*INTERNATIONAL SERIES OF MONOGRAPHS ON*
## ANALYTICAL CHEMISTRY
GENERAL EDITORS: R. BELCHER AND L. GORDON

Volume 12

# ORGANIC POLAROGRAPHIC ANALYSIS

## OTHER TITLES IN THE SERIES ON
## ANALYTICAL CHEMISTRY

Vol.  1. WEISZ—*Microanalysis by the Ring Oven Technique*
Vol.  2. CROUTHAMEL (Ed.)—*Applied Gamma-ray Spectrometry*
Vol.  3. VICKERY—*The Analytical Chemistry of the Rare Earths*
Vol.  4. HEADRIDGE—*Photometric Titrations*
Vol.  5. BUSEV—*The Analytical Chemistry of Indium*
Vol.  6. ELWELL and GIDLEY—*Atomic Absorption Spectrophotometry*
Vol.  7. ERDEY—*Gravimetric Analysis*
Vol.  8. CRITCHFIELD—*Organic Fuctional Group Analysis*
Vol.  9. MOSES—*Analytical Chemistry of the Actinide Elements*
Vol. 10. RYABCHIKOV and GOL'BRAIKH—*The Analytical Chemistry of Thorium*
Vol. 11. CALI—*Trace Analysis of Semiconductor Materials*

# ORGANIC POLAROGRAPHIC ANALYSIS

*by*

## PETR ZUMAN

*Polarographic Institute*
*Czechoslovak Academy of Science*

PERGAMON PRESS

OXFORD · LONDON · NEW YORK · PARIS

1964

PERGAMON PRESS LTD.
*Headington Hill Hall, Oxford*
*4 & 5 Fitzroy Square, London, W.1*

PERGAMON PRESS INC.
*122 East 55th Street, New York 22, N.Y.*

GAUTHIER-VILLARS ED.
*55 Quai des Grands-Augustins, Paris 6*

PERGAMON PRESS G.m.b.H.
*Kaiserstrasse 75, Frankfurt am Main*


*Distributed in the Western Hemisphere by*
THE MACMILLAN COMPANY · NEW YORK
*pursuant to a special arrangement with*
PERGAMON PRESS LIMITED

*Library of Congress Catalog Card Number 63-17229*

*Set in 11 on 12 pt. Imprint and printed in Great Britain by
Page Bros (Norwich) Ltd, Norwich*

# CONTENTS

PREFACE ix

I. INTRODUCTION 1

1.1. Basic Principles 2
1.2. Types of Polarographic Limiting Currents 6
    1.2.1. Diffusion currents 6
    1.2.2. Kinetic currents 12
    1.2.3. Catalytic currents 17
    1.2.4. Adsorption currents 20
1.3. Characterization of the Different Types of the Electrode
    Processes 22
1.4. Other Types of Currents in Polarography 27

II. POLAROGRAPHIC INSTRUMENTATION 32

2.1. Dropping Electrode 32
2.2. Reference Electrode 34
2.3. Electrolysis Vessels 35
2.4. The Polarograph 41
2.5. Derivative and Subtractive Methods 45
2.6. Auxiliary Methods 48
    2.6.1. Estimation of reversibility 48
    2.6.2. Proof of the character of polarographic processes 50
    2.6.3. Determination of the number of electrons trans-
        ferred in the electrode reaction 52
    2.6.4. Identification of the product of electrode processes 53

III. EXPERIMENTAL TECHNIQUES IN ORGANIC POLAROGRAPHY 61

3.1. Supporting Electrolyte 61
3.2. Removal of Oxygen 69
3.3. Recording of Polarographic Curves 70
3.4. The Measurement of the Limiting Current 70
3.5. Evaluation of the Wave-height: Calibration Curve and
    Standard Addition Methods 73
3.6. Sensitivity and Accuracy of the Method 77
3.7. Measurement of Half-Wave Potentials 79

IV. CLASSIFICATION OF POLAROGRAPHIC METHODS FOR THE
    ANALYSES OF ORGANIC SUBSTANCES                              83
    4.1. Polarographically Active Substances                      83
    4.2. Surface Active Substances                               101
    4.3. Direct and Indirect Methods of Analysis                 102
    4.4. Elemental Analysis                                      102
    4.5. Functional Analysis                                     103

V. DIRECT METHODS OF POLAROGRAPHIC ANALYSIS                      107
    5.1. Examination of a Compound not previously Studied        108
    5.2. Simultaneous Determination of Several Substances        110

VI. INDIRECT METHODS                                            112
    6.1. Transformations into Electroactive Form                 112
        6.1.1. Nitration                                     112
        6.1.2. Nitrosation                                   119
        6.1.3. Condensations                                 120
        6.1.4. Additions                                     129
        6.1.5. Substitutions                                 132
        6.1.6. Oxidations                                    132
        6.1.7. Complex formation                             135
        6.1.8. Other reactions                               140
    6.2. Concentration Change of Polarographically Active
        Substances                                           141
        6.2.1. Condensations                                 142
        6.2.2. Additions                                     142
        6.2.3. Oxidations                                    143
        6.2.4. Complex formation                             145
    6.3. Polarometric (Amperometric) Titrations of Organic
        Compounds                                            145
        6.3.1. Precipitation reactions                       152
        6.3.2. Oxidation-reduction reactions                 159
        6.3.3. Coupling reactions                            162
        6.3.4. Addition and substitution reactions           163
        6.3.5. Soluble complex reactions                     163
        6.3.6. Condensations                                 165

VII. SEPARATION TECHNIQUES                                        172
7.1. Precipitation and Complex Formation                         172
7.2. Extraction                                                  173
7.3. Distillation and Steam Distillation                         175
7.4. Dialysis                                                    176
7.5. Electrolysis                                                177
7.6. Chromatography                                              177

VIII. PRACTICAL APPLICATIONS                                     185
8.1. Pharmacy                                                    185
8.2. Medicine and Biochemistry                                   192
8.3. Agricultural and Food Chemistry                             198
8.4. Purity of Technical Products                                203
8.5. Petroleum and Fuels                                         206
8.6. Plastics                                                    209
    8.6.1. Monomers                                              210
    8.6.2. Catalysts and other Substances present in Polymers    212
    8.6.3. Polymers                                              213
    8.6.4. Identification of polymers                            214
8.7. Explosives                                                  215
8.8. Textile Industry                                            220
    8.8.1. Cellulosic fibres                                     220
    8.8.2. Protein-based fibres                                  220
    8.8.3. Dyeing process                                        222
    8.8.4. Auxiliary materials                                   222

IX. POLAROGRAPHY IN ORGANIC SYNTHESES AND ISOLATION OF
        NATURAL PRODUCTS                                         227
9.1. Preparative Electrochemistry                                227
9.2. Applications in Organic Synthesis                           229
9.3. Applications in the Isolation of Natural Products           230

X. POLAROGRAPHIC ANALYSIS IN THE STUDY OF REACTION
        RATES AND EQUILIBRIA                                     232
10.1. Equilibrium Constants                                      232
10.2. Homogeneous Reactions in Solutions                         238
10.3. Fast Reactions Accompanying the Electrode Process
        and Rates of Electrode Process Proper                    243

XI. EFFECTS OF STRUCTURE; POLAROGRAPHY AS A TOOL IN THE
   ANALYSIS OF STRUCTURES OF ORGANIC SUBSTANCES  245
 11.1. Effects of Structure on Half-Wave Potentials  245
 11.2. Structural Effects and Other Factors  248
 11.3. Polarography as a Tool in the Analysis of the Structure
   of Organic Substances  248
 11.4. Detection of Reactive Forms and Intermediates  250
  11.4.1. Reactions in the bulk of solution  250
  11.4.2. Chemical reactions accompanying the electrode
    process  251
  11.4.3. Electrochemical reactions  251

LITERATURE CONCERNED WITH ORGANIC POLAROGRAPHIC ANALYSIS  254

AUTHOR INDEX  261

SUBJECT INDEX  269

# PREFACE

THE great and expanding interest in the applications of polarography in the field of organic chemistry is reflected by the publication of several hundreds of papers per annum devoted to this subject. But even though organic chemists interested in physical methods, and physical and analytical chemists who handle organic substances, have contributed much to our knowledge and understanding of this branch of applied electrochemistry, organic chemists in general are still little informed about the potentialities of polarography. It is the aim of the present monograph to draw attention to the applications which have already been discovered, and especially to future trends and possibilities.

To achieve this objective the conventional approach of summarising past achievements and giving detailed descriptions of procedures, has been abandoned and, instead, the principles, techniques and apparatus of organic polarography are discussed first. Only some selected examples are given in the section devoted to the applications of organic polarography in various fields of applied chemistry. The direct methods in which the sample is simply dissolved in a suitable supporting electrolyte are treated briefly, because the problem of analysis is restricted exclusively to establishing the best electrolyte for a given type of sample. It is in the indirect methods, where a polarographically inactive substance is either converted to an active substance by a chemical reaction, or a concentration change of a reagent is followed, that chemical invention and creativity can be fully exploited; accordingly, indirect methods are treated in more detail to stress the possibilities that exist in this field. However, the more detailed descriptions of procedures in this section should not be taken as an indication that indirect methods are of greater importance or more useful in practice than direct methods, because quite the opposite is true.

The vast number of papers which has appeared during recent years—a situation which unfortunately does not distinguish organic polarography from other branches of chemistry—has made it necessary to restrict severely the number of references to original work. Wherever possible review articles are quoted. If papers from the author's own research group are more often quoted than others, this does not mean that contributions from other parts of the world have been overlooked. It is merely a reflection of the fact that the author is better informed about work done by his immediate colleagues.

Finally, the author takes this opportunity to express his gratitude to all who helped in the realization of this monograph. Professor Dr. R. Belcher (Birmingham) suggested the possibility of writing this book, and gave valuable advice concerning the arrangement of the material, and was helpful at all stages of production. Dr. R. Dagnall (Birmingham) devoted much effort to correcting linguistic errors. The rephrasing resulting from this correction and editing undoubtedly helped to clarify the text; the complicated clauses that still appear here and there are the author's fault only—as he is able to insinuate them into all the languages at his command. Dr. M. Březina (Prague) kindly revised the whole manuscript, and Dr. K. Veselý (Brno) the chapter devoted to applications in polymer chemistry. Thanks for careful preparation of the manuscript are tendered to Mrs. Hodáčová and Miss M. Stormes. It is a pleasant duty to express my thanks to Pergamon Press for their smooth co-operation and careful production of the book.

P. ZUMAN

# CHAPTER I

# INTRODUCTION

AMONG electrochemical methods of analysis the importance of polarography has been widely recognized. The possibilities that polarography offered for the understanding of basic principles of both electrochemical processes and electroanalytical methods attracted the interest of numerous workers to that field, and resulted in what is sometimes called the renaissance of electrochemistry.

The polarographic method of analysis is based on the study of electrolysis with mercury capillary electrodes and on the interpretation and measurement of the resulting current–voltage curves. The shape of the curves obtained in electrolysis with the mercury dropping electrode (or its modifications) enables us to determine quantitatively some constituents of the solution, and in some instances to detect the presence of a given compound. Polarographic determinations can be performed even at large dilutions and in small volumes of the electrolysed solution. The method can be described as economical in both time and material used. The curves recorded in polarographic electrolysis enable us to obtain information concerning the electrochemical properties of the substances involved, and of the chemical and electrochemical reactivity of these compounds.

The mercury dropping electrode was first introduced to electrolysis by J. Heyrovský.[1] The most important milestones in the theoretical development of polarography were the exact deduction of the equation for the limiting diffusion current by D. Ilkovič,[2] of the equation for the shape of polarographic wave by J. Heyrovský and D. Ilkovič,[3] the introduction of the conception of half-wave potentials by the same authors, the recognition of catalytic[4] and adsorption[5] currents by R. Brdička and the development of the theory of kinetic currents by K. Wiesner, R. Brdička, J.

Koutecký, V. Hanuš, J. Koryta and P. Delahay[6-11] as well as the observation of electrolyte motions by H. J. Antweiler.[12]

Over sixty textbooks and monographs dealing with polarography have been published in 15 different languages, and polarographic literature is being collected and registered systematically in various bibliographies (cf. Chapter XII). In recent times about 900 papers per annum devoted to polarography have been published, and the total number of papers handling various theoretical and applied aspects of polarography has reached 15,000.

About a third of these papers is devoted to the polarography of organic compounds. But although world-wide polarographic studies of organic substances have been made, few chemists working in the field of organic chemistry are familiar with the possibilities of the application of polarography to the solution of their particular problems. It is the aim of this work to show at least some of these applications.

## 1.1. BASIC PRINCIPLES

A simple polarographic arrangement is shown in Fig. 1. The solution (S) to be analysed is put into an electrolysis vessel (V) with a separated reference electrode (R), usually a calomel electrode. The indicator electrode is a dropping mercury electrode, in this case consisting of a thick-walled glass capillary (C), of 0·05–0·1 mm inside diameter and 7–15 cm in length. The slow outflow of mercury drops (every 3–5 sec) from the orifice is achieved by joining this capillary by rubber tubing (or plastic tubing) to a mercury reservoir (M) placed at a suitable height. To this cell a voltage $E$ is applied, by a slide contact P from the potentiometer (DF), connected to a storage battery B. The galvanometer G measures the current flowing in the circuit PGCRD.

Provided that the resistance in the circuit (including the wiring and the solution) is low and that the potential of the reference electrode (e.g. the calomel electrode, S.C.E.) remains constant during the electrolysis, the applied voltage is practically equal to the potential of the indicator dropping electrode. To achieve the applied potential, each particular drop of the capillary electrode has to be charged to the respective potential by a charging current (or condenser or capacity current) $i_c$, whose value, however, does not exceed $10^{-7}$ A. As electrolytic currents in polarography are usually of the order $10^{-6}$ to $10^{-5}$ A, the charging current can be neglected in most cases. It has to be taken into account only when working with very low concentrations of the substance to be analysed (less than $10^{-5}$ M), i.e. when using high galvanometer sensitivity for the measurement of small currents.

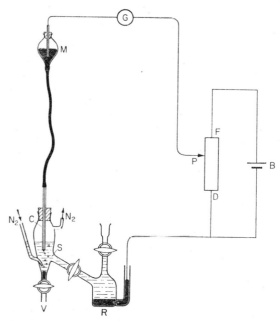

Fig. 1. Schematical view of polarographic circuit. (C) capillary of the mercury dropping electrode; (V) electrolysis vessel; (S) solution to be analysed; (R) reference electrode; (N$_2$) nitrogen inlet and outlet; (M) mercury reservoir; (G) galvanometer; (DF) potentiometer; (P) potentiometer slide contact; (B) storage battery, source of e.m.f.

The method can be illustrated when the applied voltage $E$ is increased regularly by shifting the sliding contact P (Fig. 1) from D towards F and noting, after each increase of $E$, the corresponding current $i$. When using a borate buffer of pH about 9·0 as electrolyte, the graph showing the dependence of the current $i$ on the applied voltage $E$, the "current–voltage curve", has the shape of curve 1 (Fig. 2). The slowly increasing charging current is at $E = 1\cdot9$ V followed by a steep increase of current corresponding to the electrodeposition of sodium ions (buffer components) at the dropping mercury electrode, involving the formation of a dilute

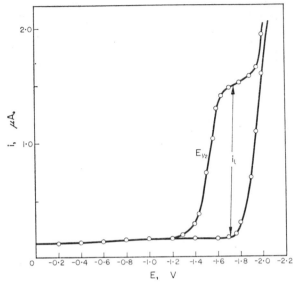

FIG. 2. Reduction of propiophenone.

Borate buffer pH 9·0; added: (1) 0;(2) 2 × 10⁻⁴ M propiophenone, 2 per. cent ethanol. Curves from 0·0 V, S.C.E., $t_1 = 2\cdot2$ sec, $m = 2\cdot1$ mg/sec.

amalgam. Similarly, an increase of current (but in the opposite direction) at the beginning of the curve (at positive potentials, *A* in Fig. 3), corresponds to the dissolution of metallic mercury with the formation of mercurous ions, reacting with components of the solution (in the example given with borate ions).

In polarography it is a convention to denote as cathodic those currents, corresponding to a reduction process, occurring above the galvanometer zero line. Currents flowing in the opposite direction, i.e. causing deflections under the zero line, are called anodic (Fig. 3).

If we now add a small amount of propiophenone (preferably of a 0·01 M ethanolic solution) to the so-called supporting electrolyte, to make the solution 2–5 × 10⁻⁴ M in propiophenone, one observes an increase of current at 1·4 V (Fig. 2). This increase corresponds to the electro-reduction of propiophenone to the corresponding 1-phenyl propyl alcohol. Such changes of the current are called "waves" and denote by their potential the nature, and by their height, the concentration of the electrolysed compound in the solution.

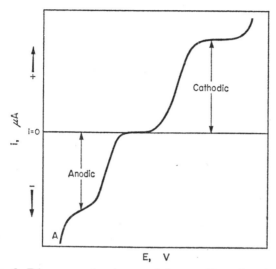

FIG. 3. Diagrammatic picture of the anodic and cathodic polarographic waves.

On a polarographic wave we observe the following important sections: Before the electro-reduction starts the current is, to a large extent, practically identical to the charging current (i.e. the current obtained before the addition of the polarographically active component—propiophenone in Fig. 2—to the pure so-called supporting or base electrolyte). This part is followed by a range of potential where a relatively steep increase of the current is observed. This steep increase of the current is followed by a range of potential where the current remains practically constant, and the current–voltage curve is again approximately parallel with that of the charging current. The difference between the charging current and the portion of the polarographic wave, where the current remains practically constant, we usually describe as the "limiting current" ($i_l$ in Fig. 2) often called "wave-height".

When the polarographic wave is preceded by another wave, the limiting current is the difference between the parallel currents in the region where they are independent of potential. The limiting current is usually proportional to the concentration of the polarographically active substance.

The potential, at which the current reaches the half value of the limiting current, is called the "half-wave potential" ($E_{\frac{1}{2}}$ in Fig. 2). This value of the oxidation or reduction potential is a physical constant, in most instances practically independent of the concentration of the particular compound and characterizing qualitatively the electroactive compound. The half-wave potential ($E_{\frac{1}{2}}$) is dependent on the nature of the electroactive species, and on the composition of the supporting electrolyte. Only in some instances, and to a comparatively small degree, is the half-wave potential dependent on the concentration of the polarographically active substances, temperature and the characteristics of the capillary used.

## 1.2. TYPES OF POLAROGRAPHIC LIMITING CURRENTS

### 1.2.1. *Diffusion Currents*

The most important type of polarographic limiting currents used for practical purposes are the diffusion limiting currents, usually described briefly as "diffusion currents". The diffusion current is a type of limiting current, the magnitude of which is limited by the rate of diffusion of electroactive species from the bulk of solution to the surface of the mercury electrode. The constant value of the limiting diffusion current is given by the particular number of particles, reaching the surface of the dropping electrode during the drop-time. The magnitude of the diffusion current ($i_d$) is given by the Ilkovič[2] equation*:

$$i_d = 0\cdot627\ nF\ D^{\frac{1}{2}}\ m^{\frac{2}{3}}\ t_1^{\frac{1}{6}} \cdot c$$

---

* It has been shown recently[13] that in the derivation of the simple Ilkovič equation, some factors have been neglected, and that for the most accurate theoretical calculations an additional correcting factor must be considered. For all practical purposes the above form is completely satisfactory.

This equation can be changed into a form, which shows the linear dependence of the diffusion current on concentration, (important for practical applications).

$$i_d = \kappa.c$$

The linear relationship between the diffusion current ($i_d$) and concentration $c$ (in moles per litre) holds true, if the factor $\kappa$ remains constant. This factor includes all the other variables given in the preceding equation, and $n$, $D$, $m$ and $t_1$ must also be constant for $\kappa =$ constant. Hence the rate of outflow of mercury $m$ (in mg per sec) and the drop-time $t_1$ (in sec) (together called capillary characteristics) remain constant when the same capillary is used and the same mercury pressure is applied. Thus, the mercury head and the position of the capillary must remain constant for the comparison of curves. The rate of diffusion and therefore the diffusion coefficient $D$ of the polarographically active species increases with rise in temperature. A rise in temperature of 1 °C causes an increase in the height of the diffusion current by about 1·5 per cent of the original value. Thus the temperature at which the curves to be compared are registered must not change greatly. The number of the exchanged electrons $n$ is also a constant for a given type of electrode process; $F$ is the Faraday, i.e. a charge of 96 500 Coulombs.

To ensure the linear relationship between the diffusion current and concentration advantageous for analytical applications of polarography, it is necessary to maintain the temperature and mercury pressure constant, and to use the same capillary for all curves compared. An example of this type of behaviour is demonstrated by the curves of maleic acid at various concentrations (Fig. 4).

Generally speaking, most polarographic limiting currents (diffusion currents as well as others) are additive, i.e. the final limiting current of a solution containing two or more electroactive species, corresponds to the sum of the limiting currents of the individual substances. Because the half-wave potentials are not usually influenced by other electroactive compounds, the wave of a distinct substance remains unchanged after addition of another polarographically active substance. This usually holds true, when

B

the half-wave potentials differ sufficiently (i.e. by more than about 0·1 V) and when the ratio of concentrations of both substances is not too great (i.e. not more than a hundred times excess of a substance, the half-wave potential of which differs by about 0·2 V).

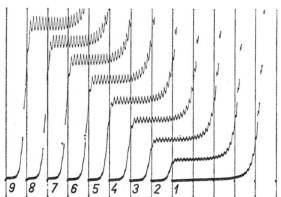

FIG. 4. Dependence of the height of the maleic acid wave on its concentration.

0·1 N hydrochloric acid with 0·005 per cent gelatine, concentration of maleic acid. (1) 0; (2) $1 \times 10^{-4}$ M; (3) $2 \times 10^{-4}$ M; (4) $3 \times 10^{-4}$ M; (5) $4 \times 10^{-4}$ M; (6) $5 \times 10^{-4}$ M; (7) $6 \times 10^{-4}$ M; (8) $7 \times 10^{-4}$ M; (9) $8 \times 10^{-4}$ M. Curves starting at $-0.4$ V, S.C.E., 200 mV/absc., $t_1 = 2.3$ sec, $m = 1.9$ mg/sec, full scale sensitivity 8 μA.

When the product of the electrode process reacts chemically with other components, the above is not true. Such examples, observed with inorganic systems, have rarely been described for organic substances. A more complicated example of this type of system (i.e. the non-additivity of waves) is formaldehyde and acetaldehyde (Fig. 5). Here, probably, the radicals formed as intermediates in the formaldehyde reduction, react with the acetaldehyde diffusing towards the electrode. The amount of acetaldehyde reaching the surface of the electrode is thus diminished and the acetaldehyde wave is decreased (Fig. 5, curve 2), compared with the wave obtained with solutions containing the same concentration of acetaldehyde, but no formaldehyde (Fig. 5, curve 3).

The reduction of systems, in which hydrogen ions are consumed during the electrolysis, represents yet another example of this type. During the course of the reduction the pH-value in the neighbourhood of the electrode is changed, causing a complicated polarographic wave. Four examples can be mentioned: In solutions containing a nitro-compound and a small concentration of a strong acid (hydrochloric, sulphuric etc.) comparable with that of

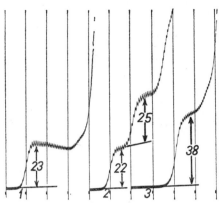

FIG. 5. Mutual influence of formaldehyde and acetaldehyde.
0·1 N lithium chloride with 0·01 N lithium hydroxide, added: (1) 5 ×
$10^{-3}$ M formaldehyde; (2) $5 \times 10^{-3}$ M formaldehyde and $9 \times 10^{-4}$ M
acetaldehyde; (3) $9 \times 10^{-4}$ M acetaldehyde. Curves starting at
−1·4 V, S.C.E., 200 mV/absc., $t_1 = 3·2$ sec, $m = 1·9$ mg/sec,
full scale sensitivity 15 μA.

the nitro-compound, the wave for the reduction of hydrogen ions is lower in the presence of the nitro-compound than in the same unbuffered solution containing no nitro-compound. This is due to the fact that in the reduction of the nitro-group (to the hydroxyl-amino or amino state), hydrogen ions are consumed. As there is no buffer to deliver the necessary hydrogen ions, it is the hydrogen ions from the strong acid which are consumed during the reduction of the nitro-group at the surface of the electrode The number of hydrogen ions undergoing the electro-reduction is thus lowered and the limiting current, corresponding to the reduction of free hydrogen ions, is lowered.

Another example is the reduction of an organic substance, involving proton-transfer, in a neutral salt medium. As the reduction proceeds with such substances at a different potential in acidic media and at another in alkaline media, two waves can be observed. An example of this type of system is the behaviour of quinhydrone, which in poorly buffered solutions shows two separate waves (Fig. 6). The anodic wave corresponds to the oxidation of the hydroquinone. Because in the oxidation of hydroquinone hydrogen ions are set free, the anodic wave occurs at potentials

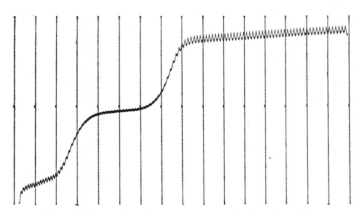

Fig. 6. Wave of quinhydrone in unbuffered media.
0·1 N potassium nitrate, $2 \times 10^{-4}$ M quinhydrone. Curve starting at +0·1 V, S.C.E., 100 mV/absc., $t_1 = 3·2$ sec, $m = 1·9$ mg/sec, full scale sensitivity 8 $\mu$A.

corresponding to the oxidation-reduction potential in acidic media. On the other hand, in the reduction (shown by the cathodic wave at more negative potentials), hydrogen ions are consumed and become attached to the hydroquinone dianion formed in the electrode process. The hydrogen ions are supplied by water, and thus a surplus of hydroxyl ions exists at the surface of the dropping electrode. Consequently, the half-wave potential of the more negative wave corresponds to the oxidation-reduction potential at higher pH-values.

Other examples are irreversible systems, in which the electrode process is accompanied by a proton-transfer reaction. Such systems, e.g. benzaldehyde, also show two waves on polarographic curves in unbuffered solutions. The more positive wave corresponds to the reduction at lower pH-values. When the rate of supply of hydrogen ions is not sufficient, the reduction occurs at

more negative potentials with the formation of a wave, corresponding to that of reduction at higher pH-values. In such examples we cannot easily distinguish whether the proton-transfer
occurred during the electrode process or as an antecedent reaction.
There are, however, some examples in which the hydrogen-ion
transfer definitely occurs in a reaction, preceding the electrode
process proper.

Such types, which constitute our last group, are represented by
the reduction of weak acids, involving a recombination, e.g.
pyruvic acid in poorly buffered solutions. Polarographic curves
under such conditions give rise to two waves. The more positive
corresponds to the reduction of free acid, and the more negative
to the reduction of the anion of pyruvic acid. The whole picture is
here complicated by the fact that free pyruvic acid is present in
the solution and, in addition, is formed from the anion and water,
and from the anion and hydrogen ion, resulting in the dissociation
of pyruvic acid. Thus, the wave-height ratio of the more positive
wave for the free acid and the wave height of the more negative
wave are also dependent on the concentration of the weak acid
(pyruvic acid, Fig. 7).

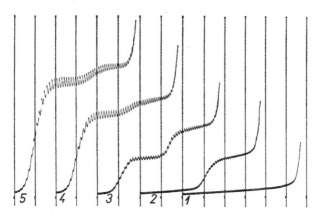

Fig. 7. Waves of pyruvic acid in unbuffered media.

$0.1$ N potassium chloride, concentration of freshly distilled pyruvic
acid: (1) 0; (2) $2 \times 10^{-4}$ M; (3) $4 \times 10^{-4}$ M; (4) $6 \times 10^{-4}$ M; (5) $8 \times 10^{-4}$ M. Curves starting at $-0.8$ V, S.C.E., 200 mV/absc., $t_1 = 3.2$
sec, $m = 1.9$ mg/sec, full scale sensitivity 6 $\mu$A.

Thus, in unbuffered solutions several complications can be encountered; but when using a properly buffered solution for the polarography of organic substances which consume hydrogen ions, the additivity of limiting currents can be expected, though a proof of this rule is always necessary.

### 1.2.2. *Kinetic Currents*

In some cases, an electroactive form, other than the substance present in the bulk of solution, is formed by a chemical reaction in the neighbourhood of the electrode, and consequently undergoes reduction or oxidation at the mercury dropping electrode. In such instances, when the rate of a chemical process is slow enough to be the determining step of the electrode process, we use the term kinetic or reaction currents ($i_k$).

An example of such a current occurs in the reduction process in which the reducible form is formed from another species (present in excess in the bulk of the solution). This second form is either polarographically inactive or reducible at considerably more negative potentials. E.g. in aqueous solutions of formaldehyde, the nonreducible hydrated form predominates.[14-16] The reducible dehydrated aldehydic form is formed from the hydrated form by a general acid-base catalysed reaction:

$$
\begin{array}{ccc}
\text{H} & \text{OH} & \text{H} \\
\diagdown \diagup & & \diagdown \\
\text{C} & \xrightarrow{k} & \text{C=O} + H_2O \\
\diagup \diagdown & & \diagup \\
\text{H} & \text{OH} & \text{H}
\end{array}
$$

The rate of this reaction ($k$) determines the height of the polarographic reduction wave, and since the rate is strongly influenced by changes in pH (Fig. 8) and temperature, the polarographic limiting current is also greatly dependent on the pH of the supporting electrolyte and the temperature of the electrolysed solution.

A similar behaviour was observed with several other aliphatic aldehydes, together with compounds, such as erythrose[17] (see Fig. 9).

A similar example is the reduction of aldoses, in which only the

free aldehydic form undergoes reduction. This situation is somewhat more complicated, because the rate of formation of the aldehydic form, from both cyclic ($a$ and $\beta$) forms, must be taken into
account.[18-21]

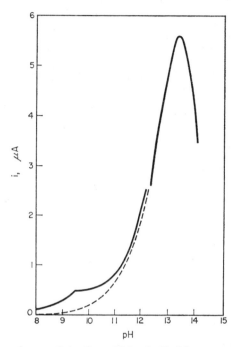

FIG. 8. Dependence of the formaldehyde limiting currents on pH-
values. $4 \times 10^{-3}$ M formaldehyde in borate buffers and lithium
hydroxide solutions. Full line; experimental; dotted line: theoretical
for OII⁻ catalysis only. The increase at pII 9–10 is due to
borate catalysis. According to R. Brdička.

Likewise, the aldehydic and not the hemiacetal form of pyridoxal undergoes polarographic reduction.[22, 23] Because the ring-
opening reaction of the hemiacetal group is acid-base catalysed,
an increase of the limiting current at low and high pH-values was
observed (Fig. 10). The acid-base catalysis can probably be ex-
plained by the difference in reactivity of different protonized
forms of pyridoxal. In agreement with the explanation of the

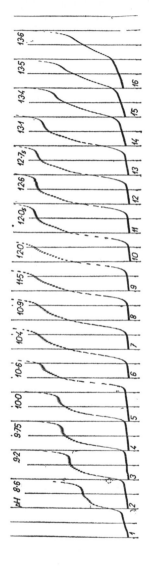

FIG. 9. Dependence of erythrose reduction waves on pH.

5 . 10⁻⁴ erythrose, pH of the final solution indicated on the polarogram. (1)–(5) 0·1 N ammonia, ionic strength $\mu = 1\cdot0$ regulated by addition of sodium chloride, with (1) 1·0 N; (2) 0·2 N; (3) 0·1 N; (4) 0·04 N; 0·01 N ammonium chloride; (6)–(9) phosphate buffers prepared from 0·05 N H₃PO₄ titrated with 0·1 N NaOH; (10)–(16) lithium hydroxide solutions: (10) 0·01 N; (11) 0·03 N; (12) 0·05 N; (13) 0·1 N; (14) 0·3 N; (15) 0·5 N; (16) 1·0 N; concentration of lithium sulphate: (10)–(12) 0·5 N; (13) 0·4 N; (14) 0·2 N; (15) and (16) 0·0. Curves (1)–(5) starting at −1·0 V, (6)–(16) at −1·2 V; S.C.E., 200 mV/absc., $t_1 = 2\cdot8$ mg/sec, full scale sensitivity 4·2 $\mu$A.

pH-dependence of the pyridoxal waves is the behaviour of pyridoxal-5-phosphate. This substance, in which the formation of a hemiacetal form is prevented by esterification of the methylol group in position 5, shows a pH-independent diffusion controlled wave in the same pH-region where an S-shaped decrease of current with decreasing pH-values was observed with pyridoxal.

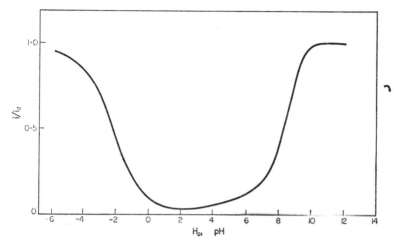

FIG. 10. Dependence of the pyridoxal wave height on pH. According to J. Volke and O. Manoušek.

Another common example of kinetic currents is observed with reducible acids and substances that are reduced in protonized and unprotonized forms (e.g. some keto-acids[7, 8, 24] and other acids,[25, 26] oximes[27, 28] nitrones[29] etc.). For such substances two waves are observed on the polarographic curve, the ratio of which changes with the pH-value of the solution in the shape of a dissociation curve (Figs. 11 and 12). The more positive wave corresponds to the acidic form, and the more negative one to the reduction of the corresponding base. However, the ratio of the two waves does not correspond to the equilibrium conditions in the bulk of the solution. The height of the more positive wave is considerably higher than it would be if it corresponded to the equilibrium concentration of the acidic form. Additional acidic form is formed around the electrode by recombination from the corresponding base (e.g. from anions) and proton donors. The rate of this recombination reaction thus governs the height of the more positive wave.

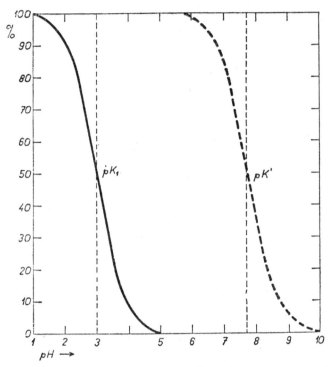

Fig. 12. Comparison of titration (full line) and polarographic (dotted line) dissociation curves. The shift is due to the recombination reaction.

It has been shown recently that in a reaction of this type proton donors (e.g. acid buffer components) other than hydroxonium can participate.[30-35] Moreover, with some reducible acids (e.g. keto-acids) the electrode process can be complicated by solvation effects[24, 36] and even the effect of keto-enol tautomerism cannot be completely excluded.[24]

A special example of a proton-transfer reaction is shown by the azulenes.[37, 38] Hence, the protonized azulenium ion is reduced at substantially more positive potentials than the conjugated base, azulene, and its wave-height increases with increasing acidity. However, in aqueous solutions the conjugated base (free azulene) is only slightly soluble, and the equilibrium between the electroactive and inactive form is here a heterogeneous one.[37]

A Lewis acid can also take part in acid-base equilibria preceding the electrode process proper. An example is the behaviour of the reducible tropylium ion,[39, 40] which is formed from tropyl alcohol by the reaction:

In all the above-mentioned examples it is possible to calculate, from the polarographic limiting currents, the rate constant for the particular chemical reaction that determines the electrode process (provided that the equilibrium constant is known). These calculations can be rigorously performed only when the chemical reaction proceeds homogeneously, i.e. in a layer of solution in the neighbourhood of the electrode. In some instances one of the reacting components may be adsorbed, that is, a heterogeneous reaction occurs at the surface of the electrode, and consequently the quantitative treatment presents difficulties.[41-43] Moreover, even with a homogeneous process it remains questionable whether the value of the equilibrium constant (mainly when concentration of charged particles is involved) used in calculations remains unchanged in the strong electric fields around the electrode. Thus, at present, the physical meaning of the calculated rate constants of antecedent reactions involving ions (mainly recombination reactions) is a little doubtful.

## 1.2.3. *Catalytic Currents*

Principally, two types of polarographic currents are described as catalytic currents. In the first type the limiting current of an electroactive substance is increased in the presence of a catalyst, which itself is either polarographically inactive or reduced at considerably more negative potentials. In the second group, the polarographically inactive catalyst causes a shift in the reduction potential of the polarographically active substance towards more positive potentials.

Examples of the first type, which belong to the most precisely treated polarographic currents, are the reductions of $Fe^{III}$ or $Ti^{IV}$ in the presence of different oxidizing agents, such as hydroperoxide, hydroxylamine, chlorate etc. The waves measured are those corresponding to the reduction of the metallic ions to the lower valency state, and the limiting currents of these waves are increased in the presence of oxidizing agents (owing to the regeneration of the reducible form from the product of the electrode process). The reaction proceeds as follows:

$$Me^{n+} + e \underset{k\,[Ox]}{\overrightarrow{\phantom{xxxxxxx}}} Me^{(n-1)+}$$

where Ox represents the oxidizing agents. The limiting value of such catalytic currents, also described as regeneration currents ($i_{reg}$), is given by the following equation (provided that $k[Ox] \gg l/t_1$):

$$\frac{i_{reg}}{i_d} = 0.81 \sqrt{(4.2k\,[Ox]\,t_1)}$$

This shows the dependence of the current on the concentration of the oxidizing agents.

Catalytic currents were first observed[6] with indigosulphonates in the presence of a palladium sol saturated with hydrogen (here the oxidized form is reduced with hydrogen in a heterogeneous reaction). However, there are still few examples of organic systems involving homogeneous reactions of this type.[44] Recently, an increase in the anodic waves of hydroquinones was described[45] in the presence of illumination by u.v. light in isopropanol solution. In the photochemical reaction, the quinone, formed at the

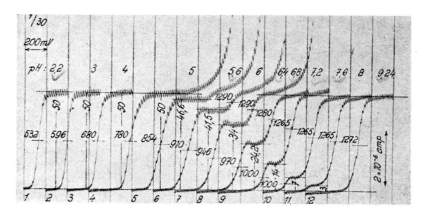

FIG. 11. Dependence of the phenylglyoxylic acid waves on pH.
$5 \cdot 5 \times 10^{-4}$ M Phenylglyoxylic acid McIlvain buffers, pH of the
electrolysed solution indicated on the polarogram. N.C.E.,
200 mV/absc., $t_1 = 2 \cdot 3$ sec, full scale sensitivity 7.2 $\mu$A. According
to R. Brdička.

electrode, is activated, and by a reaction with the solvent forms a radical which in turn leads to the formation of hydroquinone. Thus in this sequence of reactions the electroactive form, hydroquinone, is regenerated by a chemical reaction.

The second group of catalytic currents are due to the presence of some substances which lower the hydrogen overvoltage. In such instances, the curves of which often possess sharp peaks, the hydrogen ions are reduced at more positive potentials than those corresponding to the reduction of protons from solutions of strong acids or buffered solutions at the given pH. The hydrogen ion is reduced after interaction with the catalytically active substances, and in the course of the reaction the catalyst in the unprotonized form is regenerated. Thus, such catalytic waves are often many times higher than the corresponding diffusion current

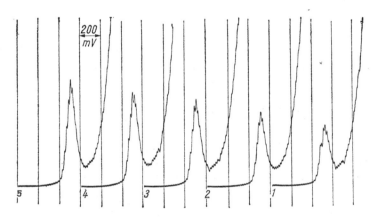

FIG. 13. Catalytic curves of cobalamin (vitamin $B_{12}$).
Acetate buffer pH 4·7, concentrations of vitamin $B_{12}$: (1) 2·3 $\mu$g/ml; (2) 3·2 $\mu$g/ml; (3) 4·1 $\mu$g/ml; (4) 4·95 $\mu$g/ml; (5) 5·6 $\mu$g/ml. Curves starting at $-1·2$ V, S.C.E., 200 mV/absc., $t_1 = 2·4$ sec, $m = 2·1$ mg/sec, full scale sensitivity 150 $\mu$A.

at the given concentration (Fig. 13). Catalytic currents, in most instances, are not a linear function of concentration, but they reach a limiting value with the increasing concentration of the catalytically active substance. Most catalytic currents increase with decreasing pH and with the increasing concentration of the buffer solution used. Some catalytic currents are also sensitive to the ionic strength. Typical examples of such catalytic currents occur in the presence of different organic heterocyclic nitrogen compounds, some weak acids and bases in buffers, in ammoniacal cobalt solutions and in the presence of some simple sulphur derivatives, e.g. cystine (Fig. 14) or proteins.[46] The mechanism of most reactions which cause catalytic currents, has not yet been determined with certainty, but some observations show that a different mechanism occurs with different substances.[47] In some instances, the adsorption of the catalyst[48-52] and possibly of the buffer[53] together with the motion of the solution[48, 49] are claimed to play an important role. On the other hand, the typical catalytic maximum for cystine (Fig. 14) is accompanied only by an unsubstantial motion of the solution.

### 1.2.4. Adsorption Currents

Some forms of polarographically active substances are adsorbed at the mercury dropping electrode. In such instances two waves may be observed on polarographic curves, one of which corresponds to the reduction (or oxidation) of the free form and the other of the substance in the adsorbed state. The adsorption current increases with the increasing concentration of the electroactive species, but only to a certain value, which is a function of the surface of the electrode. No further increase of current is observed with further increases of concentration, and we suppose that the surface of the electrode under such conditions is covered by a layer of the adsorbed substance. The adsorption current ($i_a$) is given by the equation[5]

$$i_a = 0 \cdot 85n. \; F.z.m^{\frac{2}{3}}t_1^{-\frac{1}{3}}$$

where $z$ is the number of moles adsorbed on 1 cm² of the surface of the electrode. The other symbols are the same as in the Ilkovič equation (p. 6). Characteristic adsorption currents were observed with methylene blue,[5] in which the reduced form is adsorbed, and thiols and related compounds[46] in which the insoluble mercury salt is adsorbed (Fig. 15). In all these examples

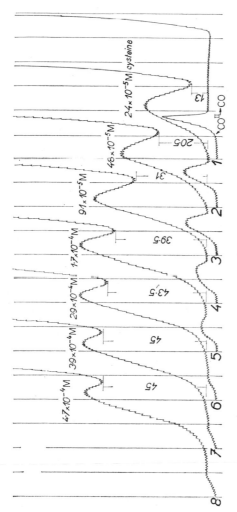

Fig. 14. Dependence of catalytic wave of cysteine in ammoniacal buffered cobaltous solutions. 0·002 M Cobaltous chloride, 0·1 M ammonia, 0·1 M ammonium chloride; concentration of cystine: (1) 0; (2)–(8) given on the polarogram. Curves starting at 0·8 V, Hg-pool, 200 mV/absc., $t_1 = 2·4$ sec, $m = 3·0$ mg/sec, full scale sensitivity 100 $\mu A$.

the adsorption energy causes a shift in the half-wave potentials to more positive or more negative values.

Another type of adsorption current was observed, (e.g. with quinine) probably due to the slow formation of the adsorption layer. In other instances the reduction process is hindered by a formation of an adsorbed layer. This layer can be formed either by the

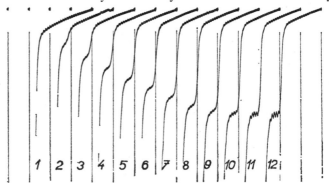

FIG. 15. Mercury salt formation. Dependence of anodic waves of uracil on concentration.

0·05 M borate buffer pH 9·3, concentration of uracil: (1) 0; (2) $2 \times 10^{-5}$ M; (3) $4 \times 10^{-5}$ M; (4) $6 \times 10^{-5}$ M; (5) $8 \times 10^{-5}$ M; (6) $1 \times 10^{-4}$ M; (7) $1·2 \times 10^{-4}$ M; (8) $1·4 \times 10^{-4}$ M; (9) $1·6 \times 10^{-4}$ M; (10) $1·8 \times 10^{-4}$ M; (11) $2·0 \times 10^{-4}$ M; (12) $5 \times 10^{-4}$ M. Curves recorded from $-0·4$ V towards positive potentials, mercurous sulphate reference electrode, 200 mV/absc., $t_1 = 2·85$ sec, $m = 3·3$ mg/sec, full scale sensitivity 1·5 $\mu$A. Galvanometer null line shown by dots on abscissae.

electroactive form itself, by the product of the electrode process, or by another electro-inactive compound (e.g. pyridine or higher fatty alcohols) present or added to the solution.[54]

### 1.3. CHARACTERIZATION OF THE DIFFERENT TYPES OF ELECTRODE PROCESSES

To distinguish between the different types of electrode processes, we take as a guide the dependence of the limiting current on the mercury pressure, concentration of the polarographically active substance and buffer, and the dependence on pH and temperature. Further diagnostic tools are the shape of the polarographic wave, the changes of half-wave potentials and auxiliary methods discussed in Chapter II.

Diffusion currents are proportional to the root of the height of the mercury column (measured between the level of mercury in the reservoir and the tip of capillary) denoted by $h$, which is corrected for the interfacial tension at the surface of the growing drops ($h_{back}$).

$$h = h_{exp} - h_{back}, \text{ where } h_{back} = 3 \cdot 1/m^{\frac{1}{3}} t_1^{\frac{1}{3}} \text{ cm}$$

Kinetic currents are independent of $h$, and adsorption currents are directly proportional to $h$ (not to its root) (Fig. 16). For catalytic currents, different functions of $h$ were observed. When a current is increasing with the decrease of the mercury head, a catalytic effect can be suspected but such currents can also be a linear function of $h$, independent of $h$ or possess an intermediate function.

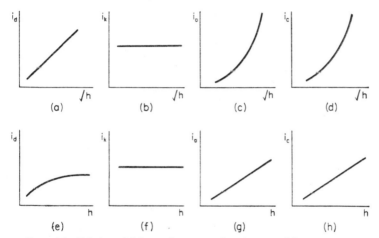

FIG. 16. Distinguishing of types of polarographic currents using the effect of mercury pressure ($h$).
(a)–(d) Dependence of the limiting current on $h$, (e)–(h) dependence of the limiting current on $\sqrt{h}$. (a) and (e) diffusion current, (b) and (f) kinetic current; (c) and (g) adsorption current, (d) and (h) capacity current.

Diffusion and kinetic currents (for reactions of first order) are usually a linear function of the concentration of the substance to be analysed. The height of the adsorption and catalytic waves

C

reaches a limiting value with increasing concentration, and at higher concentrations the waves are practically concentration independent (Fig. 17).

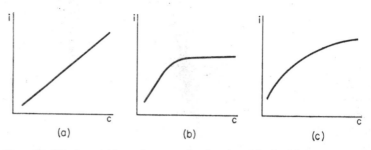

FIG. 17. Distinguishing of types of polarographic limiting currents using the effect of depolarizer concentration.
(a) Diffusion and first order kinetic currents; (b), (c) adsorption and catalytic currents.

Whereas diffusion and adsorption currents are usually independent of the buffer concentration, kinetic currents (in some instances) and catalytic currents are very often a function of the concentration and composition of the buffer. The ionic strength was also observed in some instances to affect catalytic currents.

The pH of the supporting electrolyte often influences kinetic currents, and is of the utmost importance in the catalytic evolution of hydrogen.

Finally, a substantial increase with increasing temperature was observed with some kinetic currents. However, not all kinetic currents show a large temperature coefficient.

The characteristics of the most important types of currents are summarized in Table 1.

The shape of the wave and the position of the half-wave potential enable us to gain a further insight into the electrode reaction.

For diffusion controlled reactions, in which both the oxidized and reduced forms are soluble, and in which the electrode reactions are mobile (i.e. for so-called reversible systems) the wave is S-shaped and the dependence of $\log (i_{\lim} - i)/i$ on potential is linear. The linear plot has a slope of $RT \,.\, 2{\cdot}303/nF$ (here $n$ is the

TABLE 1

DISTINGUISHED DIFFERENT TYPES OF LIMITING CURRENTS

| Current | Symbol | $h$ | $c$ | Buffer | pH | $\dfrac{1}{i}\dfrac{di}{dT}$ |
|---------|--------|-----|-----|--------|-----|-------|
| Diffusion | $i_d$ | $k \cdot h^{1/2}$ | $k \cdot c$ | independent | independent | 1·6% |
| Kinetic | $i_k$ | $k \cdot h^0$ | $k \cdot c$ | dependent (sometimes) | dependent | 5–20% |
| Adsorption | $i_a$ | $k \cdot h^1$ | lim | independent (usually) | independent | different |
| Catalytic | $i_{cata}$ | different | lim | dependent | dependent | — |

*Note:* lim = the current reaches a limiting value with increasing concentration of the substance.

number of electrons transferred in the electrode reaction, $i_{lim}$ the limiting current and $i$ the current at a given potential) (Fig. 18). When, in addition, the half-wave potential is independent of the concentration of the substance and the drop-time, and when the half-wave potentials of the oxidized and reduced forms are identical and equal to the oxidation-reduction potential measured by equilibrium methods (e.g. potentiometry), then and only then, can

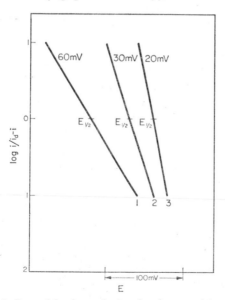

FIG. 18. Logarithmic analysis of polarographic curves.
(1) $n = 1$; (2) $n = 2$; (3) $n = 3$ for $t = 30°C$.

the system be called "reversible". This statement assumes that both oxidation and reduction processes are fast, so that the passage of current does not alter the value of the ratio of the concentration of the oxidized and reduced forms corresponding to the applied potential.

When the dependence of $\log(i_{lim} - i)$ with potential is linear and the slope is $RT \times 2\cdot303/nF$, an insoluble product of the electrode reaction is formed. Such curves, resulting in sharp bends, were observed for some anodic waves corresponding to a formation of an insoluble mercury compound, e.g. diethylbarbituric acid.[55]

If the shape of the wave shows a reversible process, when the limiting current is diffusion controlled, but the half-wave potentials differ from those measured at the equilibrium conditions and are dependent on the drop-time ($E_{1/2}$ = const. $\pm$ $2\cdot303RT/nF \log_{10} t_1$), then the product of the reversible electrode reaction is inactivated by a fast chemical reaction, e.g. in the case of the anodic waves for ascorbic acid.[56, 57] It was supposed that the inactivation reaction is the hydration of dehydroascorbic acid, but the polarographic behaviour of dehydroascorbic acid does not agree with this simple explanation.

When the shape of the wave corresponds to a reversible process, the limiting current is diffusion controlled, but the half-wave potential is a function of the concentration of the electroactive species ($E_{1/2}$ = const. $+ 2\cdot303RT/3nF \log ckt_1$), a fast and mobile electrode reaction accompanied by a dimerization can be anticipated.[58] Dimerization of radicals formed in the reduction of tropylium ion[39, 40] is supposed to be of this type.

When dissociation occurs for oxidized or reduced forms of a reversible system, the half-wave potentials are shifted with the pH of the solution. The shift depends on the number of electrons transferred, the number of protons dissociated, the pH-value and the standard potential of the substance studied. From polarographic measurements of reversible systems the approximate values for the dissociation constants can be estimated.

Some irreversible electrode processes cause drawn-out polarographic waves, the slope of which is much smaller than would correspond to a reversible process of the particular type (e.g.

hydroperoxide or some halogen derivatives). The half-wave potentials, corresponding to irreversible processes, are dependent on pH-value when a proton-transfer reaction precedes the slowest step in the electrode reaction.

For some substances the half-wave potential of the oxidized form differs substantially from that of the reduced form. The shape of these waves, as well as the shifts of the half-wave potentials, are such as we would expect for a reversible process. Sometimes, the slope of the wave and the dependence of half-wave potentials on pH correspond to a transfer of a smaller number of electrons than is deduced from the limiting current. In such instances we assume that a part of the electrode process is mobile, but usually we describe such total processes as irreversible. Examples of such behaviour are the reductions of carbonyl compounds. For irreversible systems the exchange of water for an organic solvent, e.g. dioxane or dimethylformamide, can disclose whether or not, in the electrode process in aqueous solution, there is interaction with a molecule of water.

## 1.4. OTHER TYPES OF CURRENTS IN POLAROGRAPHY

*Charging* or *condenser current*, due to the charging of the electrode (each drop) to the respective potential, observed even in pure supporting electrolyte, has already been mentioned (p. 2). This current depends on the magnitude of the surface of the mercury drop and is thus proportional to the height of the mercury column $h$, similar to the adsorption current.

*Migration current* is observed in addition to the diffusion current in solutions with insufficient concentration of supporting electrolyte. This current is due to the migration of ions in the electric field between the two electrodes. Under normal conditions, in which the molar concentration of the supporting electrolyte is more than twenty times higher than that of the substance studied, this current is negligible.

On polarographic curves a sharp or rounded rise of current in the form of a maximum is often observed. These *maxima* are accompanied by motion of the solution near the dropping electrode. This movement causes an increased transport of the electroactive substance to the surface of the dropping electrode. The maxima are usually divided into maxima of the first and second kind.[59, 60] Both kinds can be suppressed by gelatin or some other surface active substance.

The maxima of the first kind, arising usually at the beginning of the polarographic wave, are sharp or rounded, and are often observed with low concentrations of electrolytes. Their height varies with the height of the mercury column in different ways, according to the concentration of the supporting electrolyte and the nature of the depolarizer.

The maxima of second kind, observed in the middle of the diffusion current, are never sharp. They can possess the form of a rounded maximum, a general increase of the limiting current or even a form of a false wave. They are usually observed at concentrations of the supporting electrolyte higher than 0·2 M. Their dependence on the mercury pressure is characteristic, and they increase with increasing height of the mercury column (substantially more than the diffusion or adsorption current) (Fig. 19).

In polarographic analysis it is often necessary to suppress these maxima to enable the precise measurement of the limiting current. For such purposes the addition of gelatin or other surface active

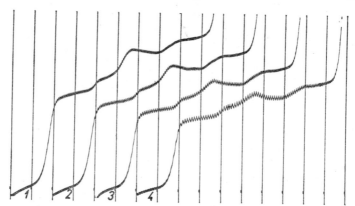

FIG. 19. Dependence of the waves of 2-methyl-1,4-naphthoquinone on mercury pressure.
$2 \times 10^{-4}$ M 2-Methyl-1,4-naphthoquinone in 0·1 N KCl $h =$ (1) 75 cm; (2) 65 cm; (3) 55 cm; (4) 45 cm. Curves starting at 0·0 V, S.C.E., 200 mV/absc., $t_1 = 2·8$ sec, $m = 2·2$ mg/sec, full scale sensitivity 4·2 $\mu$A.

substances is used, but as waves are sometimes distorted by high concentrations of surface active substances, the lowest possible concentration of these substances is added. Alternatively, we may use the fact that the suppression of a maximum is a function of the concentration of surface active substances, for the estimation of the total concentration of such substances. The presence of surface active compounds can serve, e.g. to distinguish a natural product (including always some surface active agents) from artificially prepared products.[46]

## REFERENCES

(1) HEYROVSKÝ, J., Chem. listy 16, 256 (1922); Phil. Mag. 45, 303 (1923).
(2) ILKOVIČ, D., Collect. Czechoslov. Chem. Commun. 6, 498 (1934).
(3) HEYROVSKÝ, J. and ILKOVIČ, D., Collect. Czechoslov. Chem. Commun. 7, 198 (1935).
(4) BRDIČKA, R., Collect. Czechoslov. Chem. Commun. 5, 148 (1933).
(5) BRDIČKA, R., Z. Elektrochem. 48, 278 (1942).
(6) WIESNER, K., Z. Elektrochem. 49, 164 (1943); Chem. listy 41, 8 (1947).
(7) BRDIČKA, R. and WIESNER, K., Naturwiss. 31, 247 (1943); Collect. Czechoslov. Chem. Commun. 12, 39 (1947); 12, 138 (1947),
(8) BRDIČKA, R., Collect. Czechoslov. Chem. Commun. 12, 212 (1947).
(9) BRDIČKA, R. and KOUTECKÝ, J., J. Amer. Chem. Soc. 76, 907 (1954).
(10) KOUTECKÝ, J. and BRDIČKA, R., Collect. Czechoslov. Chem. Commun. 12, 337 (1947).
(11) BRDIČKA, R., HANUŠ, V. and KOUTECKÝ, J., General Theoretical Treatment of the Polarographic Kinetic Currents, in Progress in Polarography (P. Zuman, I. M. Kolthoff, editors), Vol. 1, p. 145. Interscience, New York (1962) and references 25–33 given herein and in Chapter X.
(12) ANTWEILER, H. J., Z. Elektrochem. 43, 596 (1937); 44, 663, 719, 831, 888 (1938).
(13) KOUTECKÝ, J. and VON STACKELBERG, M., The Equation for Polarographic Diffusion Currents and the Limits of its Validity, in Progress in Polarography (P. Zuman, I. M. Kolthoff, editors), Vol. 1, p. 21, Interscience, New York (1962) where further references are given
(14) VESELÝ, K. and BRDIČKA, R., Collect. Czechoslov. Chem. Commun. 12, 313 (1947).
(15) BIEBER, R. and TRÜMPLER, F., Helv. Chim. Acta 30, 706, 971, 1109, 1286, 1534, 2000 (1947); 31, 5 (1948).
(16) LANDQVIST, N., Acta Chem. Scand. 9, 867 (1955).
(17) ZUMAN, P. and ZINNER, H., Chem. Ber. 95, 2089 (1962).
(18) WIESNER, K., Collect. Czechoslov. Chem. Commun. 12, 64 (1947).

(19) Los, J. M. and Wiesner, K., *J. Amer. Chem. Soc.* **75**, 6346 (1953).
(20) Los, J. M., Simpson, L. B. and Wiesner, K., *J. Amer. Chem. Soc.* **78**, 1564 (1956).
(21) Los, J. M. and Gaspar, N. J., *Z. Elektrochem.* **64**, 41 (1960).
(22) Volke, J., *Collect. Czechoslov. Chem. Commun.* **23**, 1486 (1958); *Z. Physikal. Chem.* (*Leipzig*) Sonderheft 1958, 268.
(23) Manoušek, O. and Zuman, P., *Collect. Czechoslov. Chem. Commun.* in the press.
(24) Ono, S., Takagi, M. and Wasa, T., *Collect. Czechoslov. Chem. Commun.* **26**, 141 (1961).
(25) Volke, J. and Volková, V., *Collect. Czechoslov. Chem. Commun.* **20**, 1332 (1955).
(26) Volke, J., *Collect. Czechoslov. Chem. Commun.* **21**, 246 (1956); **22**, 1777 (1957).
(27) Volke, J., Kubíček, R. and Šantavý, F., *Collect. Czechoslov. Chem. Commun.* **25**, 871 (1960).
(28) Souchay, P. and Ser, S., *J. Chim. Phys.* **49**, C 172 (1952).
(29) Zuman, P. and Exner, O., *Collect. Czechoslov. Chem. Commun.* in preparation.
(30) Hanuš, V., *Proc. 1st Internat. Polarograph. Congr.*, Pt. I, 811, Prague (1951).
(31) Hans, W. and Henke, K. H., *Z. Elektrochem.* **57**, 595 (1953).
(32) Wiesner, K., Wheatley, M. and Los, J. M., *J. Amer. Chem. Soc.* **76**, 4858 (1954).
(33) Wheatley, M., *Experientia* **12**, 339 (1956).
(34) Kemula, W., Grabowski, Z. R. and Bartel, E. T., *Roczniki Chem.* **33**, 1125 (1959).
(35) Becker, M. and Strehlow, H., *Z. Elektrochem.* **64**, 42 (1960).
(36) Becker, M. and Strehlow, H., *Z. Elektrochem.* **64**, 129 (1960).
(37) Zuman, P., *Z. Physikal. Chem.* Sonderheft 1958, 243.
(38) Ždanov, S. I. and Mirkin, L. S., *Collect. Czechoslov. Chem. Commun.* **26**, 370 (1961).
(39) Zuman, P., Chodkowski, J. and Šantavý, F., *Collect. Czechoslov. Chem. Commun.* **26**, 380 (1961).
(40) Ždanov, S. I. and Frumkin, A. N., *Dokl. Akad. Nauk SSSR* **122**, 412 (1958).
(41) Volková, V., *Nature* **185**, 743 (1960).
(42) Grabowski, Z. R. and Bartel, E. T., *Roczniki Chem.* **34**, 611 (1960).
(43) Majranovskij, S. G. and Liščeta, L. I., *Collect. Czechoslov. Chem. Commun.* **25**, 3025 (1960).
(44) Berg, H. and Kapulla, H., *J. Electroanalyt. Chem.* **1**, 108 (1959/60).
(45) Berg, H., *Z. Elektrochem.* **64**, 1104 (1960); *Naturwiss.* **47**, 320 (1960); **48**, 100 (1961).
(46) Březina, M. and Zuman, P., *Polarography in Medicine, Biochemistry and Pharmacy*, Interscience, New York (1958), where the literature is extensively quoted.

(47) ZUMAN, P. and KUIK, M., *Collect. Czechoslov. Chem. Commun.* **24**, 3861 (1959).
(48) VON STACKELBERG, M. and FASSBENDER, H., *Z. Elektrochem.* **62**, 834 (1958).
(49) VON STACKELBERG, M., HANS, W. and JENSCH, W., *Z. Elektrochem.* **62**, 839 (1958).
(50) NÜRNBERG, H. S., in *Advances in Polarography* (Proc. 2nd Internat. Congr. Polarography, Cambridge 1959) Vol. 2, p. 694. Pergamon Press, London (1960).
(51) MAJRANOVSKIJ, S. G., *Dokl. Akad. Nauk SSSR* **114**, 1272 (1957); **132**, 1352 (1960).
(52) KOUTECKÝ, J., HANUŠ, V. and MAJRANOVSKIJ, S. G., *Ž. fiz. chim.* (*SSSR*) **34**, 651 (1960).
(53) PUNGOR, E. and FARSANG, GY., *Acta Chim. Acad. Sci. Hungar.* **25**, 293 (1960); *J. Electroanalyt. Chem.* in the press.
(54) REILLEY, C. N. and STUMM, W., Adsorption in Polarography, in *Progress in Polarography* (P. Zuman, I. M. Kolthoff, editors), Vol. 1, p. 81, Interscience, New York (1962), where further references are quoted.
(55) ZUMAN, P., KORYTA, J. and KALVODA, R., *Collect. Czechoslov. Chem. Commun.* **18**, 350 (1953).
(56) KERN, D. M. H., *J. Amer. Chem. Soc.* **76**, 1011 (1954).
(57) KOUTECKÝ, J., *Collect. Czechoslov. Chem. Commun.* **20**, 116 (1955).
(58) HANUŠ, V., *Chem. Zvesti* **8**, 702 (1954).
(59) VON STACKELBERG, M., *Fortschr. Chem. Forschg.* **2**, 229 (1951); *Advances in Polarography* (Proc. 2nd Internat. Congr. Polarography, Cambridge 1959) Vol. 1, p. 68, Pergamon Press, London (1960).
(60) KRJUKOVA, T. A., *Z. Phys. Chem.* (*Leipzig*) **212**, 247 (1959).

# CHAPTER II

# POLAROGRAPHIC INSTRUMENTATION

FOR measuring polarographic currents, an arrangement must be available consisting of a mercury dropping electrode (or another type of indicator electrode), a reference electrode, both placed in an electrolysis vessel containing the solution to be analysed, and a polarograph.

## 2.1. DROPPING ELECTRODE

The dropping mercury electrode, already mentioned on p. 2 consists of a capillary connected to a mercury reservoir, whereby the pressure of mercury ensures that the drops fall regularly from the capillary's orifice. The capillary, used for a dropping electrode, is an ordinary thick-walled glass tube (as used for thermometer stems). The inside diameter should be 0·05–0·1 mm and for such a capillary 7–15 cm in length, the desired drop-time, of about $t_1 = 3$ sec, is achieved with the height of mercury column $h = 40$–60 cm (in 1 M KCl at 0·0 V vs. S.C.E.). For the sake of mechanical stability, the outside diameter is usually 3–6 mm, but for some microanalytical work capillaries with an outside diameter of 1 mm are used. The drawn-out capillaries, recommended in the early stages of polarographic research, have the disadvantage of poor reproducibility and fragility.

Recently, a new useful modification of a dropping mercury electrode was described by Smoleř.[1] With this capillary the tip of the glass tube is bent by some 30–90° from the vertical. This type of electrode can also be made by placing an ordinary capillary in a horizontal position and without changing the outflow velocity $m$, the drop-time is shortened. The height of polarographic waves, obtained with such capillaries, is not very much lower than of those registered with an ordinary electrode. However the oscillations on polarographic curves, due to the dropping of mercury, are smaller with the horizontal capillary, and consequently simplifies the measurement of limiting currents. Furthermore the Smoleř-type electrode is more resistant against disturbances at more negative potentials (than about $-1.9$ V) and in nonaqueous solutions.

Owing to the compensation of different effects, values for the current received with this type of electrode follow the simple equation of Ilkovič more closely than an ordinary electrode. The Smoleř-type of electrode represents a new tool in distinguishing different kinds of polarographic currents. Capillary electrodes with an artificially regulated drop-time also have a similar advantage.

The advantages of the dropping mercury electrode can be summarized as follows:

1. Every drop offers a fresh surface, unaffected (almost) by electrolysis on the preceding drop and surrounded by a practically fresh layer of the solution, so that the surface conditions are well defined and time effects excluded.

2. The large overvoltage of hydrogen at a mercury electrode prevents the evolution of hydrogen even in the deposition of the alkali metals from neutral solutions. Using tetra-alkyl-ammonium salts the study of primary processes may be extended to $-2.6$ V (using a saturated calomel electrode as reference base).

3. The changes in the composition of the solution are negligible owing to the small value of current. Consequently, current–voltage curves may be repeated several times with identical results.

4. The constancy of the dropping rate leads to reproducible results, and permits an exact mathematical treatment of the curves.

5. The small dimensions of the dropping electrode allow very small volumes to be analysed. The electrolysis is usually performed in volumes of solution of 1–10 ml. but with special precautions even 0.01 ml. is sufficient.

The great success of the mercury dropping electrode in polarographic theory and practice, led (during the past two decades) to the introduction of many different types of mercury electrodes and electrodes of different solid metals for the registration of current–voltage curves.[2, 3] Even though some of them offer advantages for solving some special problems (e.g. for the extension of the potential range to more positive potentials, or for increasing the sensitivity for some systems), none possesses the general versatility and reproducibility of the mercury dropping electrode.

## 2.2. REFERENCE ELECTRODE

In polarographic electrolysis the reference electrode can be placed either in or separated from the solution to be analysed.

When only the limiting currents (not the half-wave potentials) of cathodic waves are to be measured, provided that strong oxidizing agents and surface active compounds are not present, it is possible to use a *mercury pool electrode* as the reference electrode in polarographic analysis. The exact measurement of half-wave potentials is prevented owing to the polarization (change of potential during the registration of a curve) of the mercury pool, even in solutions containing 0·1 M chlorides. A strong oxidizing agent would interfere, because of the dissolution of metallic mercury similarly as strongly surface active substances (like proteins), covering the reference electrode with an adsorbed layer and thus increasing the cell resistance.

In the absence of substances reacting with silver ion (e.g. ammonia or barbital) a *silver chloride electrode* is useful even for precise measurements of half-wave potentials. This electrode is constructed from a silver wire, coated with electrolytically deposited silver chloride, and immersed in a solution containing 0·1 M chlorides as a component of the supporting electrolyte.

The most popular separated reference electrodes are the *calomel electrode* (usually saturated) and the *mercurous sulphate electrode*. The calomel electrode is made by adding a solution of potassium chloride of the desired concentration (1 M or saturated) to a layer of mercury. No calomel need be added because a thin layer of this salt is formed during electrolysis, and a thicker layer of calomel can cause an increase in the resistance. Because of the greater solubility of mercurous sulphate, a small amount of this salt is added to the surface of mercury in the preparation of a mercurous sulphate electrode. A solution of 1 N sodium sulphate containing 0·01–0·1 N sulphuric acid (to prevent hydrolysis) is then added. The potential of this electrode is about +0·3 to +0·4 V more positive than that of a calomel electrode. The potential of the calomel electrode is more reproducible, but the mercurous sulphate electrode is less polarizable. For special purposes other types of reference electrodes are also used.

Such reference electrodes are separated from the solution to be analysed by a liquid boundary, a salt-bridge or membranes (of Cellophane, or sintered glass). The junction is arranged in such a way as to make the resistance of the cell low, and to avoid the possibility of contamination of the solution under study by the components from the compartment containing the reference electrode.

## 2.3. ELECTROLYSIS VESSELS

A great number of different vessels for general and special purposes are described in the polarographic literature. Some examples of simple vessels are given in this chapter.

The vessels recommended differ in the volume of the solution to be analysed, in the possibility of deaeration, in the position of the reference electrode and in the possibility of temperature-control.

In the relatively rare cases of examining solutions open to the air, ordinary beakers (Fig. 20a) of 5–20 ml. capacity, containing a layer of mercury approximately 3 mm deep suffice. The solution to be examined is poured in to fill three-fourths of the vessel. The mercury layer acts as a reference electrode and is connected to the source of e.m.f. When a capillary electrode is placed in the solution, polarographic electrolysis can be performed.

When volumes of 0·2–2 ml. of solutions are to be analysed using a mercury pool reference electrode, the semimicro-vessel depicted in Fig. 20b can be used. The wide arm of the vessel serves to keep the level of mercury constant in the narrower part, where the solution to be analysed is placed. This vessel is equipped with a side arm for deaeration of the solution. The atmospheric oxygen is removed from the solution to be electrolysed by bubbling an inert gas (nitrogen, hydrogen or carbon dioxide) through the solution. The outlet of the gas is in the upper right section of the vessel and is usually connected to a water seal.

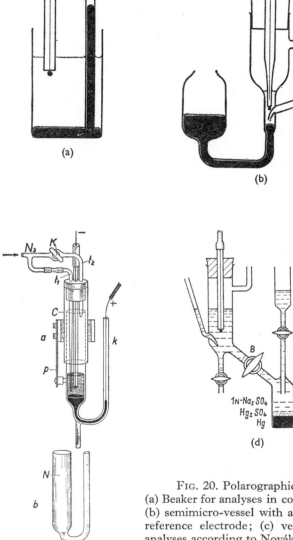

FIG. 20. Polarographic vessels.
(a) Beaker for analyses in contact with air; (b) semimicro-vessel with a mercury pool reference electrode; (c) vessel for series analyses according to Novák; (d) Kalousek vessel with a separated mercurous sulphate reference electrode (description of parts in text).

For a large series of analyses the vessel of Novák[4] (Fig. 20c) is suitable. It consists of two parts: the outer cylindrical jacket C is fixed to an ordinary laboratory stand by a clamp, so that its lower edge is 25–30 cm above the base of the stand. The long tube passing into the cylinder serves as an inlet for the inert gas. The gas is passed in from a gas reservoir (usually a steel flask) by rubber or plastic tubing connected to the horizontal part of the glass tube by the stopcock. The capillary of the dropping electrode is inserted through the neck of the jacket, so that the tip of the capillary almost reaches the exit of the gas tube. The capillary is fastened at the neck by a short piece of rubber tubing. Instead of using all-glass apparatus the upper part of the jacket can be closed by a stopper with borings for the capillary, gas inlet and outlet.

In the second part, the electrolyte vessel N consists of a glass tube fused to a narrow bent capillary tube and a solid rod base n is sealed on to the narrow tube.

It is sufficient to provide one cylinder jacket for each polarograph, and a dozen or more electrolyte vessels should be available.

The procedure for a polarographic determination using this type of vessel is as follows:

Place about 1 ml of mercury into the electrolyte vessel N, taking care to remove all air bubbles from the side-arm k. Then add 2–10 ml of the solution to be examined, place vessel N into the cylinder C (the vessel N is fixed in position by the spring p), and adjust the position of vessel N to allow the bubbles of inert gas to pass freely into the solution (the tube of the inner vessel N should fit into the cylinder C of the jacket to leave a clearance of about 0·5 mm).

Remove the oxygen from the solution by passing the inert gas through the inlet tube, keeping the stopcock closed. During the recordings of the current–voltage curve, open the stopcock in the inlet tube and allow the space in the jacket above the solution to be filled with the inert gas (excess gas escapes through the interspace between the two cylindrical tubes without disturbing the solution, thus preventing the diffusion of atmospheric air into the solution under examination).

Insert a stainless steel contact wire into the mercury, through the side arm k, to make the anode connection. When the curve of one solution has been recorded, replace the vessel N by another vessel of the same type filled with the subsequent solution; insert this vessel into the jacket and vigorously bubble the inert gas through the solution for 2–3 min. The solution is then ready for polarographic examination. For a large series of solutions a wooden or plastic block can be used with holes to support a number of electrolyte vessels on rod n. The solutions can be then deaerated simultaneously.

The vessels N are easily cleaned and dried, and with a number of such vessels the analysis of a series of samples is much faster. The capillary tip is always situated in the same position, relative to the mercury level in the reservoir and platinum metal is not necessary for contacts.

When anodic as well as cathodic waves are to be investigated and when the values of the half-wave potentials are to be determined, as in other instances where the use of the mercury pool electrode is excluded, it is necessary to have a reference electrode separated from the solution to be examined. A suitable vessel for such measurements is the Kalousek vessel,[5] shown in Fig. 20d; the solution to be investigated is separated from the electrolyte of the reference electrode by a liquid boundary. The cell consists of two compartments: the solution to be examined is placed in the left compartment (Fig. 20d); the right compartment, separated by the stopcock B, contains the reference electrode. To ensure a low resistance, the stopcock B is best constructed with a wide bore and the connecting tubes on both sides of this stopcock should be as short as possible. As reference electrodes, calomel or mercurous sulphate electrodes are usually used. The procedure for a cell containing a mercurous sulphate electrode is as follows:

With tap A open, pour enough mercury through a funnel to give a layer 3–5 mm deep at the bottom. Then add a small quantity of solid mercurous sulphate, followed by a small volume of the solution to be used in the reference electrode (1 N sodium sulphate, 0·1 N sulphuric acid). Leave the mercurous sulphate to settle and then with taps A and B open, fill the cell slowly with the solution for the reference electrode until it rises above tap B. Close stopcocks A and B after first driving any gas bubbles out through the main stopcock, B. Remove the rest of the solution for the reference electrolyte from the left compartment by opening the tap at the bottom of this compartment. Remove with air-pressure (applied with a bent glass tubing) or suction the remaining liquid in the side tube connected to stopcock B. Similarly thoroughly rinse the left compartment with distilled water and/or a part of the solution to be examined. Close both taps A and B during this treatment.

Place the solution to be analysed into the left compartment, ensuring that tap B and the stopcock at the bottom of this compartment are closed. Then place the capillary (in a rubber bung) into the solution and allow the mercury to flow out. Introduce the inert gas through the side tube into the solution (Fig. 20d, extreme left) and connect the gas-outlet, the side arm at the top of the left compartment, to a water seal. After deaeration of the sample, open the stopcock B and record the polarographic curve. When the measurements have been completed remove the capillary from the solution, close tap B and discard the electrolysed solution via the stopcock at the bottom of the left compartment. Blow out any solution remaining in the connecting tube with a bent glass tube; after rinsing the cell is ready for a further electrolysis.

*Notes.* When a sufficient volume of the solution to be analysed is available, and in situations where the differences in the composition of the solutions are small, it is unnecessary to rinse the left compartment with water and it is sufficient to wash twice with the solution to be analysed before an electrolysis.

This cell is also well suited for the analysis of a great number of samples. The main advantages are: no handling of mercury, simple, rapid cleaning and preparation of the cell, drying is not necessary and highly reproducible results can be obtained.

Kalousek's cells are usually manufactured for quantities of 5–20 ml. of solution. When smaller volumes are used, the wide bore of stopcock B, and the wide and short connections to it, become conditions difficult to fulfil when glass stopcocks are used. In such circumstances, a modification of the polarographic cell shown in Fig. 21 can be used.[6] A Cellophane or other similar plastic membrane is used for the separation of both compartments. An agar bridge can be used for the central section, but even this is unnecessary when the central part is not horizontal. The Cellophane membrane is very suitable because of its low resistance and hindrance to the contamination of the electrolysed solution with agar. Membranes of this type cannot, of course, be used in solutions containing compounds which react with the membrane itself, e.g. periodic acid. The "dead space" around the stopcock is eliminated and 0·5–5 ml. of solution can be safely electrolysed. The rinsing is more simple than with the original Kalousek's cell. Analogous cells without "dead space" can be made from plastic materials.

In the above cell, a silver chloride reference electrode can also be used. The silver wire is inserted into a rubber plug which lies horizontally in the side arm. A sintered glass disc is less suitable for the separation of the reference electrode because of the relatively high resistance of such cells. The solution to be electrolysed can also be contaminated by agar, and the cleaning operation for subsequent analyses is lengthy and difficult.

D

Vessels with temperature control are used mainly for precise theoretical measurements, especially when kinetic currents are involved, for methods using a calibration curve, and for the measurements of homogeneous kinetics, with a mercury dropping electrode as an indicator, for the changes of concentrations of polarographically active substances with time. These vessels usually

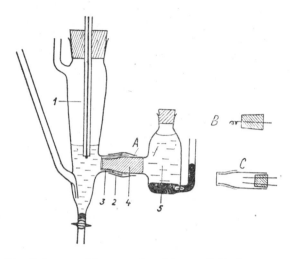

FIG. 21. Polarographic vessel with a Cellophane separated reference electrode.
(1) Capillary electrode; (2) rubber connection; (3) Cellophane diaphragm; (4) agar–potassium chloride bridge; (5) calomel electrode; (A) compartment with calomel reference electrode; (B) silver chloride electrode (put instead of A); (C) compartment with two silver chloride electrodes for three electrode system measurements.

consist of a water jacket, either around the section where the electrolysed solution is placed or also around the reference electrode. However, it is often easier to immerse a normal vessel in a waterbath at a controlled temperature.

Among the special-purpose cells are those vessels used for continuous analysis.[7, 8] In this type of measurement the limiting current is measured for control or automation purposes over a long period of time. Thus both the reference electrode and the indicator electrode properties must not change with time. This type of instrument is used for process streams, and the usual types of indicator and reference electrodes are inconvenient. In the most successful forms of continuous analysers, the stream of analysed gas or solution streams against the indicator electrode. The potential of the reference electrode is kept constant by a slow but steady stream of an appropriate solution around the electrode. Cells enabling the continuous flow of both analysed solution, or gas and solution around the reference electrode (which can also serve as a supporting electrolyte for the electrode process taking place at the indicator electrode) have different forms according to the specific analytical problems.

## 2.4. THE POLAROGRAPH

A polarograph is an apparatus which registers the current–voltage curves. Since 1925, when J. Heyrovský and his Japanese co-worker M. Shikata constructed the first polarograph, many instruments of varying complexity have been constructed and are now produced all over the world.

Most of the instruments used contain the following basic parts, shown in Fig. 1: (i) A source of e.m.f. enabling a continuous or step-wise change of the voltage which is applied to the electrolysis cell. (ii) An indicator showing the current flowing during electrolysis. (iii) An arrangement enabling the recording of the current indicated by the indicator as a function of the applied voltage. The various types of apparatus differ mainly in the way that the resulting current–voltage curve is registered. The three main types can be distinguished by the use of the photographic, manual or pen-recording principle.

The various types of polarographs and their uses have been described in several other monographs and commercial literature, and thus only the principles and comparison of these three groups are given here (Cf. references 9–11).

In photographically recording instruments, the continuous increase of the applied voltage (usually from a potentiometer drum) is synchronized with the movement of photographic paper. The current flowing through the electrolysis cell is indicated by a sensitive mirror galvanometer. A beam of light deflected by the galvanometer mirror falls through a slit on the photographic paper, where the increase in current causes a deflection perpendicular to the direction of movement of the paper (corresponding to increasing applied voltage). Hence the increase of current and the increase of applied voltage in the perpendicular direction enable the recording of current–voltage curves. When developed, a "polarographic curve" is observed on the photographic paper, the abscissa denoting the voltage and the ordinate the current (cf. Figs. 2, 4 etc.). When several polarographic curves of this type are recorded on the same sheet of photographic paper it is then called a polarogram.

Photographically-recording instruments are in our opinion the most suitable for research purposes, for they enable one to distinguish minor details on polarographic curves because the waveform is not usually distorted. On the other hand facilities for photographic developing are necessary and some time is consumed in the handling of photographic materials. Moreover, a certain amount of training is necessary to visualize the course of the polarographic curve directly from the movement of the light-spot on the slit in front of the photographic paper. Such a visualization enables one to record and place several polarographic curves on a polarogram in any way that is desired.

In manual instruments the voltage is changed manually, and at chosen potentials the current is measured by means of a sensitive indicator. The deflections corresponding to current are then plotted manually against voltage to give a current–voltage curve. In some instruments the change of applied voltage is synchronized with the shift of a translucent paper, through which the position of a light spot, reflected from the indicator galvanometer and showing the current flowing, can be observed and marked on the paper. This arrangement possesses some advantages when looking for extremely accurate values for the half-wave potentials, and other detailed information as to the wave-form. Nevertheless, the continuous record reveals more detail than discontinuous manual plotting. The automatic recording of current–voltage curves represents also a substantial gain of time in comparison with manual methods. The technique, by which the current is only measured at two potentials (at the potential more positive than that of the wave and at the potential of the limiting current) lacks certainty because other substances may be estimated together with the substance under investigation.

The main advantage of manual instruments is that they are relatively inexpensive, and possess an educational value demonstrating clearly the principles of the polarographic method. The manual instruments can furthermore be advantageously applied to polarometric titrations.

In pen- or pencil-recording instruments it is usually the shift of the paper that is synchronized with the increase of applied voltage, and the deflection of the pen or pencil is proportional to the current flowing through the electrolysis cell. Electronic or photoelectric amplification is necessary for the tracing of polarographic curves with a recorder. Only when the electronic or other amplifying system possesses the properties of a critically damped galvanometer with a period of about 10 sec can the recorded curves be identical to those recorded manually or photographically (with a slow voltage-scanning). Only a few commercially available instruments fulfil this condition, and thus curves obtained with the other instruments differ from "true" curves. Such instruments are not suitable for fundamental theoretical studies.

On the other hand, for analytical purposes, where only the values of the limiting currents are of interest, pen-recording systems are suitable. In addition, in factories or places exposed to shocks the suspended galvanometer is of no use and only the pen-recording instruments are recommended.

The use of pen-recording instruments permits routine polarographic analysis to be successfully carried out in industrial laboratories, where the primary interest lies in other fields of chemistry and only a limited knowledge of polarographic theory and practice is required.

The changes of current due to the growing mercury drop cause oscillations of the current during the life of one drop. For theoretical purposes only the mean value of these oscillations (mean current, $i$) is measured by using a critically damped galvanometer with a period of swing somewhat larger than the twofold average drop-time (i.e. $T \doteq 10$ sec) or its equivalent (discussed further in Chapter III). The mean current is read off directly with manual instruments, and in photographic and pen-recording instruments the oscillations are registered on the curves. In some commercial instruments these oscillations can be eliminated by additional damping, but we do not think that the elimination by overdamping or other methods is advantageous even for analytical purposes. The regular current oscillations are one of the factors that indicate a well functioning capillary and apparatus.

The main constituents given above are included in practically all commercially manufactured polarographs. Beside these, most commercial instruments contain some additional parts, e.g. a circuit which enables a change of sensitivity of the galvanometer (or its electronic equivalent) without changing the condition of critical damping. Different current-scales enable one to record polarographic curves with solutions of varying concentration. Another type of circuit allows the choice of the appropriate potential range and potential span for the recording of draw-out curves. Also the rate of voltage scanning can be changed with some instruments. Another type enables one to compensate for the condenser (capacity) current.

Some types of polarographic instruments introduced new principles for electrolysis with a dropping mercury electrode. Thus the current can be measured only during a period at the end of each drop-life ("Tast polarography"), and by the application of a square-wave-voltage ("square-wave polarography"), possibly with an amplitude-modulated radio-frequency current modulated by square-wave-voltage ("square-wave polarography with r.f. polarization"), or changes in limiting currents produced by rectangular voltage pulses ("pulse polarography") are recorded.[12] The change of voltage in the whole range can occur during a very short time, and cathode ray tubes are then used for tracing the current–voltage curves (single-sweep[13] and multi-sweep methods are discussed together with auxilliary methods on p. 48). The continuously increasing voltage can be superimposed by an alternating current of small amplitude (a.c. polarography).[14] Instead of voltage, a continuously increasing current can be applied to the electrolysis cell and the corresponding potential of the dropping mercury electrode is recorded (constant-current polarography).[15] Alternating current can also be applied to the electrodes in oscillographic polarography[25–27] and changes in charging current are followed. Most of these methods, developed for special branches, claim to possess analytical applications. We shall restrict ourselves to the application of conventional ("classical") polarography and some of the above mentioned methods will be discussed only among auxiliary methods.

## 2.5. DERIVATIVE AND SUBTRACTIVE METHODS

If the sample is a complicated mixture, it depends on the nature and ratio of the single constituents whether or not a polarographic method is preferable. It is a simple problem in polarography to determine a trace constituent that is reduced at more positive potentials (A) than an excess of a reducible compound (B) (Fig. 22, curve 1). Similarly a small anodic wave at more negative potentials (C') can be measured exactly in the presence of excess of a substance (D') which gives a large anodic wave at more positive potentials (Fig. 22, curve 4).

On the other hand, the situation is more difficult if a small reduction wave (B') is preceded by a large wave due to a substance in excess (A') which is reducible at more positive potentials (Fig.

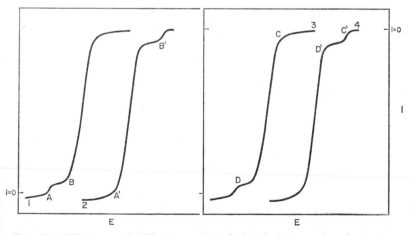

Fig. 22. Mixtures of different ratios of depolarizers reduced at more positive (A) and more negative (B) potentials or giving anodic waves at more negative (C) and more positive (D) potentials. Cathodic waves right, galvanometer zero line at the bottom. Anodic waves left, galvanometer zero line at the top.

22, curve 2). The oscillations on the limiting current of the substance in excess obscure the measurement of the height of the more negative wave. Similarly the measurement of a small anodic wave (D) preceded by a large wave due to a substance (C) in excess (Fig. 22, curve 3) also presents difficulties.

For example, a small wave due to trace of nitrobenzene, reducible at very positive potentials (at about −0·3 V) at the dropping mercury electrode, can be measured precisely in the presence of a thousandfold or even ten thousandfold excess of phenylhydroxylamine, reducible in acid solutions at above −1·0 V.

However, the determination of phthalic acid in the presence of naphthoquinone can only be performed with the usual accuracy when the naphthoquinone, reducible at positive potentials, is present in about a five-fold excess. With a larger excess of naphthoquinone, the more negative wave for phthalic acid cannot be measured very accurately. Such instances can be handled chemically with the proper supporting electrolyte or by separation methods as will be shown later. Another possible separation is provided by the derivative and subtractive methods.

Derivative methods overcome the difficulty mentioned above by plotting $di/dE$–$E$ diagrams instead of the usual $i$–$E$ graphs. The $di/dE$–$E$ diagrams are described as derivative polarograms. The method was first recommended by J. Heyrovský[16] and such curves can be obtained by using two synchronized dropping mercury electrodes in a modified polarization circuit. For practical purposes a suitable system containing only one dropping mercury electrode was proposed by J. Vogel and J. Říha[16, 17] and later described by M. P. Lévèque and F. Roth.[18]

Curves registered with this circuit (Fig. 23) show peaks corresponding to waves in ordinary polarography. The galvanometer reading remains zero before and after the completion of the wave. The position of the peak relative to the abscissa denotes the half-wave potential, i.e. the quality of the electroactive substance, because the maximum of the peak is approximately at the half-wave potential. The height of these peaks are often practically a linear function of the concentration of the electrolysed compound and are thus used for quantitative analysis. Nevertheless the use of a calibration curve (cf. p. 73) is always recommended.

Even when the derivative current drops to practically zero at the limiting current, the oscillations due to the dropping persists and these oscillations interfere in the measurement of small peaks at more negative potentials. This difficulty can be overcome by using an electrode with a regulated drop-time or a Smoleř-type electrode. [1]

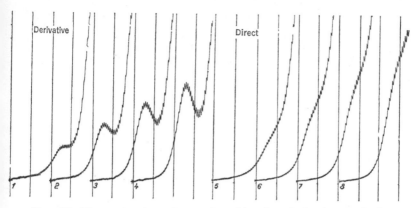

FIG. 23. Determination of pyruvic acid using derivative method. 9 ml. of the acetate buffer + 1 ml. of sauerkraut juice. Added sodium pyruvate: (1) and (5) 0; (2) and (6) $3 \times 10^{-4}$ M; (3) and (7) $6 \times 10^{-4}$ M; (4) and (8) $9 \times 10^{-4}$ M. (1)–(4) are $di/dt - E$ curves recorded using the derivative circuit of J. Vogel and J. Říha, curves (5)–(8) are primitive $i-E$ curves. Curves start at $-0.6$ V, S.C.E., 200m V/absc., 270 mV/min, $t_1 = 2.4$ sec, $m = 2.4$ mg/sec, full scale sensitivity: derivative curves $0.5$ $\mu$A, primitive curves $4$ $\mu$A.

This derivative method cannot be used with manual polarographs because a continuous linear increase in voltage is difficult to adjust.

Another method, which eliminates large limiting currents in order to facilitate the measurement of a relatively small one, is the subtractive method, devised by G. Semerano and L. Riccoboni. [19] In this method (also called differential polarography) the galvanometer measures the difference in the currents flowing through two separated electrolytic cells with identical capillaries and the same supporting electrolyte. In one cell the sample is dissolved, and in the other the same concentration of an interfering substance is added (preferably by titration). The currents due to the interfering substance, present in excess, are subtracted with this circuit and the resulting curve only shows the waves for minor constituents.

Oxygen is also present in both solutions in the same concentrations, and consequently its waves are subtracted and cause no interference. To obtain curves without disturbances as in ordinary polarography, not only the drop-time, but also the outflow velocity of mercury from both capillaries, as well as the potential of both reference electrodes must be identical. Because these conditions are not very easily obtainable with the subtractive method it has not found many applications so far.

Lastly, a circuit was devised so that an adjustable current of opposite direction to the electrolytic current could be sent through the galvanometer. However the large oscillations remaining on the curves made the measurement of small waves very difficult.

## 2.6. AUXILIARY METHODS

### 2.6.1. *Estimation of Reversibility*

The first condition for the reversibility of the electrode process (mentioned on p. 26) is the coincidence of the half-wave potentials of the oxidized and reduced forms of the system under study. It often happens that only one of these two forms is available or sufficiently stable, and then some of the auxiliary methods must be employed to prove the mobility of the system. The application of a periodically changed rectangular voltage using the instrument devised by M. Kalousek[20, 21] produces the wave for the product of the primary electrode process. Using the simple form of this circuitry, the electrolysis is carried out over several short periods during one drop-time at a chosen applied voltage (corresponding to the limiting current and branched from an auxiliary potentiometer). During intermittent short periods the current–voltage curve (corresponding to the polarography of the electrolysis product formed at the surface of the electrode) is recorded. The half-wave potential of this wave can be compared with that of the simple curve.

Similarly the reversibility can be studied with a steady mercury electrode, e.g. a hanging mercury drop electrode.[22, 23] This type of electrode is first polarized continuously from positive to negative potentials, the change is then interrupted and the polarization continued for some time at the voltage corresponding to the limiting current of the wave.* If the polarization is carried out from negative to more positive potentials, an anodic peak occurs for reversible systems at the same potential as that of the cathodic peak registered during the first period. Products formed as intermediates in the reduction of nitro-compounds[22] and hydrogen sulphide formed in the hydrogenolysis of 4-mercapto-pyridoxol (Fig. 24)[24] were detected in this way.

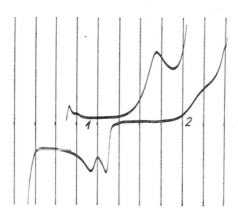

FIG. 24. Detection of electrolysis products using the hanging mercury drop method.
Borax pH 9·3, $2 \times 10^{-4}$ M pyridoxthiol polarized from positive to negative potentials (1) and from negative to positive potentials (2). Backwards tracing started immediately after (1) was recorded. Of the two anodic peaks one corresponds to the SH-group of pyridoxthiol and one to the SH-ions formed in the reduction process. S.C.E., 200 mV/absc., 250 mV/min, hanging drop electrode designed by J. Vogel, full scale sensitivity 1·5 $\mu$A.

An oscilloscope instead of a galvanometer is often used to follow rapid reactions occurring during the life of a single drop. There are two main groups of oscillographic methods used for the study of

* This period can be very short and the reversal of the direction of the polarization can follow "immediately" after arriving at negative potentials. The sufficient stability of the reduction product is anticipated.

electrode processes: the method of applied current and the method of applied voltage.

The first group is represented by oscillographic polarography, invented by J. Heyrovský and J. Forejt.[25-27] This method follows $E$–$t$, $dE/dt$–$t$ and recently mainly $dE/dt$–$E$-curves. When the cathodic and anodic "kinks" or incisions are observed at the same potential, the systems are described as reversible. The greater the difference in the potentials of the "kinks" or incisions, the more irreversible is the reaction. The "degree of reversibility" is a crude measure of the mobility of the electrode process. The period of polarization is such, that usually the whole curve from 0·0 V to 2·0 V and back to 0·0 V is traced during some 1/50 sec; the oscillographic reversibility has thus a somewhat different meaning to reversibility in classical polarography.

Single sweep oscillography, introduced independently by J. E. B. Randles[28] and A. Ševčík,[29] belongs to the second group. This method applies a single voltage-sweep to the system of the dropping and reference electrode. The voltage-sweep is applied usually in the second half of the drop-time, where there is little change in the surface of the electrode. With reversible systems the cathodic and anodic peaks, corresponding to polarization from positive to negative potentials and vice versa, occur at almost the same potential, as with the hanging mercury drop.

### 2.6.2. *Proof of the Character of Polarographic Processes*

Rapid changes in the instantaneous current during the life of a single drop can be registered with an oscilloscope or a string-galvanometer. Because of the transfer of concentration polarization, the best results are obtained when the $i$–$t$ curve is registered on the first drop after the voltage is applied.[30, 31] Parabolic $i$–$t$ curves were observed for limiting currents corresponding to the equation $i = k \times t^{0.19}$ for diffusion and $i = k \times t^{0.66}$ for kinetic currents. The measurement of the $i$–$t$ curves in the potential range corresponding to the rising part of the polarographic wave has shown the possibility of distinguishing between reversible and irreversible processes, or between processes where the reduction product is soluble and processes where the reduction product forms an amalgam. The $i$–$t$ curves for adsorption processes have the form of a peak (Fig. 25). Some catalytic processes give a linear increase of the current with time. In other instances curves rising exponentially or hyperbolically were observed.

The curves of the dependence of the instantaneous current with time, using a hanging drop electrode polarized by a voltage

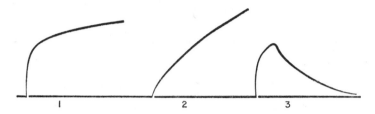

FIG. 25. Typical $i$–$t$ curves.
(1) Diffusion current; (2) kinetic current; (3) adsorption current.

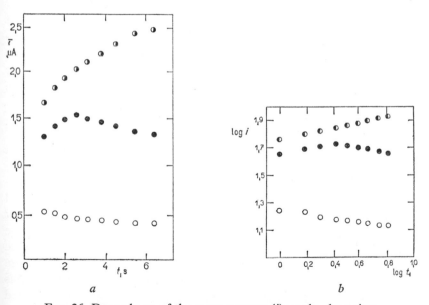

FIG. 26. Dependence of the mean current ($i$) on the drop-time.
Britton–Robinson buffer of pH 2·8; $1·2 \times 10^{-3}$ M tropylium bromide $m = 1·38$ mg/sec, regulated drop-time. (a) $i_{lim} - t_1$; (b) $\log i_{lim} - \log t_1$. $\bigcirc$—$(i_{a1})_{lim}$; $\bullet$—$(i_{a_1} + i_{a_2} + i_1)_{lim}$; $\mathbb{O}$—total limiting current.

pulse show different forms. The processes controlled by diffusion, rate of chemical reaction, or rate of autocatalytic reaction have recently been shown to be distinguishable.[32]

It is possible to register, by regulation of the drop-time with mechanical, electrical or electronic devices, the dependence of the mean current on the drop-time, i.e. $i–t_1$ (Fig. 26) and on the outflow velocity $i–m$. Such curves were mainly used for the study of adsorption processes, even when the results were complicated by the transfer of concentration polarization in a similar way to classical polarography.

If there is no device for the drop-control, the drop-time can be altered in a narrower range by changing the position of the mercury reservoir (changing $m$ simultaneously) or by changing the position of the capillary tip. An extreme change in the drop-time gives the streaming mercury electrode,[2] suitable for studying kinetic currents and adsorption effects. The electrocapillary curves can also offer some information as to adsorption phenomena.

Alternating current polarography and tensametry[14] can provide valuable information on adsorption processes and on the difference between various types of adsorption. Finally, using a periodically changed rectangular voltage[20, 21] the adsorption of the product of the electrode process causes a substantial increase of current on the "switched on" curve.

### 2.6.3. *Determination of the Number of Electrons transferred in the Electrode Reaction*

The possibility of applying the simple Ilkovič equation for calculations of the number of electrons ($n$) cannot be recommended, for the exact values of the diffusion coefficients are usually unknown under the conditions used in polarography (i.e. at low concentrations). Moreover, it would be necessary to use the extended form of the Ilkovič equation[33] to obtain precise values. Thus the usual operation is to compare the height of the wave under examination, with the height for a substance in the same molar concentration in the same supporting electrolyte. The number of electrons transferred for the latter substance must be known precisely under the conditions used. The standard substance must be a well-defined chemical entity, and the molecular shape and the molecular weight should be approximately the same as the molecule under examination. It is also preferable that both the standard and the substance should contain some identical functional groupings. It is assumed that the diffusion coefficients of both the standard and substance are practically identical, and it is advisable to use more than one standard compound. Suitable standard substances are quinones, nitro-compounds and some carbonyl compounds.

The condition of identical diffusion coefficients is best fulfilled when the studied and standard groupings are contained in the same molecule. If the reduction potentials of these groupings are sufficiently separated, two waves are observed on the polarographic curve. When the number of electrons transferred in one of these steps is known, the number of electrons transferred in the other can be computed from the ratio of the wave-heights. Thus the reduction of $p$-iodonitrobenzene produced two waves in alkaline solutions: The more positive corresponds to the reduction of the nitro-group, the more negative to the reduction of the C–I bond, and the ratio of the wave-heights is 2:1. As the nitro-group is reduced with the consumption of 4 electrons, it can be deduced that the reduction of the C–I bond proceeds with the consumption of two electrons.

Coulometry, milli- and microcoulometry[9] are also used for the determination of the number of electrons transferred. In these methods the quantity of electricity necessary to reduce a distinct amount of the substance is measured at the potential of the limiting current, controlled by a potentiostat. Coulometric methods are usually not very accurate, and sometimes side reactions occur when electrodes of constant surface are used instead of a dropping electrode. An insufficient separation of cathodic and anodic spacing can also cause complications. Coulometric methods are thus best suited for systems, where $n = 1$ or 2, but for higher numbers of electrons transferred, the decision is often difficult.

The most unambiguous method for the determination of the number of electrons transferred in electro-reduction or -oxidation of organic compounds, is the identification of the product of the electrolysis with a dropping mercury electrode (discussed in the next paragraph). Knowledge of the number of bonds in the substance under examination and the product of electrolysis gives an estimation of the number of electrons needed for this transformation.

### 2.6.4. *Identification of the Product of Electrode Processes*

A most useful and very important method for the study of electrode processes is electrolysis at a constant potential. This can be performed by setting manually the appropriate potential or preferably by the use of potentiostats, which by either mechanical or electronic devices automatically keep the potential constant during the electrolysis.

The reduction process is usually followed at the potential of the limiting current. When more than one wave is observed in the given supporting electrolyte, the electrolysis can be applied successively at each limiting current.

The electrodes generally used are either a stationary mercury electrode or a dropping mercury electrode. The steady mercury pool electrode produces greater amounts of the reduction product, but the conditions can differ from those at a dropping electrode. The difference consists mainly in the prolonged time when the reduction product is in the neighbourhood of the electrode. During this time different side and competitive reactions can take place which do not affect the electrode process under normal polarographic conditions. When a dropping mercury electrode is used for the electrolysis at a constant potential, the products are usually identical with those in polarography, but the amounts of the prepared product of the electrode process are essentially lower.

The identification of the products prepared using the mercury pool electrode can be carried out with the usual methods of classical organic chemistry. With the dropping mercury electrode, the methods employed are those used for dilute solutions, e.g. paper chromatography, spectrophotometry, determination of dissociation constants, or polarography.

When the product of the electrode process is itself electroactive in the same solution in which its electrolysis is performed its identification is possible with oscillographic polarography, single-sweep oscillography, the periodical change of voltage or the hanging mercury drop electrolysis.

The incisions on the oscillographic d$E$/d$t$–$E$-curves show the presence of a reduction product, in a similar way as new peaks on the patterns obtained with the single-sweep method, or the hanging mercury drop electrolysis. Because of the short time-period used, both oscillographic methods sometimes show products or intermediates too short-lived to be detected by other methods. In oscillographic polarography the different conditions and mainly the cyclization of the polarization process, sometimes give rise to different electrolytic reaction products from those obtained in classical polarography. Polarographic waves of the reduction product can also be obtained using the periodically changing rectangular voltage method.

The product formed in the electro-reduction by the latter four methods can only be examined under the same conditions at which the reduction is performed. This is a distinct disadvantage in comparison with potentiostatic methods. It is far better, for the proof of identity, to compare the reduction product formed in one supporting electrolyte with the behaviour of a standard substance not only in the same solution, but also under different conditions.

The use of electrolysis under controlled potential is necessary when the product of the electrode process is electro-inactive under the conditions used, but polarographically active under other conditions.

Some of the methods described in preceding paragraphs were used for the identification of the electrolysis product corresponding to the four-electron wave, in alkaline buffered solutions of 3-phenyl sydnone.[34] A decrease of the four-electron reduction wave and an increase of an anodic wave at positive potentials was observed during the course of controlled potential electrolysis with a dropping mercury electrode (Fig. 27). The wave was identified as a hydrazine derivative wave (corresponding to the formation of a slightly soluble or complex mercury compound) by comparison with other hydrazine derivatives at several different pH-values. Similar results were obtained using the periodically changed rectangular polarizing voltage in the commutator method devised by Kalousek. An increase in the positive anodic wave for the hydrazine derivative was observed (Fig. 28) when the auxiliary

E

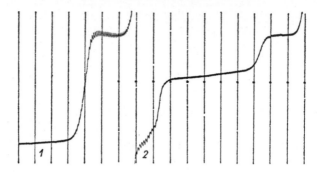

FIG. 27. Controlled potential electrolysis of sydnones.
0·005 M benzylsydnone, in a borate buffer pH 9·3, was electrolysed
using a dropping mercury electrode with potential controlled by a
potentiostat by Peizker. The electrolysis was performed for 30
hr. The resulting solution was diluted twentyfold using a borate
buffer. (1) before electrolysis; (2) after electrolysis. 200 mV/absc.,
full scale sensitivity 4·2 μA.

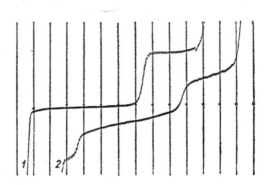

FIG. 28. Sydnone reduction using the commutator method by
Kalousek.
2·5 × 10⁻⁴ M 3-phenylsydnone, borate buffer pH 9·3 with 5 per
cent ethanol: (1) primitive curve; (2) commutated curve, auxiliary
potential corresponds to the limiting current. Frequency of
commutation: 3·5 c/sec. Curves starting at +0·2 V, S.C.E., 200
mV/absc., h = 65 cm, full scale sensitivity 10 μA.

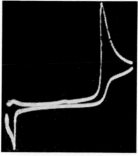

Fig. 29. Oscillographic $i$–$E$-curves of sydnone in alkaline solutions using the technique of impulse polarography.
$1.25 \times 10^{-4}$ M 3-phenylsydnone in 0·05 M borate buffer pH 9·3. Apparatus by Valenta, $t_1 = 22.7$ sec, one triangular impulse, the slope of the impulse 0·63 V/sec, $i_{max} = 1.59$ A. Starting voltage $-0.04$ V (against Hg-pool), final voltage $-1.90$ V.

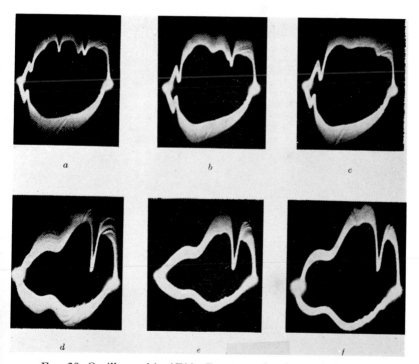

Fig. 30. Oscillographic d$E$/d$t$–$E$-curves of sydnone derivatives.
$1.25 \times 10^{-4}$ M sydnone in (A) 0·1 M-NaOH, (B) 0·5 M-H$_2$SO$_4$, (a), (d) phenyl-sydnone, (b), (e) 3′,4′-dihydroquinolo[1′,2′-c] sydnone, (c), (f) 3-phenyl-4-methylsydnone. Polaroskop, 0·2 mA, amplif. 1, S.C.E.

potential, corresponding to the limiting current of the four-electron wave, was applied.

The formation of hydrazines was further proved by the single-sweep method. The curve obtained with triangular voltage-sweep (Fig. 29) showed, in addition to a cathodic peak (corresponding to the reduction of the sydnone ring), an anodic peak, corresponding to the formation of a mercury salt with the hydrazine derivative, formed in the reduction process at more negative potentials. Finally, the oscillographic $dE/dt = f(E)$ curves in alkaline media showed a reversible incision at positive potentials (Fig. 30). This incision corresponds to the oxidation-reduction system of the mercury hydrazine derivative formed during polarization at negative potentials.

In addition to these proofs, the formation of a hydrazine derivative was detected by potentiometric titration of the solution electrolysed at a constant potential. In sydnone solutions no dissociation step was observed between pH 2 and 12, but the product of electrolysis showed a dissociation step, in agreement with model hydrazine derivatives, with a p$K$ value of about 9·8.

In addition to the auxiliary methods given above, it is sometimes possible to identify the product of the electrolysis directly from the course of the polarographic wave. Two or more waves are observed on the polarographic curves for substances that undergo polarographic electrolysis in a number of successive steps, i.e. for substances that are electrolysed with the formation of stable inter-mediates, or for substances bearing several electroactive groups. If the product formed during polarographic electrolysis at the potentials of the first step is stable, then this product can be identi-fied by comparison of the second wave of the substance with waves obtained in solutions under the same conditions, containing only the stable intermediate. The half-wave potential and the wave-form in one supporting electrolyte are not considered a sufficient proof of identity, and several media ought to be used for comparison.

This principle of identification of electrolysis products can be demonstrated by the reduction of α-aminoketones.[35] ω-Piperi-dinoacetophenone is reduced in two steps (Fig. 31) and both the potential and the pH-dependence of the more negative wave is identical with that for acetophenone. Hence, acetophenone must be the product formed in the first wave and this is possibly only when the C–N bond is broken in the first step. Thus the gross reaction can be given by the following equations:

$$\text{1st step:} -COCH_2\overset{+}{N}R_3 + 2e + H^+ \longrightarrow -COCH_3 + NR_3$$

$$\text{2nd step:} -COCH_3 + 2e + 2H^+ \longrightarrow -CHOHCH_3$$

Other examples include 4-bromosydnones,[36] diaryl iodonium salts and bromonaphthalenes.[37] The first wave in the polarographic curve of 4-bromosydnones corresponds to the reduction of the C–Br bond, while the second is practically identical to the wave of the parent sydnone. The first two waves of diaryl iodonium

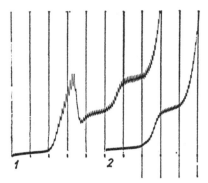

FIG. 31. Comparison of waves for ω-piperidinoacetophenone metho-iodide and acetophenone.
Phosphate buffer pH 6·95 with $2 \times 10^{-4}$ M: (1) ω-piperidonoacetophenone methoiodide; (2) acetophenone. Curves starting (1) at −0·6 V, (2) at −1·2 V, S.C.E., 200 mV/absc., $h = 65$ cm, full scale sensitivity 6·2 μA.

salts show that one C–I bond is broken and the iodobenzene formed is reduced at more negative potentials. In bromonaphthalenes, the naphthalene formed in the reduction of the C–Br bond in the more positive wave is further reduced at −2·1 V. These examples, based solely on current–voltage curves, demonstrate the applicability of the method.

POLAROGRAPHIC INSTRUMENTATION59

## REFERENCES

(1) SMOLEŘ, I., *Collect. Czechoslov. Chem. Commun.* **19**, 238 (1954).
(2) KOLTHOFF, I. M. and OKINAKA, Y., Recent Modifications of the Heyrovsky Dropping Mercury Electrode, in *Progress in Polarography* (P. Zuman, I. M. Kolthoff, editors), Vol. 2, p. 357. Interscience, New York (1962).
(3) ADAMS, R. N., Solid Electrodes, in *Progress in Polarography* (P. Zuman, I. M. Kolthoff, editors), Vol. 2, p. 503, Interscience, New York (1962).
(4) NOVÁK, J. V. A., *Collect. Czechoslov. Chem. Commun.* **12**, 237 (1947).
(5) HEYROVSKÝ, J. and KALOUSEK, M., *Collect. Czechoslov. Chem. Commun.* **11**, 464 (1939).
(6) ZUMAN, P., *Chem. listy* **51**, 993 (1957).
(7) ZAGÓRSKI, Z., Cells for Polarographic Electrolysis, in *Progress in Polarography* (P. Zuman, I. M. Kolthoff, editors), Vol. 2, p. 549, Interscience, New York (1962).
(8) NOVÁK, J. V. A., Continuous Polarographic Analyzers, in *Progress in Polarography* (P. Zuman, I. M. Kolthoff, editors), Vol. 2, p. 569, Interscience, New York (1962).
(9) MEITES, L., Advances in Polarographic Instrumentation in the United States, in *Progress in Polarography* (P. Zuman, I. M. Kolthoff, editors) Vol. 2, p. 515, Interscience, New York (1962).
(10) TANAKA, N., Polarographic Instrumentation in Japan, in *Progress in Polarography* (P. Zuman, I. M. Kolthoff, editors), Vol. 2, p. 523, Interscience, New York (1962).
(11) ŠERÁK, L., Advances in Classical Polarographic Instrumentation in Europe, in *Progress in Polarography* (P. Zuman, I. M. Kolthoff editors), Vol. 2, p. 535, Interscience, New York (1962).
(12) BARKER, G. C., Square-wave and Pulse Polarography, in *Progress in Polarography* (P. Zuman, I. M. Kolthoff, editors), Vol. 2, p. 411, Interscience, New York (1962).
(13) VOGEL, J., Single-sweep Method, in *Progress in Polarography* (P. Zuman, I. M. Kolthoff, editors), Vol. 2, p. 429, Interscience, New York (1962).
(14) BREYER, B., Alternating Current Polarography and Tensammetry, in *Progress in Polarography* (P. Zuman, I. M. Kolthoff, editors), Vol. 2, p. 487, Interscience, New York (1962).
(15) FUJINAGA, T., Constant-Current Polarography and Chronopotentiometry at the Dropping Mercury Electrode, in *Progress in Polarography* (P. Zuman, I. M. Kolthoff, editors), Vol. 1, p. 201, Interscience, New York (1962).
(16) HEYROVSKÝ, J., *Chem. listy* **43**, 149 (1949).
(17) VOGEL, J. and ŘÍHA, J., *J. Chim. phys.* (*Fr.*) **47**, 5 (1950).
(18) LÉVÈQUE, P. and ROTH, F., *J. Chim. phys.* (*Fr.*) **46**, 480 (1949); **47**, 623 (1950).

(19) SEMERANO, G. and RICCOBONI, L., *Gazz. chim. ital.* **72**, 297 (1942).
(20) KALOUSEK, M., *Collect. Czechoslov. Chem. Commun.* **13**, 105 (1948).
(21) RÁLEK, M. and NOVÁK, L., *Collect. Czechoslov. Chem. Commun.* **21**, 248 (1956).
(22) KEMULA, W., *Advances in Polarography* (Proc. 2nd Internat. Congr. Polarography, Cambridge 1959), Vol. 1, p. 135, Pergamon Press, London (1960).
(23) ŘÍHA, J., The Hanging Mercury Drop in Polarography, in *Progress in Polarography* (P. Zuman, I. M. Kolthoff, editors), Vol. 2, p. 383, Interscience, New York (1961).
(24) MANOUŠEK, O. and ZUMAN, P., *Collect. Czechoslov. Chem. Commun.* in the press.
(25) HEYROVSKÝ, J. and FOREJT, J. *Z. physikal. Chem.* **193**, 77 (1943).
(26) HEYROVSKÝ, J. and KALVODA, R., *Oscillographische Polarographie mit Wechselstrom*, Akademie Verlag, Berlin 1960.
(27) KALVODA, R., Oscillographic Polarography with Alternating Current, in *Progress in Polarography* (P. Zuman, I. M. Kolthoff, editors), Vol. 2, p. 449, Interscience, New York (1962).
(28) RANDLES, J. E. B., *Trans. Faraday Soc.* **44**, 322, 327 (1948).
(29) ŠEVČÍK, A., *Collect. Czechoslovak. Chem. Commun.* **13**, 349 (1948).
(30) HANS, W., HENNE, W. and MEURER, E., *Z. Elektrochem.* **58**, 836 (1954).
(31) KŮTA, J. and SMOLEŘ, I., The Instantaneous Currents ($i$–$t$ Curves) on Single Drops, in *Progress in Polarography* (P. Zuman, I. M. Kolthoff, editors), Vol. 1, p. 43, Interscience, New York (1962).
(32) VOGEL, J., Unpublished results.
(33) KOUTECKÝ, J. and VON STACKELBERG, M. The Equation for Polarographic Diffusion Currents and the Limits of its Validity, in *Progress in Polarography* (P. Zuman, I. M. Kolthoff, editors), Vol. 1, p. 21, Interscience, New York (1962).
(34) ZUMAN, P., *Z. physikal. Chem.* (*Leipzig*), Sonderheft 1958, 243; *Collect. Czechoslov. Chem. Commun.* **25**, 3245 (1960).
(35) ZUMAN, P. and HORÁK, V., *Collect. Czechoslov. Chem. Commun.* **26**, 176 (1961).
(36) ZUMAN, P., *Collect. Czechoslov. Chem. Commun.* **25**, 3252 (1960).
(37) LEVIN, E. S. and FODIMAN, Z. I., *Ž. fiz. chim.* **28**, 601 (1954).

CHAPTER III

# EXPERIMENTAL TECHNIQUES IN ORGANIC POLAROGRAPHY

In polarographic electrolysis the substance to be investigated must be present in a true solution. A suitable electrolyte is added to the solution and the oxygen present in solution is removed. The solution is then ready for the recording of polarographic curves.

Wherever possible aqueous solutions are preferred, but substances of low solubility prevent the use of water as a solvent and consequently the solvents normally used are aqueous alcohols, dioxane–water or Cellosolve–water mixtures. Sometimes even nonaqueous solutions are used (e.g. glacial acetic acid, N,N'-dimethylformamide, benzene–methanol mixtures etc.). Usually it is necessary to purify the solvent in order to prevent contamination by substances which give waves in the same potential range as the substance under examination. Often procedures developed for the purification of solvents for spectrophotometric purposes have proved useful.

Another possibility involves the use of detergent-like substances first recommended by G. Proske for the solubilization of organic solvents in water. The principle has been so far little exploited.

## 3.1. SUPPORTING ELECTROLYTE

The solution to be polarographed must contain in addition to the substance to be determined, a so called "supporting electrolyte", dissolved in an ionized state. A supporting electrolyte has three main functions: to maintain the conductivity of the solution, to eliminate the effect of migration and to prepare the conditions that give the best developed wave. The supporting electrolyte usually consists of an acid, hydroxide or other base and a salt or buffer-solution. The concentration of the supporting

61

electrolyte (or its ionized form) has to be at least twenty times higher than that of the substance to be studied. Usually 0·1–0·5 M solutions are used.

However, the usefulness of a supporting electrolyte is limited by the available potential range. This range is given by the potential of the dissolution of mercury (at positive potentials) and by the potential of the reduction of the cation (at negative potentials). Solutions containing sulphates, perchlorates, nitrates or acetate and borate buffers are recommended for reaching positive potentials (about +0·3 V vs. S.C.E.). Such supporting electrolytes are suitable for the registration of anodic waves with a positive half-wave potential (e.g. barbiturates, ascorbic acid, adrenaline etc.). In supporting electrolytes containing halogenides, phosphates, veronal-buffers or amines, the dissolution of mercury occurs at considerably more negative potentials. Thus solutions containing potassium iodide as a supporting electrolyte are not suitable for obtaining well-developed waves at potentials more positive than about −0·3 V.

Usually salts of potassium or sodium (as buffer components or hydroxides) allow the study, in neutral or alkaline solutions, of waves at potentials more positive than about −1·8 V. More negative potentials are reached with lithium salts (e.g. in the determination of acetaldehyde or sugars). This extends the useful negative potential range by about 0·1 V. For even more negative potentials (up to −2·5 V) (e.g. the determination of some halogen derivatives or unsaturated hydrocarbons) salts or hydroxides of quaternary amines, e.g. $N(CH_3)_4Cl$, $N(C_2H_5)_4OH$ or $N(C_4H_9)_4OH$, are recommended. The correct use of a solvent can also extend the available potential range, but with organic solvents the correction of potentials for the $i.R$-drop must not be omitted. Lithium and tetra-alkyl ammonium salts, inorganic acids, hydroxides and alkoxides are usually sufficiently soluble in organic solvents.

Contrary to the situation in inorganic polarography where complex formation (the main function of the supporting electrolyte) is most important, the basic problem in organic polarography is pH control. As most of the reductions of organic compounds are dependent on the pH of the solution, the polarographic analysis must be carried out in solutions of strong acids and bases (the concentration of which is more than twenty times greater than that of the substance under consideration), or in well buffered solutions. General information can be obtained with mixed buffers with a broad pH-range such as a Britton–Robinson buffer, or McIlvaine buffer. Exact measurements should be made with simple buffer solutions, e.g. acetate, phosphate, borate, veronal or glycine buffers, ammonia–ammonium chloride etc.

It must be remembered that with a buffer solution there is always the possibility of interaction between the substance under examination and the buffer components. The best known example of this type is the effect of borates which form complexes with e.g. a-dihydroxy or a-hydroxycarbonyl compounds and result in shifts, diminutions or complete suppressions of their polarographic waves (e.g. with benzil[1] or ninhydrin[2]). Similarly, the interaction of primary amines (ammonia, glycine) with carbonyl compounds may cause a change in polarographic behaviour. The ketimines formed by condensation are reduced in a new wave at potentials more positive than that of the carbonyl form. A simple wave for carbonyl compounds can be obtained with a veronal buffer or buffers prepared from tertiary amines over the pH-range 8–10.

The role and control of acidity represents a difficult problem in nonaqueous polarography, and the presence of proton donors often changes markedly the polarographic behaviour. Extensions of the acidity scale, like $H_0$ and $H_-$ functions, have been successfully employed in some instances.

The function of a solution, of a distinct pH-value, is to obtain well developed waves, to eliminate interfering components and to separate coinciding waves.

An example of the first kind is the behaviour of $\Delta^4$-3-ketosteroids.[3] The protonized forms of these substances are reduced in well developed waves usually between pH 4 and 7. At lower pH-values the wave is obscured by catalytic hydrogen evolution. Moreover, the well developed waves of the unprotonized form are observed in 0·1 N lithium hydroxide containing 50 per cent ethanol. Between pH 8 and 10 two waves are observed, which are interesting from the theoretical point of view, but not very suitable for analytical purposes.

The difference in shifts of the half-wave potentials of organic substances with pH are usually not as large as in the complexation of inorganic cations. Elimination of an interfering wave can be achieved only if, in a given pH-range, the half-wave potential of the substance to be studied remains practically constant, and the half-wave potential of the interfering substance shifts to more negative values. Another possibility is to choose the conditions so that the interfering substance decomposes or changes its structure, e.g. used in the analysis of mixtures of nicotinic acid and its amide. In acid solutions both protonized forms of the free acid and amide give a reduction wave. In alkaline solutions, containing alkali metal ions, the wave for the anion of nicotinic acid is not evident before the final rise of the current, which corresponds to the reduction of the cation of the supporting electrolyte. Under such conditions in mixtures containing nicotinic acid and its amide, only the wave of the amide is observed.[4, 5]

Whereas two coincident waves, corresponding to two different reducible groups, are not too often encountered in practice, a current problem is in distinguishing two structurally similar substances with the same polarographically active group. The half-wave potentials of two closely related substances only occasionally differ sufficiently to allow two separate waves to be measured.

Examples for distinguishing closely related substances can be chosen among the aromatic nitro-compounds. Dinitrobenzene in the presence of nitrobenzene can be determined over practically the whole pH-range. On the other hand the waves for nitrobenzene and $p$-nitrophenol almost coalesce in acid solutions, whereas at pH 10 the wave of $p$-nitrophenol is about 0·2 V more negative than the wave of nitrobenzene.

Isomers also differ in their half-wave potentials, but only rarely to such a degree that separated waves can be obtained. An example of the separation of waves of isomers are $o$- and $p$-nitrophenols. Their waves in alkaline solutions, corresponding to the dissociated phenolate form, coalesce, but at pH 2·0 the wave for $o$-nitrophenol is about 0·12 V more positive. This is just sufficient for a measurement of both waves provided that their concentrations are not too different.

In some instances, the difference in acid-base behaviour can be utilized for the discrimination of some *cis-trans*-isomers and structurally related substances. Undissociated forms of maleic and fumaric acids are reduced practically at the same potentials. An acid buffer with a pH value lower than 3 allows only a determination of the sum of maleic and fumaric acids. If small concentrations of maleic acid are to be determined in the presence of an excess of fumaric acid, a phosphate buffer of pH about 7 containing ammonium ions must be used.[6, 7] The more negative wave corresponds to the univalent anion of fumaric acid, preceded by a wave of the more readily reducible corresponding form of maleic acid. The role of ammonium ions is two-fold: to shift the half-wave potentials of anions to more positive values, and to change the acid base equilibria in the neighbourhood of the electrode. In 1 N lithium hydroxide the wave of the divalent anion of fumaric acid is reduced at more positive potentials than that of maleic acid. In 1 N LiOH it is thus possible to determine smaller amounts of fumaric acid in the presence of maleic acid.

The difference in polarographic p$K'$-values can be used for the determination of progesterone at pH 9·2 in the presence of methyltestosterone.[3] The polarographic curve of progesterone, at this pH, only shows the wave corresponding to the reduction of the protonized form. Methyltestosterone under these conditions is reduced in the unprotonized form at more negative potentials. Similarly it is possible at pH 9·5 to determine the protonized form of deoxycorticosterone in the presence of testosterone, which is reduced in an unprotonized form.

A further example is the determination of pyridoxal and pyridoxal-5-phosphate mixtures.[8] In alkaline solution the phosphoric acid grouping of the pyridoxal-5-phosphate undergoes dissociation. The effect of the ionized group causes a shift more than 0·3 V to more negative values when compared with pyridoxal (Fig. 32). At pH values below 10 the half-wave potentials of pyridoxal and pyridoxal-5-phosphate differ so little that their waves coalesce. However, if transformed into the corresponding oximes, it is possible to distinguish the waves by employing a derivative circuit (Fig. 33). Finally in acid solution, where the half-wave potentials coincide, the analysis of the mixture can be

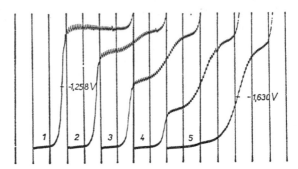

FIG. 32. Mixtures of pyridoxal and pyridoxal-5-phosphate
in 0·1 M-NaOH.
Concentrations of pyridoxal-5-phosphate: (1) 0; (2) 1·25 × 10⁻⁴ M;
(3) 2·5 × 10⁻⁴ M; (4) 3·75 × 10⁻⁴ M; (5) 4·9 × 10⁻⁴ M: concentration of
pyridoxal: (1) 5·0 × 10⁻⁴ M; (2) 3·75 × 10⁻⁴ M; (3) 2·5 × 10⁻⁴ M; (4)
1·25 × 10⁻⁴ M; (5) 1·10⁻⁵ M. Half-wave potentials given against the
S.C.E., 159 mV/absc., full scale sensitivity 4·06 $\mu$A.

performed by the application of the difference of wave-heights
(Fig. 34). At pH 3–5 the wave of pyridoxal is very low owing to the
effect of hemiacetal formation (see p. 13), whereas the wave of
pyridoxal-5-phosphate remains unchanged and corresponds to a
two-electron reduction process which is diffusion controlled.
From measurements of wave-heights obtained with a mixture of
pyridoxal and its 5-phosphate derivative at pH 4 and 9, it is
possible to calculate the composition of the mixture using the
following equations:

$$(P) = \frac{1 \cdot 06 \, i_2 - i_1}{\kappa_{PH} - \kappa_P} \qquad (PH) = \frac{i_1 - \kappa_P/\kappa_{PH}}{\kappa_{PH} - \kappa_P} \cdot 1 \cdot 06 \, i_2$$

where P is pyridoxal, PH is pyridoxal-5-phosphate, $i_1$ is the limiting
current at pH 4, $i_2$ is the limiting current at pH 9 and $\kappa$ are for
the particular Ilkovič constants. Of the three methods for the
analysis of the above mixtures, the one is selected which corresponds to the analytical requirements of the particular example.

Besides the pH and the presence of some typical complexing
agents (e.g. boric acid), the type of buffer and especially the
cation present in the solution also play an important role. An
example, the reduction of maleic acid, has already been

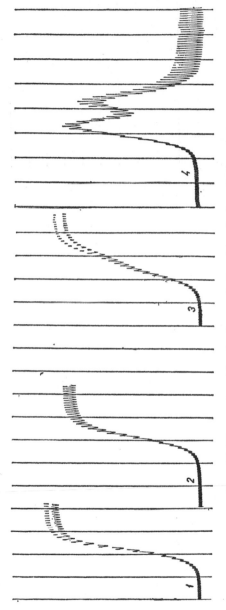

FIG. 33. Waves of pyridoxaloxime and of pyridoxaloxime-5-phosphate.
Veronal buffer pH 8·95, 0·01 M hydroxylamine hydrochloride, added: (1) 7·2×10⁻⁴ M pyridoxal; (2) 7·2×10⁻⁴ M pyridoxal-5-phosphate; (3) and (4) mixture of 7·2×10⁻⁴ M pyridoxal, 7·2×10⁻⁴ M pyridoxal-5-phosphate. Reaction mixture heated for 10 min to 70°C, curves recorded after cooling. Mercurous sulphate electrode, 88 mV/absc., 160 mV/min, $t_1 = 3·2$ sec, $m = 2·9$ mg/sec, full scale sensitivity (1) to (3) 14 $\mu$A, (4) 0·9 $\mu$A.
Curves (1)–(3) primitive, (4) derivative using the circuitry by J. Vogel and J. Říha.

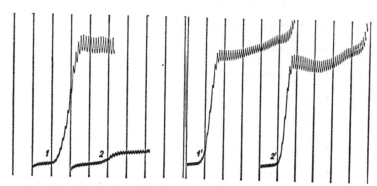

FIG. 34. Wave of pyridoxal and pyridoxal-5-phosphate in acid
media and trimethylamine buffers.
$8 \times 10^{-4}$ M Depolarizer, (1) and (1') pyridoxal-5-phosphate, (2) and
(2') pyridoxal. Supporting electrolyte: (1) and (2) 0·08 M perchloric
acid; (1') and (2') trimethylamine buffer pH 9·8. Mercurous
sulphate electrode 186 mV/absc., $t_1 = 3·2$ sec, $m = 2·9$ mg/sec,
full scale sensitivity 7 $\mu$A.

mentioned. Especially polyvalent cations (e.g. $Ca^{2+}$, $La^{3+}$ etc.) exert
an influence on the half-wave potentials of anions and on the half-
wave potentials of some polarizable molecules (e.g. halogen
derivatives). Large cations, mainly of the tetra-alkylammonium
type, can also eliminate the minima on limiting currents observed,
e.g. with benzyl chloride or $p,p'$-DDT. These minima are ex-
plained by the repulsion of negatively polarized particles from
the negatively charged double-layer[9] and the effect of $NR_4^+$-ions
is ascribed to a change in the charge of the double-layer. On the
other hand when positively charged particles are reduced, e.g.
dialkylphenacyl sulphonium ions, the addition of tetra-alkylammonium ions can on the contrary cause a formation of such
minima, because positively charged $NR_4^+$-ions repel the sulphonium ions from the double-layer.

In some instances tetra-alkylammonium ions possess some
specific properties. Thus in the solutions of cyclo-octatetraene
no reduction waves were observed in the presence of ammonium
nitrate or sodium hydroxide, but well developed waves were
obtained at $-1·5$ V in the presence of tetramethylammonium ions.

It should also not be forgotten that tetra-alkylammonium ions
are strongly adsorbed and can act as surface active substances.

When maxima are observed on polarographic curves, gelatin or other surface active substances are sometimes added to the solution. The concentration of surface active substance should be as low as possible, because a higher concentration of gelatin, deforms the polarographic curve. The surface active agent damps the streaming of electrolyte around the polarized mercury drop.

## 3.2. REMOVAL OF OXYGEN

In solutions in contact with air, atmospheric oxygen is dissolved at a concentration of about 8 mg/l., i.e. 0·001 N (at normal room temperature). This oxygen is reduced at the dropping mercury electrode and produces a double wave. The first step is due to the reduction $O_2 \rightarrow H_2O_2$ and the second to $H_2O_2 \rightarrow H_2O$.

These waves obscure the polarographic waves of other substances and hence usually oxygen must be removed from the solution. There is however, another reason why oxygen must be removed, especially when unbuffered solutions are used as a supporting electrolyte. During the reduction of oxygen, hydrogen ions are consumed leaving in the neighbourhood of the electrode an excess of hydroxyl ions. These ions can react with substances which diffuse from the bulk of the solution to the electrode surface and consequently change their wave-form and wave-height.

The most general method for removing oxygen is deaeration by a polarographically indifferent gas. In some instances it is possible to reduce oxygen using some reducing agents.

Nitrogen is usually preferred for the indifferent gas, but hydrogen, methane, the inert gases and, in acid solution, even carbon dioxide can also be used. With carbon dioxide, open vessels can be used for the polarographic electrolysis.

The gas is introduced in a stream into the solution through a small orifice or sintered glass so as to form small and frequent bubbles. The vessels used are those described earlier. In a few minutes the oxygen pressure above the solution to be polarographed, and hence also the oxygen-concentration in the solution, is sufficiently lowered so as not to interfere with the determination. If the concentration of the oxygen in the indifferent gas is below about 0·2 per cent, the gas can usually be applied directly. When removing the last traces of oxygen, washing bottles containing hydrosulphite or a chromous salt with a zinc amalgam are placed between the gas source and the polarographic vessel. In addition, a washing bottle containing distilled water is placed immediately in front of, and in line with, the polarographic cell. If the solution to be analysed contains electro-inactive volatile components, the volatile component has to be added to the last washing bottle. The concentration of the volatile component should be somewhat higher than that in the polarographed solution. This is necessary for solutions containing ammonia or organic solvents.

The removal of oxygen with sulphite, sometimes used in the analysis of inorganic substances, cannot be recommended for organic polarographic analysis as many organic compounds react with sulphite ions. Recently the removal of oxygen using enzymatic systems has also been suggested.

### 3.3. RECORDING OF POLAROGRAPHIC CURVES

The solution containing the sample with the indifferent electrolyte (sometimes with the addition of a surface active agent), is placed into an appropriate polarographic cell, and the mercury pressure is adjusted to a required value by altering the height of the mercury reservoir. The dropping electrode is inserted into the solution to be polarographed and the solution is then freed from air. When the deaeration has been completed, the gas stream is stopped and the solution is then ready for a polarographic examination. The curve is recorded after adjusting the sensitivity of the galvanometer (to obtain measurable waves).

The following entries are usually registered for each polarogram: The source of e.m.f., type of vessel used, reference electrode, the starting potential, the voltage used, the indifferent gas, drop-time, out-flow velocity of mercury, temperature and the sensitivity of galvanometer used, or the relation of the deflection on the ordinate to current. For each curve the exact composition of the solution must also be noted.

### 3.4. THE MEASUREMENT OF THE LIMITING CURRENTS

There are two important principles to follow in measuring the wave-height. For exact theoretical work only the measurement of well developed waves is recommended. For approximate theoretical measurements, as well as for analytical purposes, it is most important to measure all the curves to be compared in the same way as precisely as possible.

All curves are corrected first for capacity (condenser, residual) current. This can be done in two principal ways: either by geometrical subtraction of the condenser current, registered separately in the pure supporting electrolyte, or by extrapolation of the linear flat portion of the curve before the wave-rise. The second kind of correction is used when the registration of pure condenser current is inaccessible (e.g. in analysis of biological liquids), or when the wave is well developed with linear portions (both of the current before the current-rise and of the limiting current) extending over a broad potential range. It is suggested that the first technique should always be used for measurement of the wave height of cathodic waves at negative potentials near the decomposition potential of the supporting electrolyte. The same is also true for anodic waves which are not well developed owing to the vicinity of the potential of mercury dissolution. We do not suggest the first kind of measurement as a general rule because the structure of the double layer, and hence the capacity current, in the pure supporting electrolyte and in the electrolysed solution, sometimes differs substantially owing to the adsorption of a depolarizer. Moreover, the change in adsorbability of reduced and oxidized forms can also influence the measurement. Thus the extrapolation technique can sometimes be a better approximation. When impurities giving measurable waves are present in the supporting electrolyte, a blank correction must be made in every method.

The measurement of three types of polarographic waves (after correction for condenser current) will be discussed here:

(a) Those in which the course of the current–voltage curve before and after the rise of the wave is linear (Fig. 35 a, b, c).

(b) Those in which only that part of the course which precedes or follows the rise of the wave is linear (Fig. 35 d, e).

(c) Those in which no linear portion of sizeable length is observed on the curve either before or after the rise of the wave.

*Waves of the first kind (a);* the linear portion before and after

F

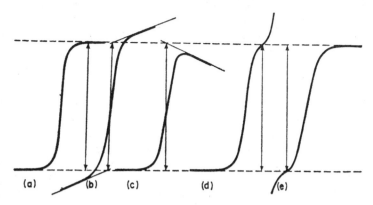

FIG. 35. Methods of measurement of polarographic waves.
(a)–(e) Different types of polarographic curves (described in the
text).

the rise of the wave must be prolonged. The half-wave potential
is approximately estimated by halving the distance between the
two lines, or from the inflexion of the curve. At this point a line
is marked, parallel to the ordinate. The intersections of this line
with the prolonged linear portions are marked and the distance
between them on the ordinate is described as the wave height
(Fig. 35 b, c). For waves where the course of the current before
and after the wave rise is parallel, it is unnecessary to carry out the
measurement at the potential of the half-wave; it may however be
performed at the ordinate at any arbitrary potential (Fig. 35 a).
Instead of the prolongation of the part of the curve before the
wave rise, a geometrical correction for the condenser current can
be applied. Again the limiting current is measured on an ordinate
at the half-wave potential of the distance between the intersections of the ordinate with the condenser and limiting currents.

*Curves possessing only one linear section (b);* this part must be
prolonged. We then try to find an inflexion point on the second
(non-linear) part of the wave (either the non-linear part of the
limiting current or the non-linear part of the current before the
wave rise). From this inflexion point, a line parallel to the ordinate
is drawn to meet the prolonged part of the linear portion of the
wave (Fig. 35 d, e). The intercept on this ordinate, limited by the
intersections with the prolonged part (or with the condenser

current) and with the polarographic wave (at the point of the inflexion of the curve) corresponds to the wave height.

*If the wave is limited by two curved sections (c);* the distance between the two inflexion points is measured on an ordinate.

The techniques of measurement described above proved to be the best in numerous instances. However it is sometimes necessary, in view of the unusual shape of the wave or of special requirements, to choose an alternative measuring technique. Maxima and catalytic currents come into this category. Here the rules of identical measurement techniques in the measurement of compared curves (e.g. of analysed solution and calibration curves) should be followed. It should be stressed that the wave-height is always measured in the direction of one of the ordinates, never on a line perpendicular to some part of the polarographic curve. The use of a soft pencil and ruler to draw lines, and by carrying out the measurements directly on the polarogram, proved to be the most suitable method.

For theoretical purposes the mean value of the current oscillations, recorded with a critically damped galvanometer with a period of oscillation of about 10 sec must be measured, because most equations have been derived to incorporate this quantity. For analytical purposes, on the other hand, the upper or lower peaks of the current oscillations of a critically damped galvanometer can be measured as well. It is important that all waves to be compared are measured in the same way. The measurement of the peak current obtained with an undamped galvanometer cannot be recommended.

### 3.5. EVALUATION OF THE WAVE-HEIGHT: CALIBRATION CURVE AND STANDARD ADDITION METHODS

The calibration curve is constructed by successively adding different amounts of the substance to be studied, to a supporting electrolyte which contains all components with the exception of the one under study.

The principle of the determination using a calibration curve is shown in Figs. 36 and 37. The component to be determined is here ascorbic acid and this method is used for its determination in pharmaceuticals.

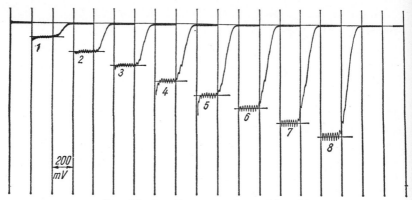

FIG. 36. Anodic waves of ascorbic acid.
0·1 M Acetate buffer pH 4·7, ascorbic acid concentration (mg %): (1) 1·2; (2) 2·1; (3) 3·3; (4) 4·3; (5) 5·2; (6) 6·1; (7) 7·1; (8) 8·0. Curves recorded from negative to positive potentials, mercurous sulphate electrode, 200 mV/absc., $t_1 = 2·8$ sec, $m = 2·2$. mg/sec, full scale sensitivity 20 $\mu$A.

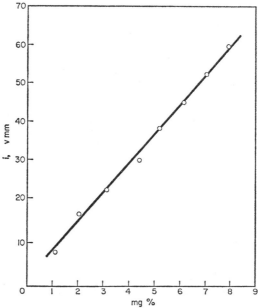

FIG. 37. Plot of the dependence of the limiting current on ascorbic acid concentration.

*Procedure*—Add a freshly prepared stock solution of ascorbic acid successively to a supporting electrolyte, consisting of an acetate buffer pH 4·7, containing 0·2 M acetic acid and 0·2 M sodium acetate and 0·005 per cent gelatin. Deaerate the solution with an indifferent gas and record the anodic curves (Fig. 36). Then plot the heights of the waves on a graph to show the dependence of the diffusion current with the concentration of ascorbic acid (Fig. 37). Finally transfer the samples to be analysed into the same supporting electrolyte as that used for the construction of the calibration curve.

The polarographic curves must be recorded under exactly the same conditions as those used to obtain the calibration values, i.e. with the same capillary, the same pressure of mercury, the same sensitivity of the galvanometer and at exactly the same temperature. The measured wave-height of the sample is then compared with the calibration curve. The electrolytic cell should be placed in a thermostat.

*Note.* The procedure given above is the simplest one and it is supposed that the other components present in the sample do not interfere. Nevertheless this assumption is not always valid. To avoid the uncertainty, caused by unknown factors, it is advisable to keep the composition of the electrolyte in the preparation of the calibration curve as similar as possible to that of the solution containing the sample. This can be achieved either by using in the preparation of the supporting electrolyte a synthetic solution of a sample, or a solution of the sample without the substance under study. This is difficult in biological analysis because of the difficulty of obtaining the sample without the constituent to be determined. A certain improvement can be achieved when the polarographic curves of several samples are registered on one polarogram, and in addition one curve of a standard solution is also recorded on the same polarogram. Smaller changes in the conditions can be detected and eliminated in this way, e.g. small changes of temperature.

The condition that the temperature does not change during the time between the registration of the calibration curve and the curve of the sample, and the condition of identical composition are best fulfilled if the method of standard addition is applied. In this method an addition of a known amount of a standard stock solution is made to each sample after its curve has been recorded. When *a* millilitres of the standard solution is added to *v* ml. of the solution, and the polarographic wave height is increased from *h* with the sample to *h'* (after the standard addition), the unknown concentration of the sample *x* is given by the following equation:

$$x = \frac{hc}{h' + [h' - h] \cdot v/a}$$

where $c$ denotes the concentration of the standard solution.

Where a more exact procedure is necessary, two equal volumes are taken from the dissolved sample or two parallel samples are prepared. One sample is diluted to a known volume with the supporting electrolyte. A known amount of the component to be determined is added to the other portion, and thereafter diluted with the indifferent electrolyte to the same volume as the first portion. The solution containing the standard gives a higher wave ($h'$) than the first solution, which gives a wave of height $h$. The concentration $x$ of the component in the sample is given by:

$$x = \frac{100 \cdot a\,h}{[h' - h] \cdot w}\ \%$$

where $a$ is the weight of the standard added and $w$ that of the sample. This method has the advantage that possible losses during the preliminary operation, e.g. due to adsorption, which should be almost identical in both solutions, are eliminated.

The procedure known as "quotient of two waves" is independent of temperature. In this method a known quantity of a certain polarographically active substance is added to each solution in which another component is to be determined. It is assumed that the ratio of the two waves (for the unknown and for the added standard or pilot) is independent of temperature, viscosity, rate of flow of mercury etc. The calibration curves are constructed by plotting the ratio of the two waves against the concentration of the substance to be determined, keeping the concentration of the "pilot" constant. These calibration curves are used in the same way as the ordinary curves.

The calibration curve method is to be preferred in serial analyses of samples of similar composition, but when precise results are required temperature control is necessary. When the capillary is broken or blocked, the construction of new calibration curves is necessary.

The method of "quotient of two waves" can be applied in all instances, as with the calibration curve method. The temperature control is unnecessary, but more calibration curves for different concentrations of the "pilot" are usually necessary, and when the capillary is broken all curves must be reconstructed.

The method of standard addition is useful for the analysis of a limited number of samples. In such instances the construction of a calibration curve would be too time-consuming. The temperature control is unnecessary but, on the other hand, for each sample the addition of a standard and the recording of two curves are necessary, and consequently the time spent on a single analysis is somewhat longer. Also the precision of this method is somewhat lower than the calibration curve method, because direct proportionality is assumed (calibration curve going through the zero point) and this rarely holds with high accuracy. The method of standard addition is extremely useful for the analysis of biological systems where it is often difficult to obtain a "pure" sample containing none of the substance to be determined.

Beside the above mentioned methods which use a relative comparison with a standard, the so called "absolute methods" are sometimes recommended. For this method the "constants of the diffusion current" are determined for every supporting electrolyte used. From these "constants" and the values for the out-flow velocity of mercury and the drop-times, the wave-height for a given concentration of the electroactive substance can be calculated.

The basic assumption in this method, namely that the product $m^{\frac{2}{3}} \cdot t^{\frac{1}{6}}$ remains constant and independent of the actual drop-time or the value of $m$, is not exactly true. This introduces an uncertainty when comparing results with different capillaries. Moreover, owing to the effect of other compounds in the sample and the supporting electrolyte on the limiting current, the conditions used in the determination of the "constants of diffusion current" are rarely identical with those in the practical analysis of complex samples.

## 3.6. SENSITIVITY AND ACCURACY OF THE METHOD

The sensitivity of the polarographic method is limited partly by the oscillations of the galvanometer, owing to the dropping of mercury, and partly by the condenser current, which charges the dropping electrode to the applied potential. The latter is of the order of $10^{-8}$ to $10^{-7}$ A. Polarographically active substances in $10^{-3}$ to $10^{-5}$ M concentrations give limiting currents of the order $10^{-5}$ to $10^{-7}$ A. These currents are but little influenced by the condenser current. The concentration range $10^{-4}$ to $10^{-3}$ M is therefore most suitable for polarographic determinations. A compound in a concentration of $10^{-6}$ M would give a limiting current of the order $10^{-8}$ to $10^{-9}$ A, that is a wave hardly distinguishable from the capacity current.

The compensation method, mentioned in Chapter II, partly counterbalances the capacity current, so that it remains almost constant: with this method, concentrations of the electroactive substance as low as $5 \times 10^{-6}$ M can be estimated.

The condenser current can be automatically subtracted from the registered curve with an electronic memory device.[10, 11] This enables traces as low as $10^{-7}$ M to be determined. With the square-wave polarograph, concentrations one order lower can be analysed. The most sensitive method as yet seems to be the method of "anodic stripping". In this method reduction products can be formed at the surface of the electrode and then stripped anodically. The anodic current corresponding to the dissolution process is either followed polarographically or with an oscilloscope. Similarly oxidizable substances can be stripped cathodically. These methods enable polarographically active substances to be detected in $10^{-9}$ or even $10^{-10}$ M solutions.[12]

Concentrations of the order $10^{-7}$ or even $10^{-8}$ M can be achieved by means of some catalytic waves, e.g. vitamin $B_{12}$ (cobalamin). On the other hand waves for some kinetic currents, where the limiting current is only a fraction of the hypothetical diffusion current, 0·01 to 0·1 M solutions are used for polarographic investigations.

Polarographic measurements are usually carried out with liquid volumes of about 20–0·5 ml., but when special cells are used, volumes as small as 0·01 ml. can be analysed. This corresponds to a sensitivity of about $5 \times 10^{-9}$ g of the component to be determined.

The accuracy of the results depends on the shape of the wave under study. For well developed waves, the limiting current (wave-height) can be measured with an accuracy of $\pm 1$ to 2 per cent. Considering the required constancy of factors controlling the limiting current (composition and the temperature of the supporting electrolyte, capillary constants) and the inaccuracies in the preparation of the sample, an overall accuracy of about 3 per cent can be claimed for ordinary polarographic determinations. In high precision serial analyses the accuracy can be increased to 1 per cent. On the other hand for badly developed waves, e.g. for those obtained with biological materials, the accuracy drops to $\pm 5$ per cent or even $\pm 10$ per cent. However, this lower accuracy is quite sufficient for most biochemical work.

### 3.7. MEASUREMENT OF HALF-WAVE POTENTIALS

The half-wave potential is measured by first determining the limiting current. The point on the curve where the current reaches half the value for the limiting current is found, and the applied voltage at this point is then determined. Two further possibilities now exist: either the half-wave potential is expressed against the reference electrode used, or its value is recalculated against another standard electrode. As standard reference electrodes the saturated potassium chloride–calomel electrode (S.C.E.) or sometimes the 1 N potassium chloride–calomel electrode (N.C.E.) are used.

In polarographic practice the most important reference electrodes are separated calomel electrodes, a mercurous sulphate electrode, or, especially for small volumes, a silver chloride electrode immersed into an electrolysed solution containing 0·1 M chlorides. This electrode proved satisfactory over the pH-range 1–13 when sodium or potassium chloride was added to the buffer solutions. Measurements in solutions forming complexes with silver e.g. glycine, veronal or ammonia buffers are precluded. The use of this electrode eliminates the uncertainty concerning the liquid junction potential.

The mercury pool electrode, so often used as the simplest electrode for analytical purposes, is completely unsuitable as a reference electrode in aqueous solutions for the measurement of half-wave potentials. Even the passage of small currents causes this type of electrode to become polarized, and polarization effects have been observed even in the presence of 0·1 M chlorides.

For nonaqueous solutions, several reference electrodes have been suggested, e.g. a mercurous sulphate electrode in concentrated sulphuric acid for measurements in solutions of sulphuric acid; calomel, mercurous sulphate and sodium acetate electrodes in glacial acetic acid for work in this solvent, etc. A graphite rod is an excellent reference electrode in glacial acetic acid containing strong acids, whereas in aqueous solutions its application as a reference anode cannot be recommended.

The basic condition to be fulfilled by a reference electrode for half-wave potential measurements is the constancy of its potential over the whole course of measurement. The reproducibility of the potential of the reference electrode is of secondary importance.

Thus of the separated reference anodes, the mercurous sulphate electrode is even somewhat superior to the calomel electrode because of its lower polarizability. As reference cathodes, amalgam electrodes have proved to be best.

The potentials of these reference electrodes can be checked against a standard half-cell, but another method must be used when the reference electrode is not separated from the electrolysed solution, when the liquid junction potential is unknown or when the potential of the reference electrode is not very reproducible— as with the mercurous sulphate electrode. In this method the unknown half-wave potential is measured against the half-wave potential of a standard substance, whose half-wave potential against S.C.E. or N.C.E. in the used supporting electrolyte is accurately known.

For aqueous solutions, additions of thallous salts proved to be advantageous because the half-wave potential of the $Tl^+$ ion is almost independent of the composition of the supporting electrolyte, provided that strong complex forming agents such as concentrated solutions of sulphuric acid, solutions containing ethylenediaminetetraacetic acid or pyrophosphates are absent. The value for the half-wave potential of thallous ions is $-0.45$ V (S.C.E.) and $-0.49$ V (N.C.E.). For very negative potentials the wave for potassium ions proved useful, and for nonaqueous solutions derivatives of naphthoquinone and rubidium have been found to be suitable.

When using photographic registration and voltage span of 200 mV/absc., the accuracy of the measured half-wave potentials is not very much better than 0·01 V. For 100 mV/absc. and with only one curve recorded, an accuracy of 0·005 V can be achieved. When recording the curves from positive to negative potentials, and then starting from negative to positive values (and thus eliminating the hysteresis or overdamping of the galvanometer), the mean values of half-wave potentials are reproducible to 0·002– 0·003 V. For pen-recording instruments the reproducibility and accuracy of potential measurements depends on the response characteristic of the recording system. The reproducibility previously mentioned only concerns the relative values obtained with any given type of experimental equipment. The absolute precision of most polarographic data does not usually exceed $\pm 0·005$ V, but this is quite sufficient for most instances, e.g. for studies of the effect of the supporting electrolyte, or for the investigation of the influence of a substituent on half-wave potentials. A higher accuracy can be obtained for use in some theoretical studies (e.g. for the measurement of the effect of drop-time) by employing the three electrode system. Here the potential of the dropping electrode is measured against a reference electrode potentiometrically in a state in which practically no current flows. The reproducibility of this method, using manually operated instruments, is claimed to be 0·0005 V.

Most of our theoretical work has been recently carried out in solutions containing from $2 \times 10^{-4}$ to $5 \times 10^{-4}$ M depolarizer; $5 \times 10^{-5}$ to $1 \times 10^{-3}$ M are considered as the practical limits of concentrations for polarographic electrolysis. At higher concentrations irregularities may sometimes occur.

In the given concentration range and in aqueous solutions containing 0·1 to 1·0 M solutions of strong electrolytes, no corrections for the potential drop $iR$ are usually necessary. A silver chloride electrode or reference electrode separated by a liquid junction or Cellophane membrane should be used. When sintered glass of higher density is used for separating the reference electrode, or when lower concentrations of supporting electrolyte are employed, or with nonaqueous solutions, a correction for the $iR$ drop should always be applied.

Because the exact measurement of the resistance across the dropping electrode and electrolytic cell presents difficulties, indirect methods are suggested. A suitable technique is represented by measurements from the shift of the relative half-wave potential with concentration of a reversible depolarizer (e.g. $Tl^+$), or from the change in the difference between the relative half-wave potentials (including the $iR$ drop) of two reversible depolarizers with concentration.

The temperature at which the measurements of half-wave potentials are performed should be stated.

REFERENCES

(1) PASTERNAK, R. *Helv. Chim. Acta* **30**, 1948 (1947).
(2) VLČEK, A. K., ŠPALEK, E. and KRÁTKÝ, L., *Techn. hlídka koželužská* **24**, 258 (1949).
(3) ZUMAN, P., TENYGL, J., and BŘEZINA, M., *Collect. Czechoslov. Chem. Commun.* **19**, 46 (1954).
(4) WENIG, K. and KOPECKÝ, M., *Čas. českého lékarn.* **56**, 49 (1943).
(5) KNOBLOCH, E., *Collect. Czechoslov. Chem. Commun.* **12**, 581 (1947).
(6) ELVING, P. J., MARTIN, A. J., and ROSENTHAL, I., *Anal. Chem.* **25**, 1082 (1953).
(7) ELVING, P. J. and ROSENTHAL, I., *Anal. Chem.* **26**, 1454 (1954).
(8) MANOUŠEK, O. and ZUMAN, P., *J. Electroanalyt. Chem.* **1**, 324 (1960); *Collect. Czechoslov. Chem. Commun.* **27**, 486 (1962).
(9) FRUMKIN, A. N. and NIKOLAJEVA-FEDOROVIČ, N., The Electroreduction of Anions, in *Progress in Polarography* (P. Zuman, I. M. Kolthoff, editors), Vol. 1, p. 223, Interscience, New York (1962).
(10) KELLEY, M. T. and MILLER, H. H., *Anal. Chem.* **24**, 1895 (1952).
(11) KELLEY, M. T., JONES, H. C. and FISHER, D. J., *Anal. Chem.* **31**, 1475 (1959).
(12) KEMULA, W., in *Advances in Polarography* (Proc. 2nd Internat. Congr. Polarography), Vol. 1, p. 135, Pergamon Press, London (1960).

# CHAPTER IV

# CLASSIFICATION OF POLAROGRAPHIC METHODS FOR THE ANALYSES OF ORGANIC SUBSTANCES

### 4.1. POLAROGRAPHICALLY ACTIVE SUBSTANCES

ACCORDING to the type of electrode process the following kinds of electroactive compounds can be distinguished: reducible compounds, showing a cathodic wave above the galvanometer zero line, and oxidizable compounds, giving an anodic wave below the galvanometer zero line. In addition we can observe on polarographic curves anodic waves corresponding to a formation of an insoluble or complex compound with mercury, waves corresponding to regeneration processes and cathodic waves due to the catalytic evolution of hydrogen. Furthermore, surface active substances can be estimated polarographically by the suppression of maxima, as mentioned earlier.

Organic compounds which are *reduced* at the mercury dropping electrode must contain a highly polar or unsaturated bond. Examples of the most common irreversibly reducible bonds and functional groupings are given in Table 2. Reversible electrode processes have been claimed for quinoid compounds (derivatives of *o*- and *p*-benzoquinones, naphthoquinones, anthraquinones, *p*-aminophenols, different types of dyestuffs like indophenols, thiazines, phenazines, indigosulphonates, and riboflavin etc.), for systems: nitrosobenzene-N-phenylhydroxylamine, azobenzene-hydrazobenzene, alloxan-dialuric acid etc.

Besides the reduced forms of reversible systems, e.g. hydroquinones, *p*-phenylendiamines, leuco forms of dyestuffs, hydrazobenzenes, N-phenylhydroxylamines etc. *oxidation waves* have been described so far only for the derivatives containing an enediol group (e.g. ascorbic acid). The system formed during the oxidations of 5-hydroxychromane and of 5-hydroxycoumarane is similar to a quinoid system.

TABLE 2. BONDS AND ATOM GROUPINGS IN ORGANIC COMPOUNDS REDUCIBLE AT THE DROPPING MERCURY ELECTRODE

| Reducible bonds, groupings | Examples | Reducible bonds, groupings | Examples |
|---|---|---|---|
| **Carbon–Carbon Bonds** | | | |
| $>C=C-C=C<$ | butadiene | (biphenyl) | diphenyl, 2,2-dinaphthyl |
| $>C=C-C\equiv C-$ | divinylacetylene | (cyclooctatetraene) | cyclo-octatetraene |
| $-C\equiv C-C\equiv C-$ | diacetylene | (tropylium, +) | tropylium ion |
| (phenyl)$C=C$ | styrene, stilbene, 1,1-diphenylethylene | (azulene) | azulene, guajazulene |
| $>C=C-Het^{a}$ | dipyridylethylene | $>C=C-COOH$ | crotonic acid[c, d] |
| (phenyl)$C\equiv C$ | diphenylacetylene | $-C\equiv C-COOH$ | phenylpropiolic acid |

| Structure | Examples | Structure | Examples |
|---|---|---|---|
| (naphthalene ring with two methyl groups) | naphthalene, anthracene, 3-methylcholanthrene, coronene | HOOC—C=C—COOH | maleic acid,[c] aconitic acid,[c] muconic acid |
| $\diagup$C=C—CN | acrylonitrile,[b] tetracyanoethylene | (benzene ring with COOH, COOH) | phthalic acid,[b,c] terephthalic acid,[b,c] |

**Carbon–Halogen Bonds**

| Structure | Examples | Structure | Examples |
|---|---|---|---|
| =C—F | 6-trifluoromethyl-7-sulphamyl-3,4-dihydro-1,2,4-benzothiadiazine | =C—Br | methylbromide, carbon tetrabromide |
| —CO—C—F | phenacyl fluoride | C=C—Br | dibromoethylene |
| =C—Cl | chloroform, DDT, hexachlorocyclohexane, benzyl chloride | C=C—C—Br | allylbromide |
| | | —CO—C—Br | phenacyl bromide |

TABLE 2. (continued)

Carbon–Halogen Bonds

| Reducible bonds, groupings | Examples | Reducible bonds, groupings | Examples |
|---|---|---|---|
| $-CO-\overset{\displaystyle\vert}{\underset{\displaystyle\vert}{C}}-Cl$ | dichloroacetaldehyde, 2,6-dichlorocyclo-hexanone, phenacyl chloride, trichloro-acetic acid | $O_2N-\overset{\displaystyle\vert}{\underset{\displaystyle\vert}{C}}-Br$ | trinitrobromomethane |
| | | 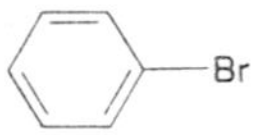 (bromobenzene ring) C$_6$H$_5$—Br | bromobenzenes |
| | | Het—Br | bromopyridines |
| | | C—I | benzyl iodide |
| | | 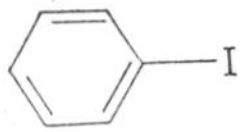 (iodobenzene ring) C$_6$H$_5$—I | iodophenol, diiodotyrosine |
| | | Het—I | iodopyrrole, iodo-pyridines |

G

## Carbon–Oxygen Bonds

| Structure | Examples | Structure | Examples |
|---|---|---|---|
| $-CO-C-O-$ | 2-acetoxyacetophenone, phenylacetyl carbinol, 16-hydroxy-17-keto-steroids | $-CO-$ | acetone, 6-ketocamphor, fructose |
| $C=O$ , $H$ | formaldehyde, citronellal, myrtenal, 8-oxo camphor, chloral, glycolaldehyde, erythrose, glucose, maltose | $C=C-CO-$ | mesityloxide,[d] isothujone,[d] $\Delta^4$-3-ketosteroids,[d] tropone, colchicine, tetraphenylcyclopentadienone |
| $C=C-C=O$ , $H$ | acrolein,[d] citral,[d] cinnamaldehyde | (phenyl)$-CO-$ | acetophenone, benzophenone, benzil, chalk-ones |
| (phenyl)$-C{=}O$ , $H$ | benzaldehydes, vanillin, 9-anthracenealdehyde | $Het-CO-$ | acetylpyridines, pyridoin, acetylpyrroles, thienylmethyl ketone |

TABLE 2. (continued)

| Reducible bonds, groupings | Examples | Reducible bonds, groupings | Examples |
|---|---|---|---|
| **Carbon–Oxygen Bonds** | | | |
| Het—C=O<br>⎟<br>H | pyrrolaldehyde, fural, pyridinealdehydes (formylpyridines) | | fluorenone |
| —CO—C=O<br>⎟<br>H | glyoxal, methylglyoxal | | anthrone, bianthronyl |
| | p-benzoquinones, naphthoquinones, anthraquinones | —CO—CO— | biacetyl, cyclooctadione, camphorquinone, benzil, pyridil |
| | | HOOC—CO— | pyruvic acid, glyoxylic acid, phenylglyoxylic acid |
| | | HOOC—COOH | oxalic acid |

## Carbon–Nitrogen Bonds

| | | | |
|---|---|---|---|
| $-CO-\overset{+}{C}-N<$ | phenacylamine, piperidinoacetophenone methoiodide, trimethyl aminoacrolein perchlorate, phenacylpyridinium ion | $>C=N-$ | acetonimine, butyraldoxime, isobutyraldehyde hydrazone, acetaldehyde semicarbazone, 17-keto-steroid betainylhydrazones |
| | | $-C=N-$   $-N<$ | amidoximes, amidines |
| $CN-\overset{+}{C}-N<$ | aminoacetonitrile | $>C=C-C=N-$ | $\Delta^4$-3-ketosteroid betainylhydrazones |
| | | $-CO-C=N-$ | benzil monoxime |
| $Het-C-N<$ | aminomethylpyridine, pyridoxamine | $HOOC-C=N-$ | pyruvic acid ketimine, mesoxalic acid hydrazone, $\alpha$-keto-acid oximes |

TABLE 2. (continued)

| Reducible bonds, groupings | Examples | Reducible bonds, groupings | Examples |
|---|---|---|---|
| **Carbon–Nitrogen Bonds** | | | |
| ![O=⬡=N structure] | naphthoquinone imine | ![⬡—C=N—] | benzalaniline, phenyl-glyoxylic acid imine, sali-cylaldoxime, benzo-phenone hydrazone, benz-hydrazidine |
| ![N=⬡=N structure] | p-benzoquinone di-oxime, p-phenylene diamine (oxidised form), Variamin Blue | Het—C=N— | pyridinaldoxime |
| | | —N=C—C=N— | diacetyldioxime |
| **Nitrogen–Nitrogen Bonds** | | | |
| —N=N— | azobenzene, methyl orange, benzocinnoline, formazane | —N⁺≡N | benzenediazonium chlor-ide, diazotised sulfanilic acid |
| —N=N—→O | azoxybenzene, benzo-cinnoline monoxide | | |

Nitrogen–Oxygen Bonds

| Structure | Examples | Structure | Examples |
|---|---|---|---|
| $-NO_2$ | nitromethane, nitro-cyclohexane, 1-nitro-2-butanol | $\diagup N-NO$ | N-nitrosodimethylamine, N-nitrosoproline, N-nitrosophenylhydroxyl-amine |
| $>C=C-NO_2$ | 2-nitro-1-butene | $-O-NO_2$ | ethylnitrate, cyclo-hexylnitrate, nitroglycerine |
| ⬡$-NO_2$ | nitrobenzenes, picric acid, nitroacetanilides, chloramphenicol, parathione, nitrona-phthalene sulfonic acids, nitrotetraline, dinitrofluorenone | $\diagup N \rightarrow O$ | adenine-N-oxide |
| $Het-NO_2$ | nitrothiophenes, nitro furanes, nitropyridines | pyridine-N→O | pyridine-N-oxide, fenazine-N-oxide, quinoxaline-N-oxide, pyridoin bis-N-oxide |
| $-NO$ | pinene nitrosochloride | $\diagup C=N-\, \rightarrow O$ | nitrones |
|  |  | $-NHOH$ | cyclohexylhydroxylamine |

TABLE 2. (continued)

| Reducible bonds, groupings | Examples | Reducible bonds, groupings | Examples |
|---|---|---|---|
| **Nitrogen–Oxygen Bonds** | | | |
| ⬡—NO | nitrosobenzene, 1-nitroso-2-naphthol,2,2-dinitrosobiphenyl | ⬡—NHOH | phenylhydroxylamine |
| | | C=N—O— | O-methylbenzaldoxime |
| **Carbon–Sulphur Bonds** | | | |
| —CO—C—S— | phenyl phenacyl sulphide | —CO—C—SCN | 2-thiocyanatoacephenone |
| C=C–⁺S (sulphonium) | triphenyl sulphonium chloride, methyl butyl phenacyl sulphonium ion | ⬡—SCN | rhodanbenzenes |
| ⬡—SO₂— | benzene sulphochloride, diphenyl sulphone, thionaphthene-1-oxide | ⬡—NCS | phenylisothiocyanate |
| ⬡—SO₂SO₂— | diphenyl disulphone | ⬡—C=S | thiobenzophenone, thiobenzamide |

## Oxygen–Oxygen and Sulphur–Sulphur Bonds

| Group | Examples |
|---|---|
| —O—OH | ethylhydroperoxide, cumenehydroperoxide, pinene hydroperoxide, ascaridol |
| —CO—O—OH | peracetic acid |
| —O—O— | dimethylperoxide, benzoylperoxide |
| —S—S— | diethyldisulphide, diphenyldisulphide, cystine, bis (di-ethyl-thiocarbamyl) disulphide, oxidized form of thiamine, lipoic acid |
| —S—SO$_2$— | thiothiosulphonates |

## Five-Membered Reducible Heterocycles[e]

| Structure | Examples |
|---|---|
| (structure) | phthalides, phenolphthalein |
| (structure) | phthalimidine, 3-phenyl isoindoline |
| (structure) | 2-benzoylthiobenzoic acid (ψ-phenylester) |
| (structure) | indolenine |
| (structure) | carbazolenine |
| (structure) | pyrazolanthrone |

TABLE 2. (continued)

| Reducible bonds, groupings | Examples | Reducible bonds, groupings | Examples |
|---|---|---|---|
| Five-Membered Reducible Heterocycles | | | |
| | maleic and citraconic acid anhydride | | thiazole-5-carboxamide |
| | indandione, ninhydrin | | 5-dimethylamino-3-phenyl-1,2,4-thiadiazole |
| | phthalanhydride | | 5-methylimino-3-phenyl-4-methyl-1,2,4-thiadiazoline |
| | phthalimides | | diphenyldipiazselenole |
| | dioxindole, isatine | | 3-methylbenzothiazolonimide |
| | saccharine | | sydnones |

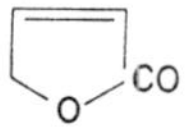

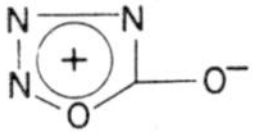

ψ-oxotriazoles

tetrazolium salts

penicillic acid, protoanemonin, angelica lactone, digitoxine

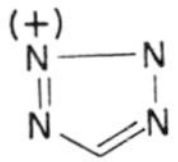

maleic hydrazide, pyridazine-4-carboxylic acid

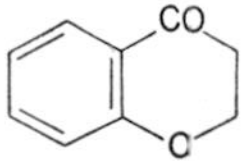

pyrimidines, adenine

pyrazinic acid amide

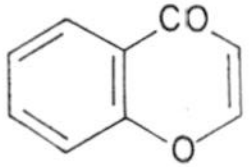

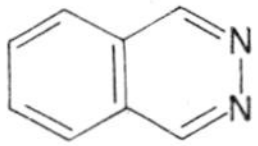

1-hydrazinophthalazine

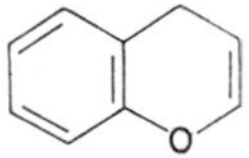

quinoxalines

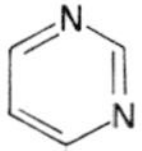

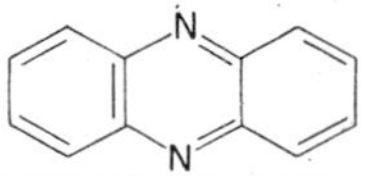

phenazines, neutral red, phenosafranine

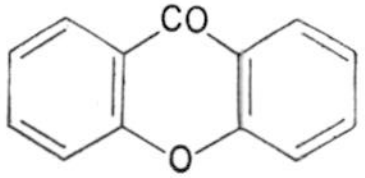

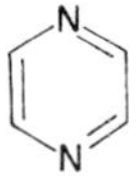

Six-Membered Reducible Heterocycles[e]

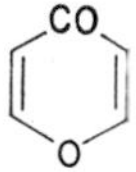

meconic acid, γ-pyrone

flavones, flavanoles

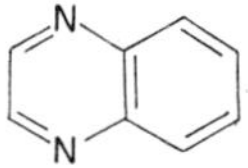

xanthone

flavanones

anthocyanins

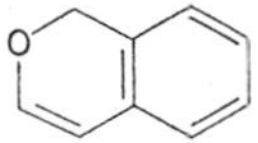

isobenzpyrylium salts

TABLE 2. (continued)

| Reducible bonds, groupings | Examples | Reducible bonds, groupings | Examples |
|---|---|---|---|
| Six-Membered Reducible Heterocycles | | | |
| (xanthylium-type structure, O(+)) | rhodamine | (phenoxazine-type structure, N=, O(+)) | oxazines, gallocyanine, actinomycine, cinnabarine |
| (acridone-type structure, CO, NH) | acridone | (phenothiazine-type structure, N=, S(+)) | phenothiazines, methylene blue |
| (thioxanthone-type structure, CO, S) | thioxanthones | (pyrimidine ring, N) | azauracil |
| (coumarin-type structure, CO, O) | coumarines | (pteridine ring structure) | pteridines, folic acid, pterines |
| (pyridine ring, N) | nicotinamide, N-alkyl pyridinium ions, pyridinium cyclopenta-dienylide | (benzopteridine/isoalloxazine ring structure) | isoalloxazines, riboflavin |

| Structure | Compounds |
|---|---|
| | 8-hydroxyquinoline, quinoline carboxylic acids, quinine, N-alkyl-quinolinium ions |
| | hydrastinine, berberine, phthalonimide |
| | acridines, lucigenine |
| | β-naphthoquinoline |

Organometallic Compounds

| Structure | Compounds |
|---|---|
| $\diagup C{-}Hg$ | ethylmercurihalides, β-methoxyethylmer-curic chloride, p-chloromercuribenzoic acid |
| $\diagup C{-}P$ | tetraphenylphosphonium chloride |

TABLE 2 (continued)

### Organometallic Compounds

| Reducible bonds, groupings | Examples | Reducible bonds, groupings | Examples |
|---|---|---|---|
| $\diagup$C—Pb | monochlorotriethyl lead | $\diagup$C—Se | triphenylselenonium chloride |
| $\diagup$C—Sn | dichlorodiethyl tin, triphenyl tin | $\diagup$C—Te | triphenyltelluronium chloride |
| $\diagup$C—As | diphenylarsin chloride, tetraphenylarsonium chloride | —Se—$\rightarrow$O | diarylselenoxides |
| $\diagup$C—Sb | tetraphenylstibonium chloride | | |

## NOTES

a Het stays for a heterocyclic ring.
b Reduction mechanism uncertain.
c Also esters of these acids.
d Unsaturated carbonyl compounds, where according to the condition involved saturated ketone or unsaturated alcohol or pinacol is formed in the reduction, are listed among other carbonyl compounds.
e In several examples the course of reduction is unknown and the reduction can proceed in the

The functional groups of organic compounds which give *insoluble* or *complex compounds with mercury* are compiled in Table 3. In solutions of such substance the anodic waves observed are often complicated by adsorption phenomena.

TABLE 3. GROUPS FORMING COMPOUNDS WITH MERCURY AND SHOWING ANODIC WAVES

| Functional grouping | Examples |
| --- | --- |
| —SH | mercaptols, cysteine, glutathione 2,3-dimercaptopropanol, SH-thiamine |
| $R_2N—C{<}^{S}_{S^-}$ | diethyldithiocarbamate, dithiocarbamino acetic acid |
| —NH—CO—NH— | barbituric acid, uracil |
| —NH—CS—NH— | thioureas, thiobarbiturates 4-methylthiouracil dithiohydantoin mercaptobenzimidazole |
| NH—CS—S | mercaptobenzthiazole, rhodanine |
| $R—SO_3H$ | pyrrol- and indolsulphonic acids, naphthol- and naphthylaminesulphonic acids |
| $—N{<}^{R}_{R}$ | ammonia, ethylenediamine, ethylenediaminetetraacetic acid |
| $—NH\ NH_2$ | hydrazine, phenylhydrazine |

Most of the organic *catalytically active substances* studied so far exert a catalytic effect upon hydrogen evolution. There are two main types of catalytically active substances: to the first type belong substances which cause catalytic waves in unbuffered acid or buffered solutions (sometimes even at pH 11). The second class is represented by substances showing catalytic waves in the presence of some heavy metals, e.g. cobalt or nickel.

All substances belonging to the first group should have one common feature: they must be Brönsted acids with a p$K_a$ value in the medium range of the pH-scale. They must neither be strong nor too weak acids and their hydrogen must not be too firmly bound. In addition, not only the acid-base equilibrium, but also the rate of dissociation and probably the adsorbability is of importance.

It was found empirically that well-pronounced catalytic effects can be observed in the presence of nitrogen-containing heterocyclic compounds (e.g. pyridine or quinoline derivatives, a number of alkaloids, cobalamin etc.). However, aliphatic nitrogen compounds (e.g. aminoacids), carbonyl compounds, oxygen-containing heterocyclic substances, unsaturated molecules or even hydrocarbons, e.g. azulenes also give catalytic waves.

Substances showing catalytic waves in ammoniacal cobalt or nickel solutions[1] must fulfil another condition beside the two conditions mentioned above: the substance has to form a complex-compound with cobalt and other components of the solution. Moreover, the acid properties of this complex and its adsorbability also seem to be of importance. The substances showing a catalytic effect of this type usually contain at least an atom of sulphur in their molecule (e.g. cysteine, dithiopyrimidine or proteins). Whether or not the presence of sulphur in the catalytically active molecule is a sufficient condition has yet to be decided. It was shown that e.g. gelatin or casein containing little or no sulphur atoms do not produce any catalytic wave of this type. Similarly, in the series of hydantoin, thiohydantoin and dithiohydantoin as well as pyrimidine, thiopyrimidine, and dithiopyrimidine, the catalytic effect was only observed for the thioderivative and it increased with the number of sulphur atoms in the molecule.[2]

Conversely the presence of such a catalytic wave was claimed for some substances containing no sulphur. From the study of the influence of the composition of the buffer solution, of the ionic strength and of the concentration of cobalt as well as of the concentration of the catalytically active substance, it has recently been possible to distinguish at least three different types of catalytic currents. Thus it is possible that the catalytic effects e.g. for uric acid,[3] glycerinaldehyde, or dihydroxyacetone,[4] have characteristics other than the catalytic waves due to thio-compounds.

The catalytic waves are often very sensitive, enabling the

detection of catalysts in $10^{-6}$ M and sometimes even $10^{-8}$ M solutions. However, these waves are not selective and often several catalysts in a mixture cannot be distinguished. Moreover, the heights of catalytic waves are very sensitive to pH, buffer composition, buffer concentration, ionic strength etc. It is thus only possible to recommend the application of these waves for pure solutions, e.g. for the determination of some alkaloids in pharmaceuticals.

### 4.2. SURFACE ACTIVE SUBSTANCES

By following the suppression of the polarographic maxima, the total amount of surface active substances present in the electrolysed solution can be estimated. Similarly, as with catalytically active substances, it is impossible to determine a single constituent in a mixture.

Most of the organic substances can serve as surface active agents. There is only one general rule concerning the extent of the suppressive effect, namely that the activity increases with increasing molecular size. This rule only strictly holds for structurally similar substances (e.g. in the homologous series of substituted thiobarbiturates[5] or for some related dyestuffs[6]). In all other instances a variation of the suppressive effect was observed with the structure. Substances of the same molecular weight often show very different surface activities. The hydrophobity of the substance also plays an important role.

The strong surface activity of macromolecular and natural substances can be used to distinguish synthetic and natural products (as mentioned earlier).

Similarly, the effects of molecular weight, as well as other specific structural influences, were observed for other polarographic phenomena in which adsorbability plays an important role: adsorption currents were observed especially for substances of higher molecular weight containing hydrophobic groups, e.g. for those with more condensed aromatic rings. In some instances free radicals are adsorbed and a chemisorption can be assumed. Such adsorption probably also operates in the adsorption of mercury compounds. Another factor which can play a role in the adsorbability of mercury salts is the polymerization of those salts.

## 4.3. DIRECT AND INDIRECT METHODS OF ANALYSIS

The methods of polarographic analysis of organic substances can be divided into two main groups: direct and indirect methods. In direct methods it is sufficient to dissolve the sample in an appropriate supporting electrolyte, register and measure the waves. In indirect methods the polarographically inactive substance is transformed by a chemical reaction into a substance which shows a wave on polarographic curves in an appropriate supporting electrolyte. In another type of indirect determinations, the substance to be determined reacts with a reagent which gives a polarographic wave. After the reaction, the wave of the reagent is measured. From the change in the height of this wave before and after reaction, the concentration of the analysed substance is computed. To this same group also belongs a part of polarometric (amperometric) titrations. Here the equivalence point is determined from the dependence of the wave-height on the volume of titrants added.

## 4.4. ELEMENTAL ANALYSIS

Polarography, because of its sensitivity, is well suited for the evaluation of the concentration in the final stages of analysis of certain elements. Thus the application of polarography was suggested long ago for the determination of sulphur after combustion.[7] The concentration of sulphates was determined from the decrease of the wave-height for barium or lead ions or by retitration.[8] Another method uses the peroxide bomb decomposition and retitration of an excess of a barium salt added, by amperometric control of potassium chromate.[9]

Similarly, anodic waves for halides can be used for the determination of halogens. The usual reductive degradative processes can also be used.

Dissolve some 20 mg of sample[10] in 5 ml. of absolute ethanol and over a period of 30 min add 0·7 g of sodium metal in small portions. At the completion of the reaction add a trace of metallic potassium. After refluxing for 30 min, cool, dilute with water, acidify the solution to litmus paper with nitric acid and make up to 100 ml. with water. Finally record the anodic waves of chlorides.

Another method[11] is as follows: fold 10 mg of the organic substance in a piece of filter paper, which has been previously soaked in potassium nitrate solution and dried. Fasten the small paper roll to the end of a platinum wire, place in the plug and burn in a 500 ml. flask containing 10–50 ml. of 0·1 N $H_2SO_4$ and filled with oxygen. Cool, well shake the bottle and finally record the anodic waves of chloride.

As ammonium ions give a reduction wave in tetra-alkyl-ammonium hydroxide solutions, a method for the determination of nitrogen was devised.[12] The method consists of mineralization by the conventional Kjeldahl method used in the semimicro or micro modification. Because waves at very negative potentials (e.g. of ammonium ions) are usually less reproducible than waves at more positive potentials, the accuracy of this method is somewhat lower than that for ordinary polarographic analysis. Other types of polarographic determinations of ammonium ions could be applied, e.g. using the anodic waves corresponding to the formation of salts with mercury or the condensation with phthalic dialdehyde (p. 142).

## 4.5. FUNCTIONAL ANALYSIS

Most polarographic methods used for the analysis of organic substances were devised for the determination of certain definite compounds. Nevertheless in some instances polarography is unavoidably applied as a functional analysis. Such instances are represented when, together with the given substance $A$, some other structurally related substances are determined and the result is expressed as a concentration of $A$. As the polarographic behaviour depends first of all on the type of the polarographically active group, it would seem natural to regard polarographic electrolysis as a method of functional analysis. However this application of polarography has certain limitations.

Polarographic waves can be taken as a measure of the amount of certain polarographically active substances, only when the substances in which the functional grouping has to be determined are structurally related. An extension of the conjugated system, or a substantial steric effect can change considerably the polarographic behaviour. Thus it is possible to determine polarographically the concentration of thiol groups in a mixture of substances

H

bearing the sulphhydryl group on aliphatic chains. Similarly the total aldehydic groups can be determined in a mixture of higher fatty aldehydes, but benzaldehyde or fural, if present, show a separate wave. Also the behaviour of aliphatic unsaturated aldehydes such as acrolein, differ substantially from that of saturated aldehydes, and hence these compounds give completely different waves. Substituted nitrobenzenes do not differ substantially from each other (with the exception of nitrophenols and nitranilines, which involve a change of the mechanism involving a quinoid intermediate) but differ from that of nitroalkanes. The following should be mentioned as other examples of a functional group determination: the nitrosamines derived from aliphatic amines and saturated heterocyclic amines, N-oxides derived from a certain type of nitrogen heterocyclics (e.g. from quinoxaline and its derivatives), $\Delta^4$-3-ketosteroids, 11-steroid aldehydes or betainyl-hydrazones of 3-ketosteroids (enabling the determination of the total amount of 3-ketosteroids in biological material) (p. 194).

The introduction of an additional active grouping in the immediate neighbourhood of the polarographically active group, can have a substantial effect on the behaviour of the latter. This effect can result not only in a shift of the half-wave potential, but in the change in reduction mechanism as well. Thus, whereas monobromo-derivatives are reduced by a substitution mechanism involving two electrons per bromine atom, α-dibromo-derivatives involve an elimination reaction corresponding to a transfer of only one electron per bromine atom. If in a reducible ketone an amino, hydroxy, alkoxy, thiol etc. group is introduced into the α-position, the hydrogenolysis of the C–$\overset{+}{N}$, C–O or C–S bonds proceeds at more positive potentials than that of the carbonyl group[13, 14] and the whole reduction pattern is changed.

Finally, the application of polarography for the determination of functional groups cannot be recommended in instances, where the half-wave potential of the polarographically active group is strongly influenced by the presence of a substituent on a remote part of the molecule.* The relatively smaller effects of substituents

---

* The susceptibility of the polarographically active group, on a given type of molecular skeleton, to the effect of substituents that exert polar, steric and resonance effects on half-wave potentials, but do not alter the

in the benzenoid series, which would assist functional analysis, are seen from the extent of potential ranges by the monosubstituted derivatives, given in Fig. 38.

Although the direct application of polarographic waves as a measure of the functional group content is limited to certain groups of compounds, there is a whole field to be explored in which polarography can be used to evaluate the existing chemical methods of functional analysis. It should be, for example, possible to determine the total amount of oximes, or the decrease of the

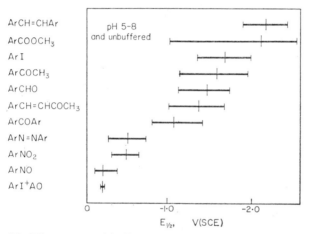

FIG. 38. The ranges of half-wave potentials in which the reductions of monosubstituted benzenoid compounds at pH 5–8 and in unbuffered solution take place, provided that the reduction follows the same mechanism as that for the parent compound.

concentration of hydroxylamine in the determination of carbonyl group, or to determine the sulphonium salts formed or the phenacyl chloride or bromide consumed in the determination of

reduction mechanism, is best expressed by reaction constants $\rho$ or $\rho^*$ in the modified Hammett and Taft equations (cf. Chapter XI). If the value of these constants exceeds 0·5 V, the half-wave potentials of substance bearing the same reducible group can be so different that the use of the method for functional analysis cannot be recommended. This rarely occurs with benzenoid substances, but was sometimes observed in the aliphatic series.

dialkylsulphides.[15] In a similar way, by degradation of the corresponding thiouronium salts in alkaline solutions to the corresponding anionic form of the mercaptan, it was possible to determine several carboxylic acids.[15]

## REFERENCES

(1) BŘEZINA, M. and ZUMAN, P., *Polarography in Medicine, Biochemistry and Pharmacy*, Interscience, New York (1958), where further references are quoted.
(2) ZUMAN, P. and KUIK, M., *Collect. Czechoslov. Chem. Commun.* **24**, 3861 (1959).
(3) BÜCHNER, M., BREHMER, CH., PIETZSCH, A., and LICKINT, F., *Naturwiss.* **43**, 423 (1956).
(4) LAMPRECHT, W., GUDBJARNASON, S., and KATZLMEIER, H., *Z. Physiol. Chem.* **322**, 52 (1960).
(5) ZUMAN, P., *Collect. Czechoslov. Chem. Commun.* **20**, 883 (1955).
(6) RUSZNÁK, I., FUKKER, K., and KRÁLIK, I., *Z. phys. Chem.* (*Frankfurt*) **17**, 56, 61 (1958).
(7) RULFS, C. L. and MACKELA, A. A., *Anal. Chem.* **25**, 660 (1953).
(8) TRIFONOV, A., IVANOV, C. and PAVLOV, D., *Collect. Czechoslov. Chem. Commun.* **19**, 1133 (1954).
(9) WARSHOWSKY, B., SHOOK, T. E., and SCHANTZ, E. L., *Anal. Chem.* **26**, 1051 (1954).
(10) SAPARA, V., *Časopis Československ. lékarnictva* **62**, 132 (1949).
(11) NOVÁK, J. V. A. in J. HEYROVSKÝ: *Polarographie*, p. 361, Springer, Wien (1941).
(12) GYÖRBÍRÓ, K. and MAJOR, E., *Kohászati Lapok* **11**, 112 (1956).
(13) LUND, H., *Acta Chem. Scand.* **14**, 1927 (1960).
(14) ZUMAN, P. and WAWZONEK, S., Trends in Organic Polarography, in *Progress in Polarography* (P. Zuman, I. M. Kolthoff, editors), Vol. 1, p. 303, Interscience, New York (1962).
(15) ZUMAN, P. and HORÁK, V., Unpublished results.

# CHAPTER V

# DIRECT METHODS OF POLAROGRAPHIC ANALYSIS

DIRECT methods of polarographic analysis can only be used in instances where there are no interfering substances present in the sample.

Interfering substances are substances with a similar half-wave potential to that of the substance to be analysed. 0·1–0·2 V (according to the slope of the waves and their relative concentration) is the smallest potential difference possible for a separate measurement to be made of both waves. Those substances which are reduced at more positive potentials than the compound under examination, and are present in a tenfold or even greater excess over the substance to be analysed, are also considered as interfering substances.

The influence of these interfering substances can be eliminated (or at least reduced) by a correct choice of the supporting electrolyte (as mentioned in Chapter III), using derivative or subtractive methods (cf. Chapter II) or using preliminary separation methods (as discussed in Chapter VII). In order to choose the correct supporting electrolyte (i.e. to obtain a well developed wave and to eliminate the interferences) it is necessary to know, and when possible to understand, the polarographic behaviour of the substance to be analysed. Polarographic behaviour (for aqueous solutions) is a general expression used to indicate the changes of the form, height and half-wave potentials of polarographic curves with pH and composition of the supporting electrolyte. The polarographic behaviour is clarified by studying the effect of the depolarizer concentration, the mercury pressure and by determining the number of electrons transferred. The auxiliary methods quoted in Chapter II are often used for this purpose. In nonaqueous solutions, the number of variable parameters is more limited, mainly by the little understood acid-base equilibria and by the limited solubility of salts. The necessity for such an experimental and theoretical treatment for achieving a solid foundation for an analytical procedure has been recently widely recognized. The practice of deliberately choosing a certain buffer solution (based only on a trial and error method or on personal preference) for the measurement of wave-heights or half-wave potentials, seems to have been gradually abandoned.

### 5.1. EXAMINATION OF A COMPOUND NOT PREVIOUSLY STUDIED

The elaboration of an analytical method is facilitated when the polarographic behaviour of the compound to be analysed is already described in the literature, using experimental conditions that do not differ substantially from those planned for the particular analysis.

On the other hand when the behaviour of the substance for the particular analytical method to be used is unknown, a systematic and thorough study must precede the analytical application. A simple scheme which has been successfully applied to several systems will now be outlined.

The first problem is the preparation of an appropriate stock solution.

Prepare, if possible, an aqueous, 0·01 M solution. Use ethanol as a solvent for substances with no or few hydrophilic groups, and then add small amounts of water and observe the concentration at which the substance becomes insoluble.

The aim is to prepare a stock solution with as little organic solvent as possible. Sometimes organic solvents other than ethanol can be used, or even non-aqueous solutions. However, the following is restricted to the most common example of aqueous solutions and water-organic solvent mixtures. Solubility data for the less common substances are not usually available, so the only guide is information concerning crystallization from solvents. Whenever possible prepare the stock solution without the application of heat, but if heating is necessary to accelerate the dissolution, it is essential to make sure that the behaviour of the "saturated" solution before heating, and the warmed solution (after heating), is identical. In addition it is necessary to control the stability of the stock solution towards long periods of standing and to the effect of diffuse day-light. These factors are sometimes overlooked and cause confusion.

When the stock solution has been prepared a few typical supporting electrolytes are choosen, e.g. 0·1 M sulphuric acid, acetate buffer pH 4·7, phosphate buffer pH 6·8, borate buffer pH 9·3 and 0·1 M NaOH. According to the character of the substance under study some other buffers may be added to these, e.g. for α-hydroxy carbonyl compounds the inclusion of veronal buffer pH 8·5, and 0·1 M ammonia 0·1 M ammonium chloride is advisable.

First add some of the stock solution of the substance under study to each of these buffers, so that the final concentration of the depolarizer is $2 \cdot 10^{-4}$ M. Examine to see if true solutions result and, if necessary, add an organic solvent to ensure the formation of a true solution. Again, use the smallest possible concentration of organic solvent in the mixture with water in the final buffer or supporting electrolyte. Now subject the $2 \cdot 10^{-4}$ M solutions in all five (or more) supporting electrolytes to polarographic electrolysis.

It is preferable to deaerate the supporting electrolyte first and then add the stock solution of the depolarizer.

Then inspect the resulting curves to discover whether there is a cathodic or an anodic wave and in what pH-region. When a reduction wave is obtained make sure that it does not change with time, measured at 10 and 20 min intervals. Then study the dependence of the concentration of the depolarizer, as well as the effect of the mercury pressure, to obtain information concerning the character (the type) of the electrode process involved. Such measurements are even more important for systems, where two or more waves are observed simultaneously on a polarographic curve at different potentials. Follow also the changes in the ratio of the two waves with the parameters mentioned above.

When these preliminary measurements have been performed make a detailed study of the pH-dependence. The choice of the buffers used (cf. Chapter III) and the pH-range studied, is based on the results of these preliminary experiments. So is, for example, a special temperature control or control of the time elapsed after addition of the stock solution to the supporting electrolyte (when time-changes occur), a change toward higher or lower concentration of the depolarizer, a regulation of the drop-time (for waves at −2·0 V and more negative, slowly dropping electrodes are preferred) etc. Based on the detailed survey of the pH-dependence the following factors are studied (according to principles given in Chapter II):

(1) The number and character of waves, their changes with pH, concentration, time and temperature. (Dependence of $i_l/c$ or $i_l/c \times m^{2/3} \, t^{1/6}$ on pH can be recorded, but usually the plot of $i_l$ − pH dependence is sufficient.)

(2) The effect of pH, concentration of the polarographically active substance and temperature on half-wave potentials.

(3) The number of electrons transferred in an electrode process, the shape of the waves (the transfer coefficient α from logarithmic analysis and from $dE_{1/2}/d$ pH) and the type and mechanism of the electrode process (based on

identification using auxiliary methods given in Chapter II, not merely on guess-work).

(4) The role and concentration of the buffer used and the presence of neutral salts (effects of the type and valency of cation and anion respectively) on the character and number of waves and on half-wave potentials.

(5) The effect of solvent composition.

(6) If necessary, the smallest possible concentration of gelatin or other surface active substances.

(7) Based on the results of all these experiments, the optimum supporting electrolyte for the particular analytical problem is chosen.

This general scheme cannot exhaust all possibilities and modifications are necessary for every particular purpose. In general, the emphasis placed on the individual points changes according to the type of the particular problem, e.g. for catalytic currents, special attention is paid to the role of buffer composition, buffer concentration and ionic strength effects.

## 5.2. SIMULTANEOUS DETERMINATION OF SEVERAL SUBSTANCES

The additivity of limiting currents (the deviations of which have already been mentioned in Chapter II) forms the basis for a simultaneous determination of two or more substances in the same sample, in the same supporting electrolyte. Usually no mutual influence is observed on limiting currents at two selected potentials (this can be compared, for example, with the more complicated behaviour of extinctions of two substances at two wave-lengths). The conditions for the simultaneous determinations can be formulated as follows: the half-wave potentials of the two substances to be distinguished have to be substantially different (cf. beginning of this chapter). When this condition is fulfilled, the simultaneous determination of both components can be carried out with an accuracy of $\pm 1$ to 5 per cent if the concentrations of all components to be determined are of the same order. This condition can be considered to be fulfilled when the excess of one component is not greater than about five fold. If a greater excess of one of the components is present, two possibilities exist: when the component in excess is reduced at more negative potentials (or gives an anodic wave at more positive potentials, cf. Fig. 22), the optimum accuracy for the determination of both compounds can be preserved. The more positive reduction wave (the more negative anodic wave) can be measured with a high galvanometer sensitivity, and the wave for the excess component is measured at a reduced sensitivity.

The situation is more complicated if the component in excess is reduced at more positive potentials than the other components. Here a highly accurate determination is only possible for the component in excess when classical polarography is used. In some instances the application of derivative and subtractive methods can also be applied for the solution of these problems (Chapter II).

# CHAPTER VI

# INDIRECT METHODS

In indirect methods, as mentioned in Chapter IV, polarographically inactive substances are transformed into compounds showing waves on polarographic curves, or concentration changes of a polarographically active substance which reacts with the electroinactive compound to be determined, are measured. Finally, polarometric (amperometric) titrations can be included in this group of analytical methods.

## 6.1. TRANSFORMATION INTO ELECTROACTIVE FORM

Several classes of compounds can be determined when transformed by a chemical reaction into an electroactive form, and for analytical purposes the waves for various substances resulting in such reactions can be followed. In this section a classification is used according to the type of reaction involved in the transformation. The most frequently used methods are nitration, nitrosation, condensation, addition, substitution, oxidation and complex formation. It should be stressed that these types of chemical reactions have so far been relatively unexploited. The analytical chemist, when using polarographic methods, should always bear in mind the possibility of using those types of chemical reactions which give a high yield of an electroactive compound.

### 6.1.1. *Nitration*

One of the most general and frequently applied indirect methods is the transformation of an organic compound into a nitrocompound. The method is applied to hydrocarbons and other aromatic compounds, mainly those bearing a phenyl ring, e.g. phenols, substituted anilines, phenyl-bearing amino acids etc. The nitrating mixture consists of nitric acid, either pure or

112

containing potassium nitrate or sulphuric acid (to increase the acidity, the formation of $NO_2^+$ ions and possibly also in some instances to act as a dehydrating agent). Nitro-compounds formed in nitration give well-developed waves at relatively positive potentials, which often enables the determination to be made in complicated mixtures (waves at more negative potentials do not interfere). The composition of the reaction mixture, the temperature and duration of nitration are dependent on the compound to be determined. In every particular situation the conditions best suited for obtaining one single nitrated product (if possible) in a quantitative reaction should be carefully checked. A careful choice of reaction conditions sometimes enables on the other hand a mixture of aromatic compounds to be analysed. The polarography is done in slightly acidic or slightly alkaline solutions (usually pH 4–10); in strongly acid solutions the waves are often complicated by the reduction of the hydroxylamine intermediate and by sharp maxima; in strongly alkaline solutions the polynitro-compounds, which are usually formed, often undergo transformations accompanied by a time-change in the height of the polarographic curves.

A method for the determination of *benzene*[1] in liquid samples (blood, urine) is as follows:

*Procedure.* Transfer the benzene from the sample in flask G with air which has been previously passed through concentrated sulphuric acid, the nitration mixture D, water E and 20 per cent sodium hydroxide F (Fig. 39). Regulate the air-flow from the flask B by means of hydrostatic pressure in the flask A (Fig. 39) and measure with the manometer K. Treat samples containing proteins with 0·5 ml. of paraffin oil, which has been previously heated to 160°C and mixed while still luke-warm with 5 per cent calcium stearate, to prevent foaming. Carry out the analysis of gaseous samples (e.g. atmosphere or breath) by introducing the sample directly in to the nitration mixture, which is placed in the U-tube (right in Figs. 39 and 40).

This U-tube, filled with glass beads, contains 0·5 ml. of the nitration mixture (Fig. 40) and is prepared from the same volumes of concentrated sulphuric acid and nitric acid ($d = 1·5$). The benzene carried by the air from flask G or by gas is trapped and nitrated to *m*-dinitrobenzene. 1·5 l. of air passed through the sample and nitration mixture in the course of 3 hr, is usually sufficient to transfer all the benzene from the flask G to the nitration mixture in the U-tube.

Next dilute the nitration mixture, and prepare it for a polarographic examination after deaeration with nitrogen (suggested deaeration by photographic developer cannot be recommended).

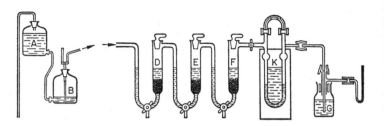

FIG. 39. Apparatus for determination of benzene in blood and in urine. (A) Reservoir of water; (B) source of air; (D) nitration mixture; (E) water; (F) 20 per cent solution of sodium hydroxide; (K) manometer; (G) sample of blood or urine; according to S. Škramovský and J. Teisinger.

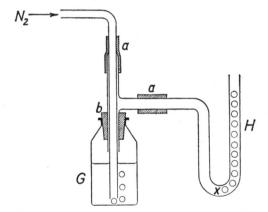

FIG. 40. Nitration compartment of the apparatus on Fig. 39.
(G) Sample of blood or urine; (H) nitration mixture with glass beds; (a) rubber tubing; (b) rubber stopper; ($N_2$) inlet of nitrogen or air.

*Notes.* (1) Instead of the previous neutralization with sodium hydroxide to tropaeolin O, the addition of carbonate (to pH about 10) or pyridine (to pH about 5·7) is now recommended. The two nitro-groups of *m*-dinitrobenzene are reduced in two four-electron polarographic waves.

(2) In the determination of *toluene*[2] the sample, from which toluene has been driven off, is heated to 60–70°C. The nitration solution consists of concentrated nitric acid ($d = 1·5$). The double wave of dinitrotoluene can be recorded after alkalization at a pH of 11. This method is used for the determination of toluene in air, blood and urine.

(3) *Naphthalene*[3] is nitrated in nitric acid ($d = 1.33$) and the sample is polarographed in an acetate buffer (pH 5·4) containing 50 per cent methanol. The reduction wave of α-nitronaphthalene can be used for the analysis of the atmosphere.

A method[4] has been recommended for the determination of *benzene in the presence of its homologues.* It is based on nitration of a mixture of aromatic hydrocarbons, extraction with ether of the nitro-compounds formed from the reaction mixture, evaporation of the solvent, oxidation with chromic acid and dissolution of the residue in acetic acid.

The nitration products of toluene and xylene are oxidized to the corresponding acids and the dinitrobenzene is extracted, after alkalization, with petroleum ether. The solvent is evaporated off and the residue is transferred into a carbonate-containing supporting electrolyte containing 50 per cent ethanol.

This method consists of two extractions, each with several portions of solvent and a twofold evaporation of the solvent. Consequently it is time-consuming and the accuracy is lowered by the volatilization of dinitrobenzene during the evaporations.

The modified method[5] suggests the following procedure:

Dissolve the sample containing 5–100 mg of benzene in 10 ml. of glacial acetic acid. To a 50-ml. flask add 2 ml. of the nitration mixture (10 g dessicated ammonium nitrate in 100 ml. of concentrated sulphuric acid) and a 0·5 ml. aliquot of sample. After 5–10 min add 1 ml. of water and 0·1 ml. of a saturated aqueous solution of chromic acid, and heat the reaction mixture on a water bath at 90–100°C for 30 min. If a blue-green colour is observed, add more chromic acid solution and then cool the solution; drop-wise add methanol until the solution is blue-green in colour. Dilute the resulting solution with 10 ml. of water and add 10 ml. of redistilled pyridine. After cooling, add 15 ml. of a 40 per cent solution of sodium hydroxide and again mix and cool. With the aid of a separating funnel discard the lower green solution, wash the colourless pyridine layer* with 5 ml. of a 20 per cent solution of sodium hydroxide and again separate. Transfer the pyridine layer to a 50-ml. flask, add 10 ml. of 1:5 diluted nitration mixture, together with 2 ml. of a 0·5 per cent solution of gelatin, and make up the solution to 50 ml. with water.
The curves recorded for such solutions are given in Fig. 41.

---

* Insufficient oxidation would be detected at this stage by the blue-green colour of the pyridine layer, resulting from the presence of dinitro-toluenes and dinitroxylenes.

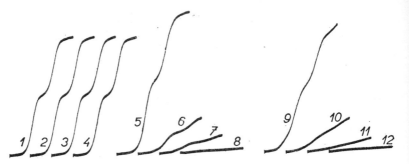

FIG. 41. Nitration and oxidation of benzene, toluene and xylene. (1)–(4) Benzene (3·1 mg); (5)–(8) to luene (8·8 mg); (9)–(12) xylene (8·8 mg). (1), (5) and (9) after nitration, the other curves after oxidation for: (2), (6) and (10) for 5 min; (3), (7) and (11) for 10 min; (4), (8) and (12) for 20 min. Curves starting at −0·1 V,S.C.E., full scale sensitivity (1)–(4) 8 $\mu$A; (5)–(12) 14 $\mu$A.

If the *sum of all the aromatic hydrocarbons* present is to be determined the following procedure is used:

Cool 2 ml. of the nitration mixture in ice and add 0·5 ml. of the sample solution in glacial acetic acid. When the nitration is complete, dilute the mixture and add 10 ml. of pyridine. After cooling, add 2 ml. of a 0·5 per cent solution of gelatin and make up the solution to 50 ml. with water.

*Phenols* have been determined after nitration (in a 2–3 per cent solution of nitric acid) to a mixture of o- and p-nitrophenols.[6, 7] By carefully selecting the nitration conditions under which phenol does not interfere[8], p-cresol can be determined in the urine of a poisoned individual.

$$OCON(CH_3)_2$$

$$\overset{+}{N}(CH_3)_3$$

$$CH_3 \ SO_4^-$$

(I)

Among the aniline derivatives, the determination of *dulcin* and *phenacetin*[9] can be mentioned. This method utilizes the formation of the o-nitro derivative. The methyl sulphate of 3-trimethyl-ammonium phenyl N,N-dimethyl-carbonate (I) (pharmaceutical trade names of Proserine, Neoeserine, Neostigmine, Prostigmine etc.) can be polarographically determined after saponification and nitration in a medium consisting of a 65 per cent solution of nitric acid.[10] Polarographic curves of the resulting nitro-compounds have been recorded in alkaline media.

Great interest has been devoted to the phenyl-bearing natural amino acids, *tyrosine, tryptophane* and *phenylalanine*.[11-18] After a detailed study of the conditions of nitration,[12, 13] nitration with $0.15$ N $HNO_3$ was recommended for tyrosine,[13] $1.5$ to $3.0$ N $HNO_3$ for tryptophane[14] and a mixture of potassium nitrate and sulphuric acid for phenylalanine[11] was suggested.

For the determination of tyrosine in the presence of tryptophane and phenylalanine the following procedure is recommended:[18]

Place a sample containing 10–20 mg of tyrosine into a centrifuge tube, add 30 ml. of $0.15$ N $HNO_3$ and crystalline phenylalanine to correspond to about three-quarters of the weight of tryptophane present (if unknown, add preferably an excess of phenylalanine) and heat the solution to 50–60°C. Then slowly add a 2 per cent solution of mercuric acetate (in $0.15$ N $HNO_3$) until the solution remains clear, add a further $0.5$ ml. in excess and, after standing 2 hr at 50–60°C, centrifuge the solution and make up the supernatant to 20 ml. with $0.15$ N $HNO_3$. Transfer the sample into an appropriate flask, add 20 ml. of $0.15$ N $HNO_3$ together with a few crystals of sodium nitrite and boil under reflux for 2 hr. Now neutralize the solution with a 20 per cent solution of potassium hydroxide and dilute to 50 ml. with water. Finally mix 5–7 ml. of this solution with 2 ml. of McIlvaine pH 5 buffer, dilute to 10 ml. and polarograph after deaeration.

For the determination of tryptophane in the presence of tyrosine and phenylalanine the analysis is carried out as follows:[18]

Decant the centrifuged precipitate of mercuric salts, disperse in $0.15$ N $HNO_3$ and centrifuge once more. Transfer the solid into a 100-ml. bottle, add 30 ml. of $1.5$ N $HNO_3$ and boil under reflux for 2 hr. After cooling, neutralize the solution with a 20 per cent solution of potassium hydroxide and centrifuge. Finally dilute the solution to 50 ml. and dilute an aliquot of 5–7 ml. to 10 ml. with the McIlvaine pH 5 buffer and polarograph after deaeration.

Finally for the determination of phenylalanine in the presence of tyrosine and tryptophane the following procedure is recommended[18]:

Heat the sample for $1\frac{1}{2}$ hr under reflux on an oil bath at 120°C. Cool the solution, neutralize by the drop-wise addition of a 20 per cent solution of potassium hydroxide and add 10 ml. of water. Reacidify the solution with dilute nitric acid to obtain pH 2–3, and add 5 ml. of a 2 per cent solution of mercuric acetate. Heat on a water-bath at about 60°C for 1–2 hr and centrifuge the sample. To the supernatant liquid add 2 ml. of 0·1 N $HNO_3$, 0·1 ml. of a 10 per cent solution of silver nitrate and 2–3 ml. of a concentrated solution of potassium permanganate so as to give a faint but persisting rose colouration. Place the mixture on a water-bath at 60–80°C for 15 min and add a few drops of hydrogen peroxide to destroy the excess of permanganate. After neutralization with a 20 per cent solution of potassium hydroxide, oxides of mercury, manganese and silver precipitate. Dilute with water to a definite volume and centrifuge the supernatant liquid. Mix a 7 ml. sample of the clear supernatant liquid with 3 ml. of McIlvaine buffer pH 5 and after deaeration polarograph the mixture.

These methods can be used for the determination of tyrosine in serum albumin and some peptides, and all three amino acids in a hydrolysate of casein (pepton).

After nitration, *phenylethylbarbituric* acid (phenobarbital) can be determined in the presence of a hundredfold excess of diethyl-barbituric acid (barbital).[19]

Although *morphine* has been frequently determined from the reduction waves resulting from the action of nitrites in acid solutions,[20, 21] it has been only recently recognized[22] that the reducible compound showing a wave at −0·9 V is 2-nitro-morphine and not a nitroso-derivative, as has been previously supposed. However, the application of the nitration mixture[23] produced no useful polarographic waves.

The recommended procedure is:

To 5 ml. of a morphine solution (containing 5–100 mg of morphine in 100 ml. of 1 N HCl) add 2 ml. of 1 M potassium nitrite; allow the solution to stand for 5 min, add 3 ml. of a 20 per cent solution of potassium hydroxide and 1 ml. of a 2 per cent solution of methylcellulose (or of 0·1 per cent gelatin) and after deaeration polarograph the solution (Fig. 42).

*Note.* Morphine has been determined by this method in poppy seed and blood after separation by paper chromatography. *Heroin* (diacetylmorphine) has also been determined after hydrolysis.[24] *Codeine,* which under the above conditions is not transformed into a 2-nitro-derivative, can be determined if treated with an acidic solution of nitrites at elevated temperatures.[25] Because this method proved unsatisfactory for the determination of codeine in mixtures, attempts were later made[26] to utilize the nitration mixture.

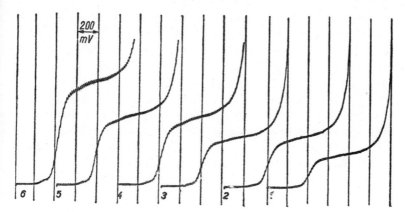

FIG. 42. Determination of morphine after nitration.
Morphine was treated in acid media with nitrite and the curves
recorded after alkalization. Concentration of morphine: (1) 200 μg;
(2) and (3) 300 μg; (4) and (5) 400 μg; (6) 600. μg Curves starting
at −0·2 V, S.C.E., 200 mV/absc., full scale sensitivity 2·2 μA.

Similarly the method devised for the determination of *estrone*[30]
gave the 4-nitro-estrone derivative.[22] The procedure is:

Dissolve the substance in 5 ml. of acetate buffer (pH 3·1–3·2) and treat
with 0·3 ml. of concentrated sulphuric acid, 0·1 ml. of 50 per cent potassium nitrite and (after 30 min) 50 ml. of alcoholic ammonia solution.

The mononitro-derivative also resulted as the main product in excess of
nitrous acid[22] in the reaction of *p*-cresol.

### 6.1.2. *Nitrosation*

*Secondary amines* can be determined in the presence of primary
and tertiary amines after transformation into nitrosamines.[27–29]

Unlike the reaction of nitrous acid with *p*-cresol, the product of
a similar reaction with *resorcinol*, has been proved[31] without
doubt, by comparison with 2,4-dinitrosorcsorcinol, to be the
nitroso-compound. The procedure is:

To 0·5 ml. of a methanolic solution of about $4 \times 10^{-4}$ M resorcinol add
0·5 ml. of methanol, 2 ml. of 3·0 M potassium nitrite and 5 ml. of 0·2 N
$H_2SO_4$. Pass nitrogen for 3 min, add 2 ml. of 2·5 M sodium hydroxide and
record the curves.

I

Catechol and hydroquinol are also attacked by nitrous acid, but the reducible products of this reaction were not identified.[31] Nevertheless, the two waves resulting from the reaction of the catechol grouping in *rutin* with nitrous acid can be used for analytical purposes.[32] Similarly *quecitrin* can also be determined. In a similar manner and by following the procedure given for morphine, *cephaeline* was determined,[33] although the structure of the reducible compound has not been proved. In the determination, a 100-fold excess of emetine does not interfere and it can be applied to *tinctura ipecacuanhae* and injections.

By essentially the same procedure *antipyrine*[34] and *Intercain* (dimethylaminoethyl ester of *p*-butylaminobenzoic acid hydrochloride)[35] were determined. The attack by nitrous acid is probably on the phenyl ring, but the reaction products, which show a polarographic reduction wave, were not identified.

Both components in *Procaine-penicillin* can be determined using nitrous acid.[36] When the samples are hydrolysed, both hydrolysis products, penillo-aldehyde and penicillamine, most likely undergo nitrosation. If hydrolysis is not carried out, Procaine forms a diazotate, the wave of which is measured.

### 6.1.3. *Condensations*

The most important condensation reactions used for analytical purposes in organic polarography are reactions of carbonyl compounds* with the formation of (1) aldimines and ketimines, (2) semicarbazones, (3) hydrazones and (4) oximes. The reactions of carbon disulphide with amines and amino acids are also used (5).

6.1.3.1. *Aldimines and ketimines* are formed by the reaction of aldehydes and ketones with solutions of primary amines or ammonia, at a hydrogen ion concentration close to the dissociation constant of the amine. With saturated aldehydes (except formaldehyde which shows a more complicated behaviour) and ketones, a well developed wave at about $-1.5$ V is observed (Fig. 43).[37-39] 2·5 N ammonia with 2·5 N ammonium sulphate, or 2 M glycine

---

* The condensation reactions of phthalaldehyde with amino acids result in the formation of electro-inactive cyclic products. The decrease of the phthalaldehyde wave is measured (p. 142).

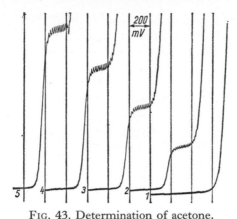

FIG. 43. Determination of acetone.
2 M Glycine, 1 M sodium hydroxide, concentration of acetone:
(1) 0; (2) $2 \times 10^{-3}$ M; (3) $4 \times 10^{-3}$ M; (4) $6 \times 10^{-3}$ M; (5) $8 \times 10^{-3}$ M. Curves starting at $-0.8$ V, S.C.E., 300 mV/absc., full scale sensitivity 1·7 $\mu$A.

pH 9·6 buffer, or 12 N ammonia saturated with ammonium chloride were used as supporting electrolytes. Under these conditions the ketimine or aldimine formed is in equilibrium with the parent carbonyl compound. The equilibrium is shifted towards the free carbonyl form, so that only 5–20 per cent of the ketone present is transformed into a ketimine, but the wave-height is strictly linearly proportional to the concentration of ketone at a given concentration of amine. More recently[40] the use of butylamine was recommended for the determination of *acetone*. This is less volatile than ammonia, and the equilibrium is shifted more towards the ketimine form than with ammonia. This is in accordance with previous experience, which has shown that solutions containing 1 M methylamine and 1 M methylamine hydrochloride were suitable for the determination of *cyclohexanone, methylcyclohexanone* and *cyclopentanone*.[39] The waves in 1 M glycine buffer were used for the determination of cyclohexanone and those in 2·5 M $NH_3$, 1·25 M $(NH_4)_2SO_4$ for the determination of *cyclohexanone-1-ol-2* in the study of the kinetics of auto-oxidation of these substances.[40a] The more negative wave in solutions of the latter substance probably corresponds to the reduction of the activated C–OH bond.

Cyclopentanone and cyclohexanone can also be determined in complex mixtures by using the formation of ketimines, from 20 per cent solutions of hexamethylenediamine, at a pH above 12.[40b] The aldehydes, when present, give aldimine waves at potentials about 0·2 V more positive than the ketimine waves. However, moderate concentrations of aldehydes do not interfere in the determination of ketones as (at the concentrations of hexamethylenediamine used) a substantial part of the aldimine is converted into a polarographically inactive compound which, during the course of the reaction, is competitive to the aldimine formation. For the determination of aldehydes, a 2 per cent solution of hexamethylenediamine proved to be the most suitable.

The aldimine formation has also been applied to the determinations of *cardiac glycosides* which bear an aldehyde grouping in position 2. Glycine (2 M) dissolved in 1 M NaOH proved best as a supporting electrolyte.[41]

Condensation with ammonia has also been exploited for the determination of *ascorbic acid*.[37, 42] When a sample containing ascorbic acid is added to 0·5 N NH$_3$ and 0·5 N NH$_4$Cl, and oxygen is slowly passed through the solution, a cathodic wave at −1·5 V is observed in addition to the smaller wave of hydrogen peroxide (Fig. 44). The dependence of the wave-height of this wave on the concentration of the ammonia buffer, shows that two moles of ammonia react with one mole of the oxidation product (probably the diketogulonic acid). The analogous behaviour of coumarindiol indicates that this reaction is common for the oxidation products of compounds containing the enediol grouping.

This cathodic wave can be used for determinations in samples containing an excess of other substances which give or influence anodic waves, e.g. chlorides, thiols, or reduced forms of some natural colouring matters. These substances interfere in the usual determination which utilizes the anodic wave of reduced ascorbic acid (cf. p. 200). However, it should not be applied when larger amounts of substances are present, which give reduction waves in this buffered solution containing ammonia at potentials more positive than about −1·5 V.

On the other hand a differentiation of carbonyl compounds and even of oxidation products of different enediols is possible,[43]

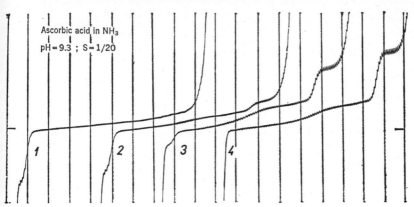

FIG. 44. Oxidation of ascorbic acid in the presence of ammonia.
0·5 N Ammonia, 0·5 N ammonium chloride pH 9·3, 3 × $10^{-4}$ M
ascorbic acid. Into this solution oxygen was introduced for: (1) 0;
(2) 7 sec; (3) 15 sec; (4) 60 sec. Curves starting at −0·2 V, $t_1 =$
2·8 sec, $m = $ 2·6 mg/sec, full scale sensitivity 4·2 $\mu$A.

e.g. if *dehydroascorbic acid* is condensed with o-phenylenediamine.
As a result of a careful study of the reaction conditions, it has been
found that when dehydroascorbic acid is treated with o-phenylenediamine (1·0–2·0 × $10^{-3}$ M) at 25°C for 50–60 min, a reduction
two-electron wave appears on polarographic curves. This wave is
well separated from the waves of dehydroreductic acid, alloxan,
mesoxalaldehyde, and even 2,3-diketogulonic acid, provided that
the pH is about 4. Under the same conditions the anodic wave for
ascorbic acid is unaltered by the presence of the condensation
product (probably II) and of excess of o-phenylenediamine. It is

$$N=C\text{———}C=O$$
$$N=C \qquad CHCHOHCH_2OH$$
(II)

thus possible to determine directly ascorbic and dehydroascorbic
acid in a mixture (and possibly also 2,3-diketogulonic acid). The

method[43] has been applied to the analysis of some natural products, and the results have been compared with the 2,4-dinitrophenylhydrazine method.

The condensation reactions with simple amines enabled the *aldehydic grouping* in artemazulene and lactarvioline to be detected. They also helped to prove that certain terpenes such as absinthindiol or guajtriol C, do not bear such a grouping.[44]

The formation of aldimines can also be utilized in the reverse way for the determination of *primary amines*. For these purposes the application of piperonal was recommended.[29] The method was used for the determination of traces of methylamine in commercial samples of dimethylamine.

### 6.1.3.2. *Semicarbazones*.

Semicarbazones[45, 46] have the advantage in comparison with aldimines and ketimines, that the equilibria between the carbonyl compound and the amine derivative are shifted more toward the condensate with semicarbazide than with simple amines. Moreover, the waves for semicarbazones are usually observed at more positive potentials, and thus the waves are better developed than those for aldimines and ketimines.

The heights of waves of semicarbazones are dependent on the equilibrium constant of the condensation reaction. This enables the analysis of some mixtures to be made. Generally speaking, the equilibrium is shifted in favour of semicarbazones more with aldehydes than ketones, and this permits the determination of *aldehydes in the presence of smaller excesses of ketones*. Thus butyraldehyde can be determined in the presence of a fourfold excess of acetone and a twofold excess of acetophenone, by recording the curves in 0·1 M HCl with 0·02 M semicarbazide.

For the converse determination, i.e. of *ketone* in the presence of aldehyde, it is necessary to remove the excess of aldehyde (e.g. by oxidation with silver oxide) as follows:

To 50 ml. of an alkaline solution containing ketone and aldehyde (e.g. acetone and butyraldehyde) add 3 g of $Ag_2O$ and heat the mixture under reflux on a water bath at about 60°C for 1 hr. Then add 25 ml. of 0·5 M semicarbazide hydrochloride together with 0·3 M NaOH and record the polarographic curve.

Any precipitate formed is claimed to be without influence. Nevertheless, in this way, the wave of cyclohexanone semicarbazone was lowered by about 30 per cent due to the treatment with silver oxide. However, the determination of acetone was uninfluenced even by a twentyfold excess of butyraldehyde.

**6.1.3.3.** *Oximes.* Although the polarographic behaviour of various oximes has been studied rather thoroughly, the waves of oximes were seldom used for the determination of carbonyl compounds.

One of the methods used for the determination of *pyridoxal* in the presence of pyridoxal-5-phosphate already mentioned on p. 65 is the transformation of both substances into oximes. This occurs quantitatively in the presence of excess hydroxylamine. But even then the separation of waves is poor, and only with the application of a derivative circuit can an analysis be made of a mixture containing comparable concentrations of pyridoxaloxime and pyridoxaloxime-5-phosphate (Fig. 33).

**6.1.3.4.** *Hydrazones.* The most widely used reaction for polarographic purposes is the condensation of carbonyl compounds with Girard reagents.[47, 48] The development of the wave of the resulting betainylhydrazone increased in the sequence: Girard's P reagent (pyridinium acethydrazide, $C_5H_5\overset{+}{N}\ CH_2CONHNH_2$) $<$ Girard's T reagent (trimethylglycylhydrazide $(CH_3)_3\overset{+}{N}$ $CH_2CONHNH_2$) $<$ Girard's D reagent (dimethylglycylhydrazide, in acid solutions as $(CH_3)_2\ \overset{+}{N}HCH_2CONHNH_2$). The condensation is performed either in acetic acid or in methanolic solutions. An excess of the reagent should always be present because the wave-height of the hydrazone product is a function of the hydrazide concentration.[49] The waves are best recorded at pH 6–9; at higher pH-values the wave-height decreases owing to the decrease in the rate of protonation; at lower pH-values the wave-height changes with time owing to the hydrolysis of the hydrazones. The ionized form of the hydrazone is reduced with the consumption of four electrons:

$$\diagdown C = NH\overset{+}{N}HR + 4e + 4H^+ \rightarrow \diagdown CHNH_3^+ + RNH_2$$

$$(\underset{=}{R} = COCH_2N(CH_3)_2 \text{ etc.})$$

The following procedure is used for the determination of straight-chain or cyclic *saturated ketones*.[48]

Dissolve 1–10 mg of ketone in 1 ml. of absolute methanol (free of carbonyl compounds) and treat with three times the excess of Girard's reagent. Carry out the condensation in a test tube with a standard joint, (for volatile ketones a sealed tube is more convenient). For non-volatile ketones, heat the reaction mixture for 2–8 hr under reflux. Heat the sealed tubes for the same period on a water-bath at 85°C. After completion of the reaction, distil off the methanol under reduced pressure at room temperature and dissolve the residue in 0·2–0·5 ml. of ketone- and aldehyde-free ethanol. Finally add an aliquot of this solution to a Britton-Robinson buffer (pH 7–8) containing 50 per cent ethanol, and record the curve.

The method was originally devised and is suitable for the determination of *ketosteroids*[47] 3-keto, 17-keto and 20-keto-steroids have been determined in mixtures. The methods were used for the analysis of biological material. Oppenauer oxidation with aluminium-*tert*butoxide of 3-hydroxy-$\Delta^5$-steroids and cholesterol gives the corresponding ketones, and it is possible[50] to devise methods even for these compounds.

For the determination of *keto-acids*, e.g. pyruvic, α-ketoglutaric and oxalacetic acids in mixtures and in biological materials, a method has been proposed employing paper electrophoretic separations of the 2,4-dinitrophenylhydrazones of these acids.[50a] After elution, the polarographic wave corresponding to the reduction of the nitro-groups (in the 2,4-dinitrophenylhydrazone formed) was followed in 0·1 N HCl and the first wave at −0·14 V measured.

*Procedure.* Transform the keto-acids into hydrazones by the addition of a 0·5 per cent solution of 2,4-dinitrophenylhydrazine in 2 N HCl. After paper electrophoresis using 0·05 N $Na_2CO_3$ (the starting point at the negative electrode), dry the paper and cut out the spots (within 12 hr after drying). Place each piece of paper in a separate test tube so that it lies flat against the wall. Add 1 ml. of distilled water and wash the nitro-compound from the paper with a gentle swirling motion. Repeat the extraction with two other 1 ml. portions of water and extract the combined liquids, after acidifying with 0·1–0·2 ml. of sulphuric acid, three times with 1·0–2·0 ml. portions of ether. Dry the combined ether extracts over anhydrous sodium sulphate and, after decantation, evaporate on a water-bath to dryness. Lastly, dissolve the residue of dinitrophenyl-hydrazone in 1·0 ml. of 0·1 N HCl and record the polarographic curve.

Transformation to 2,4-dinitrophenylhydrazones combined with the chromatopolarographic technique has also been used recently[51] for the separation and determination of *aliphatic aldehydes* (cf. p. 183). The mixture of 2,4-dinitrophenylhydrazones of propionic, butyric, and valeric aldehydes is separated on a rubber column with isooctane and 70 per cent dimethylformamide containing 0·2 M potassium chloride. If the current at −1·3 V is plotted as a function of the eluated volume, three separate elution peaks are obtained.

The optimum conditions for the reaction of acetone and hydrazine[52] have not been studied thoroughly enough for this reaction to be at present recommended for an analytical method.

On the other hand, the kinetic reduction waves of *aldopentose* hydrazones, obtained by adding the pentose to 0·053 M dibasic sodium phosphate containing 0·1 M hydrazine sulphate (final pH 2·3), can be used for analytical purposes.[52a] The governing chemical reaction, and hence the limiting current too, are pH dependent,* and it is therefore necessary to control the pH carefully. Owing to differences in equilibrium and/or, rate constants, the limiting currents at pH 2·3 vary substantially for different pentoses. This can be utilized for the analysis of certain sugar mixtures.

Conversely, using the hydrazone waves for the analysis of mixtures of *hydrazine derivatives*, it is possible to analyse mixtures of hydrazine and 1,1-dimethylhydrazine from the waves of benzalazine and benzaldehyde dimethylhydrazone.[52b]

6.1.3.5. *Reactions of carbon disulphide.* In alkaline solutions carbon disulphide reacts with amines to form dithiocarbamino-carbonic acid. This reaction was used for the determination of amino acids[53-55] and carbon disulphide.[56]

The condensation in the determination of *amino acids*, is

---

* The kinetic character is attributed to the ring opening reaction;[52a] the observed pH-dependence shows an acid-base catalysis of the governing reaction.

carried out in a pH 9·0–9·3 buffer, either in aqueous solution saturated with carbon disulphide for 4–5 hr, or in a water–acetone mixture containing an excess of carbon disulphide for 20–30 min. The dithiocarbaminocarbonic acid formed gives an anodic wave which is easily measured in a pH 11·5 buffer at about −0·4 V. The wave corresponds to the formation of a mercury salt and is proportional to the concentration of the amino acid.

The half-wave potentials of all natural amino acids are so similar that a differentiation is impossible. However, the waves for derivatives of proline, at pH 11·0, are about 0·2 V more positive than those for the remaining amino acids. The waves of these substances also differ from those of the remaining amino acids in their polarographic behaviour. Their wave-heights are dependent on pH and the ionic strength of the supporting electrolyte.

A preliminary separation is thus necessary for the analysis of mixtures of amino acids. Hence, in mixtures of histamine and histidine, the corresponding dithiocarbaminocarbonic acids were first separated by paper electrophoresis.[55] After elution, the anodic waves for dithiocarbaminocarbonic acids give the content of histamine and histidine in the mixture.

*Carbon disulphide* gives a reduction wave, but owing to its volatility and low solubility in aqueous solutions, the oxygen is not easily removed from its solutions. Thus an indirect method was used,[56] based on the introduction of the sample containing carbon disulphide into an ethanolic solution of diethylamine. The anodic wave of the diethyl dithiocarbamate formed is measured. The procedure for the analysis of gaseous samples is as follows:

Pass a known volume of gas containing 1–100 mg of carbon disulphide through a U-tube (Fig. 40, right side) containing 4 ml. of a 1 per cent solution of diethylamine in 96 per cent ethanol. Add to the U-tube 1 ml. of 2 M lithium chloride and transfer the solution to an electrolysis cell. Remove the oxygen by bubbling nitrogen for 15 min (owing to the higher solubility of oxygen in the presence of ethanol) and record the anodic waves. Measure the sum of the waves at −0·62 V (adsorption pre-wave) and at −0·46 V.

The reaction occurs practically instantaneously so that small volumes of gas passing through the trap (for 5–10 min) are sufficient.

The procedure for the determination of carbon disulphide in liquid samples is:

Place 4 ml. of the ethanolic diethylamine solution in a polarographic cell and put the sample into the U-tube (Fig. 40). Connect the U-tube to the nitrogen input on the polarographic cell and pass the stream of nitrogen through the trap. Finally after addition of 1 ml. of 2 M lithium chloride, record the anodic waves.

Volatile carbon disulphide is carried into the diethylamine solution, reacts and forms diethyl dithiocarbamate.

The method, in which a fivefold excess of hydrogen sulphide does not interfere, was used for the analysis of the atmosphere, exhalations, and wastes in the fibre industry. In an analogous way *carbon oxysulphide*[57] can be determined.

### 6.1.4. *Additions*

Addition methods* were used for the determination of *unsaturated* compounds and *olefins*. The methods are based on the additions of bromine to unsaturated bonds, and the waves for the brominated compounds corresponding to the reduction of $\alpha, \beta$-dibromides (involving elimination) are measured. Their heights are proportional to the concentration of the unsaturated compound. Thus vinylchloride and 1,2-dichloroethylene were transformed into 1-chloro-1,2-dibromoethane and 1,2-dichloro-1,2-dibromoethane, by the action of a 3 M solution of bromine in methanol saturated with sodium bromide.[58] The excess of bromine was removed with ammonia and the polarographic analysis was performed with sodium sulphite or lithium chloride as a supporting electrolyte. On the other hand, acetylene, vinylchloride, 1,2-dichloroethylene and 1,1,2-trichloroethylene were determined[59] after a 24 hr reaction with bromine in glacial acetic acid (1 : 1). The excess bromine was removed with a stream of nitrogen or carbon dioxide. An aliquot portion is diluted (1 : 10) with a 3 M solution of sodium acetate in 80 per cent acetic acid and after deaeration the curve is recorded.

Instead of the 5 M solutions of bromine, for samples only containing vinylchloride, a 1 M solution of bromine and a reaction

---

* Together with addition methods mentioned here, the reaction of unsaturated bonds with maleic anhydride is discussed in the section devoted to the decrease of polarographically active substances (p. 143).

period of 10–20 min is sufficient. The heights of the waves for all four brominated products studied are practically identical and correspond to a two-electron process involving elimination. As the half-wave potentials of the waves for the particular $\alpha,\beta$-dibromocompounds differ, the method can be used for the determination of trichloroethylene in the presence of comparable amounts of acetylene, excess of 1,2-dichloroethylene or vinyl chloride, or for the determination of acetylene in the presence of a small excess of 1,2-dichloroethylene. The determination of vinyl chloride in the presence of other unsaturated compounds is based on its substantially easier bromination.

A complicated reaction, involving addition of bromine, together with oxidation reactions and decarboxylations, is used for the determination of *citric acid*[60] after conversion to pentabromo-acetone. This reaction follows the scheme:

$$
\begin{array}{ccc}
\text{CH}_2\text{COOH} & & \text{CH}_2\text{COOH} \\
| & \text{H}_2\text{SO}_4 & | \\
\text{HO—C—COOH} & \xrightarrow{\hspace{1cm}} & \text{CO} \qquad + \quad \text{CO} \; + \; \text{H}_2\text{O} \\
| & & | \\
\text{CH}_2\text{COOH} & & \text{CH}_2\text{COOH} \\
\end{array}
$$

$$\downarrow {\scriptstyle \text{KMnO}_4 \mid \text{KBr}}$$

$$\text{CBr}_3\text{COCHBr}_2 \; + \; \text{CO} \; + \; \text{CO}_2 \; + \; \text{H}_2\text{O}$$

For this example a modification of the existing analytical method which employed titrimetry, was used. After the conversion, which is carried out essentially in the same way as in the titrimetric method, the solution (instead of extraction, oxidation-reduction treatment and final titration) is directly subjected to polarographic analysis in a pH 8·8 ammonia and ammonium chloride buffer.

In this medium, pentabromoacetone is hydrolysed to dibromo-acetic acid and bromoform. Three indistinct waves appear on the polarographic curve, the third at −1·22 V being the most suitable for analytical purposes. Divalent manganese which remained dissolved is reduced in the resulting solution at $-1.45$ V and does not interfere.

A reaction involving methylation and followed by an elimination is used for the determination of *aspartic acid*:

$$
\begin{array}{ccc}
\text{COOH} & \text{COO}^- & \text{COOH} \\
| & | & | \\
\text{CHNH}_2 \xrightarrow{\text{(CH}_2)_2\text{SO}_4} & \text{CH}\!-\!\overset{+}{\text{N}}(\text{CH}_3)_3 \xrightarrow{\text{H}_2\text{SO}_4} & \text{CH} \\
| & | & \| \quad + \text{NH}(\text{CH}_3)_3^+ \\
\text{CH}_2 & \text{CH}_2 & \text{CH} \\
| & | & | \\
\text{COOH} & \text{COO}^- & \text{COOH}
\end{array}
$$

This reaction converts aspartic acid to a mixture consisting of about 80 per cent fumaric and 20 per cent maleic acids. The sum of these acids can be determined in acid solutions polarographically.[61]

*Procedure.* Dissolve 2–10 mg of aspartic acid in 2–5 ml. of 0·01 M NaOH and add 2 ml. of dimethyl sulphate. At all times keep the solution alkaline to phenolphthalein by the addition of sodium hydroxide, and keep the temperature below 25°C by cooling. After 1½ hr acidify the solution with 1 ml. of concentrated sulphuric acid, mix and allow to stand for a further half-hour. After neutralization to phenolphthalein add 2 ml. of 6 N HCl and make up with water to 100 ml. Finally perform polarographic electrolysis on an aliquot of solution.

This method was used for the analysis of hydrolysates of proteins. Only asparagine amongst the amino acids interferes.

A method, in which probably the addition of halogen occurs is used for the determination of *carotene*.[62]

A 1 ml. petroleum ether solution of carotene reacts with 1 ml. of a 1 per cent solution of ammonium nitrate in methanol, 1 ml. of benzene and 0·3 ml. of iodine solution (0·04 g of iodine and 0·3 ml. of glacial acetic acid in 10 ml. of petroleum ether).

A substance giving an anodic wave is formed, but the mechanism of the reaction is unknown.

Finally, a base catalysed addition of water is the principle used for the determination of *vinylester of acetic acid*.[63] The reaction is:

$$R—COOCH=CH_2 + OH^- \longrightarrow CH_3CHO + R—COO^-$$

The wave of acetaldehyde formed in this reaction is measured. 0·1 N lithium hydroxide serves both as a reaction medium and a supporting electrolyte.

### 6.1.5. *Substitution*

Substitution reactions have been only rarely applied to polarographic analysis. In fact, the only method used, apart from the determination of citric acid (in which substitution as well as addition reactions occur, see p. 131), is the determination of *histidine* The method involves reaction with 1-fluoro-2,4-dinitrobenzene to yield the substituted dinitrobenzene.[64]

### 6.1.6. *Oxidations*

Even though several methods have been devised for the oxidation of *methanol* and *ethanol* to formaldehyde and acetaldehyde,[65-68] with the subsequent polarographic determination of these aldehydes, none of them has yet been widely accepted. The nonreproducibility of the oxidation, volatility of both alcohols and aldehydes formed, the reactivity and polymerization of the aldehydes and the kinetic character of the wave of formaldehyde, seem to be the main reasons for this situation.

*Ethylene* and *1,2-propylene glycols* can be determined simultaneously by oxidation with periodic acid, after distillation, to formaldehyde and acetaldehyde. The reaction proceeds according to the following stoichiometric equations:

$$CH_2OHCH_2OH + HIO_4 \longrightarrow$$
$$2HCHO + HIO_3 + H_2O$$

$$CH_3CHOH\ CH_2OH + HIO_4 \longrightarrow$$
$$HCHO + CH_3CHO + HIO_3 + H_2O$$

*Procedure.*[69] Add 3 ml. of 0·5 N periodic acid to an aqueous solution of the glycol mixture, containing approximately 5–20 mg of each of the glycols, in a 100-ml. Kjeldahl flask. Add also sufficient water to bring the total volume to about 60 ml. Distil the aldehydes into an ice-cooled receiver containing 75 ml. of water, and transfer the distillate quantitatively to a 250-ml. volumetric flask. Immediately before the polarographic determination, add 25 ml. of 1 N lithium hydroxide containing 0·1 N lithium chloride, dilute the solution to the mark and polarograph.

*Notes.* (1) The height of the second wave is proportional to the concentration of the propylene glycol. The height of the first wave, however, corresponds to two molecules of formaldehyde formed from ethylene glycol and propylene glycol. From the calculated concentration of formaldehyde, the concentration of acetaldehyde is subtracted and the remainder, divided by two, gives the concentration of ethylene glycol.

(2) Any material capable of being oxidized by periodic acid to give formaldehyde or acetaldehyde should be absent, e.g. α-amino alcohols, hydroxyamino acids and polyalcohols. Monohydroxy alcohols such as methanol or ethanol, do not interfere in the determination.

This method can be used, after hydrolysis, for the determination of *ethylene* and *propylene chlorohydrine*.[70]

Similarly, *glycerol* can be determined after oxidation with periodic acid to formaldehyde.[71] If the determination is used for fermentation products, other oxidizable substances are separated with ethanol in the presence of sodium carbonate.

The determination of glycerol and other polyalcohols which form formaldehyde, on oxidation with periodic acid, can be modified[72] so that formaldehyde need not to be separated by distillation. The excess of periodate can be removed by adding an excess of arsenite (in about 1 : 4 ratio) in a medium of 2 M HCl. When made alkaline, the wave of formaldehyde can be recorded; it is unaffected by the presence of either arsenic (III) or (V).

*Serine* can also be oxidized by periodic acid to formaldehyde. The method[73] has been used for the determination of serine in hydrolysates of proteins.

*Lactic acid* is oxidized by permanganate to acetaldehyde and it is possible, instead of the usual volumetric methods, to determine the acetaldehyde formed polarographically.[74]

*Procedure.* Transfer 1–2 ml. of the solution to be analysed to a distillation flask together with 1·9 ml. of 2 N phosphoric acid. After the addition of 5 ml. of a 10 per cent solution of manganous sulphate, dilute the solution to 50 ml. and add drop-wise 10 ml. of 0·002 M potassium permanganate, together with 0·3 ml. of 2 M phosphoric acid. Distil a portion of this solution into a receiver containing 500 ml. of 0·05 M lithium carbonate, to which 0·2 ml. of 0·5 N lithium hydroxide has been added. Carry out the polarographic electrolysis on an aliquot portion of this solution. Do not allow the solution to stand, for aldol condensation occurs. For more accurate results record several curves and extrapolate the heights to zero time.

The method can be used for determining lactic acid in biological materials and in particular for studying glycolysis.

*Mandelic acid* in bile and urine can be determined after separation of the bile acids, and conversion to benzaldehyde by means of "zinc manganite" (prepared from zinc sulphate, manganous sulphate and zinc oxide after addition of potassium permanganate).[75] The wave of benzaldehyde is measured in a phosphate pH 7·7 buffer.

A polarographic method has been described[76] for determining *acetoin*. It depends upon oxidation with ferric chloride and upon the determination of the diacetyl formed (after distillation). The method can be used for the determination of acetoin in blood and butter cultures.

Finally *noradrenaline* and *adrenaline* have been determined[76a] after oxidation with iodate to iodonoradrenochrome (III) and iodoadrenochrome (IV).

*Procedure.* Oxidize in 0·2 N sodium acetate for (III) and in a 2 per cent solution of acetic acid for (IV). Carry out the oxidation for 6 (III) or 4 (IV) min and then add 2 N sulphuric acid to change the pH to 1·0. When the purple colour of iodoadrenochrome appears add potassium iodide. Make the final polarographic electrolysis in an acetate pH 4·5 buffer, so that the quinoid system is reduced at positive potentials ($E_{1/2} = +0·03$ V).

(III) : R=H
(IV) : R=CH_3

For the analysis of biological materials, separate noradrenaline from adrenaline by paper chromatography before polarographic analysis.

The usual quantities of polyphenols do not interfere.

### 6.1.7. Complex Formation

A group of polarographic determinations that can be classified both with the determinations based upon transformation into an active compound, and with methods in which the concentration change of an active compound (reacting with the substance to be determined) is followed, are methods which are based upon the formation of complex compounds between inorganic ions and the organic compound to be determined.

The methods based upon complex formation can be divided into two groups. In the first group the analysed substance is a strong complex forming agent (usually with the possibility of formation of chelate compounds) and it reacts stoichiometrically with the inorganic ion. The wave of the complex ion is then measured. Under the given conditions (i.e. the kind of metal ion and the pH-value of the solution) the formation of complexes of this type is rather specific (each complex being characterized by a given half-wave potential). This method can also be rather selective, and even allows the determination of complex-forming reagents in mixtures. For such analysis the use of several metal ions and/or several pH-values can be recommended for increasing the selectivity and reliability of these methods. In the second group of methods, the complex-forming reagent is added to a suspension of a slightly soluble salt of a heavy metal. When the equilibrium between the solid phase and solution is established owing to complex formation, the concentration of the metal ion in the liquid phase is measured polarographically.

To the first group belongs the determination of *propylene diamine*.[77] This is based upon the formation of the copper–diamine complex, which is reduced at a potential different from that of the uncomplexed copper ion. Similarly, the determination of 1,2-*diaminocyclohexane* can be carried out in the presence of excess of hexamethylenediamine.[78] It depends upon the fact that 1,2-diaminocyclohexane forms at pH $11 \cdot 7$–$12 \cdot 2$ a complex compound with nickel ions which is reduced at $-1 \cdot 05$ V. Hexamethylenediamine at this pH does not form complexes and

K

precipitates only nickel hydroxide. In addition, another impurity, aminomethylcyclopentylamine, does not show a reduction wave of the nickel complex at this high pH-value. The importance of pH-control is clearly demonstrated, for at pH 10 both hexa-methylenediamine and aminomethylcyclopentylamine form complexes reducible at potentials more positive than that of 1,2-diaminocyclohexane. The determination of 1,2-diaminocyclo-hexane is important, because this compound appears as an impurity at low concentrations in hexamethylenediamine during the preparation of intermediates for the manufacture of Nylon 66, and thus affects the quality of the final product.

Further methods are devoted to the analysis of mixtures of amino-polycarboxylic acids. Even though it has been shown[79] that in the pH range of 7–10 there is a sufficient separation of half-wave potentials of the copper chelates to allow as little as 1 per cent of *nitrilotriacetic acid* to be detected in ethylenediamine-tetraacetic acid (EDTA), the cadmium complex was chosen as the basis for a quantitative analysis of mixtures. This was mainly because the greater difference in stability constants of the chelates of nitrilotriacetic acid and EDTA, promised a greater resolution of half-wave potentials. The study of the effects of pH on half-wave potentials and wave heights revealed that the greatest difference in half-wave potentials of cadmium complexes of nitrilotriacetic acid and EDTA is above pH 6. In the same pH-range the height of the wave for cadmium-nitrilotriacetic complex is also pH-independent. Because of the value of the solubility product of cadmium hydroxide and the stability constant, it was deduced that a small excess of cadmium ion is necessary to complex all the nitrilotriacetic acid present. Polarographic curves showed at pH 10 a small wave at $-0\cdot60$ V due to cadmium ions, a wave at $-0\cdot97$ V corresponding to the reduction of the cadmium complex of nitrilotriacetic acid and an ill-developed wave at $-1\cdot4$ V due to the cadmium ethylenediaminetetraacetic acid chelate.

The following procedure is recommended:

Dissolve 5 g of a sample of ethylenediaminetetraacetic acid, containing $0\cdot1$–$3\cdot0$ per cent of nitrilotriacetate, in 75 ml. of water and adjust the pH to 10 with 1 M nitric acid or 1 M potassium hydroxide. Then add a 1 M cadmium nitrate solution dropwise. The pH value of the solution decreases as the cadmium nitrate is added. When one drop of cadmium nitrate solution does not change the pH more than 0·1 pH unit, a sufficient amount has been added to complex all the nitrilotriacetic acid and EDTA present. Then add one or two drops in excess and again adjust the pH to 10 with potassium hydroxide. A slight precipitate of cadmium hydroxide should appear, indicating an excess of cadmium; if no precipitate is formed, add more cadmium. Finally, adjust the volume to 100 ml., dilute 10 ml. of this solution and 10 ml. of 1 M potassium nitrate to 100 ml. and record the polarographic curve.

The height of the wave at −0·97 V is proportional to the concentration of nitrilotriacetic acid over the concentration range $10^{-5}$ to $10^{-3}$ M.

*If N,N-ethylenediglycine* is present, e.g. in industrial ethylenediaminetetraacetic acid, the wave of its cadmium complex under the given conditions is only 0·1 V more positive than the wave for cadmium-nitrilotriacetic acid complex, and the resolution is thus difficult. Consequently, in the analysis of such mixtures the sum of the wave heights of the cadmium chelates of nitrilotriacetic acid and N,N-ethylenediglycine is first measured. The sample is then treated with hydrochloric acid to adjust the pH-value to 1·5–2·0 and boiled for 20 min. The cyclic imide formed from N,N-ethylenediglycine according to the reaction

$$HOOCCH_2NH-(CH_2)_2-NHCH_2COOH \xrightarrow{\text{H}^+}$$

$$\begin{array}{c} CH_2CH_2 \\ \diagup \qquad \diagdown \\ HN \qquad\qquad N-CH_2COOH + H_2O \\ \diagdown \qquad \diagup \\ CH_2CO \end{array}$$

does not form a stable chelate with cadmium ions at pH 10. The wave-height obtained with the resulting solution corresponds to the concentration of nitrilotriacetic acid. The concentration of N,N-ethylenediglycine is thus obtained by difference.

The *detection of individual amino polycarboxylic acids* has been proposed[80] based upon the separation of the mixture by zone paper electrophoresis, and by the identification of the components by comparison of the half-wave potentials of the copper chelates with those of isolated chelates.

By utilization of the waves of copper complexes, and the resolution of half-wave potentials with derivative curves, it was possible to distinguish between amino polycarboxylic acids in 20 two-component mixtures and in 4 three-component mixtures.[81] The compounds investigated were: iminodiacetic acid, methyl-iminodiacetic acid, nitrilotriacetic acid, uramil-N,N-diacetic acid, ethylenediaminetetraacetic acid, diethylenetriamine-N,N,N′,N″,N‴-pentaacetic acid, di-(2-hydroxyethyl)glycine, o-carboxyphenyliminodiacetic acid, trans-cyclohexane-1,2-diamine-N,N,N′,N′-tetraacetic acid and trans-cycloheptane-1,2-diamine-N,N,N′,N′-tetraacetic acid. The smallest possible excess of amino polycarboxylic acid was favourable for the resolution, and a difference in the half-wave potentials of even 50 mV w assufficient. A good resolution can be obtained if the ratio of the concentrations of the two components in the mixture is not greater than 4 : 1 or 1 : 4.

The following procedure is recommended[81] for distinguishing amino polycarboxylic acids:

Add 0·2 ml. of pH 6 buffer to 10 ml. of 0·002 M copper sulphate solution containing 0·025 per cent gelatin. Place the solution under an ultra-violet lamp and titrate with 0·1 M test mixture until the appearance of fluorescence is observed with a trace of o-dianisidine-N,N,N′,N′-tetraacetic acid (1 per cent dispersion in ground potassium nitrate) as indicator. Slightly over-run the end-point to ensure there is a trace in excess of the amino polycarboxylic acid solution and to this solution add 0·25 ml. of glacial acetic acid. Lastly, adjust the pH-value to 2·5 with hydrochloric acid and, after deoxygenation subject the resulting solution to polarographic electrolysis.

The second group of determinations based on complex-formation is represented by the determination of amino acids. The α-amino acids react at a controlled pH with an excess of an insoluble cupric compound. The copper taken into solution as the 1 : 2 copper-amino acid complex is then determined polaro-graphically.[82] A preliminary separation is necessary because the half-wave potentials of the complexes of individual amino acids do not differ very much. Paper-chromatography has been suggested for this purpose.[83] The paper with the spot, the position of which is determined on a parallel chromatogram with ninhydrin, is cut out, cut into strips 10 mm² and kept overnight in a suspension of copper phosphate. The increase in the height of the wave of the copper complexes of amino acids is then followed polarographically.

With different amino acids, varying heights were observed for the limiting currents of the copper complexes of individual amino acids. This behaviour was ascribed[82] to the different diffusion coefficients of the particular amino acid complexes. However the differences are so great that this explanation seems unlikely, and different stability constants of the copper complexes with individual amino acids seem to be involved.

The first factor can be overcome if the excess of the copper phosphate suspension is centrifuged off, and the copper is converted to a 1 : 1 copper EDTA chelate with excess of ethylenediaminetetraacetic acid and determined polarographically.[84] In all instances the same complex is reduced, and there is no difference in diffusing particles, and hence in diffusion coefficients.

Even though the conditions for the copper phosphate reaction have been carefully studied,[84] it does not seem possible to deduce unequivocally whether or not all amino acids only react according to stoichiometric relationships, and that the stability constants of the amino acids involved are without influence on the resulting limiting current of the copper-EDTA complex. From the measurements reported[84] it can be, on the other hand, safely deduced, that the optimum pH for the reaction between the amino acid and copper phosphate is about 8·9, and the concentration of the amino acid in the sample must be *ca.* 0·0002 M and not greater than 0·001 M for a determination with minimum error. β-Amino acids and ammonia up to a concentration of 0·001 M do not interfere, increasing ionic strength decreases the completeness of the reaction and a 0·02 M borate buffer is preferred. Furthermore, the importance must be stressed of the composition of the copper phosphate, and the following procedure is suggested for the preparation of this reagent:

Add, to 1 volume of trisodium phosphate solution (36·3 g of $Na_3PO_4$ . $12H_2O$ per litre), 1 volume of cupric chloride solution (27·3 g of $CuCl_2$ . $2H_2O$ per litre) and 4 volumes of disodium phosphate solution (25·6 g of

$Na_2HPO_4$ . $7H_2O$ per litre). Reflux the resulting slurry for 2 hr and allow to settle and age for 24 hr. Decant this suspension and store as stock in a glass-stoppered bottle. Prepare the reagent from this solution daily by centrifuging portions of the stock, rejecting the mother liquor and washing the residue with three consecutive portions of 0·02 M borate pH 8·9 buffer and 0·1 M sodium sulphate. After removal of the third wash portion, take up the residue in twenty times its centrifuged volume of borate buffer.

The recommended procedure for the amino acid determination[84] is as follows:

Add from 1 to 50 ml. of sample containing about 0·0002 M amino acid in a 100-ml. volumetric flask, 0·1 ml. of a 0·5 per cent phenolphthalein solution and neutralize with either dilute sodium hydroxide or sulphuric acid as needed. Add water to within about 30 ml. of the mark, followed by 10 ml. of a 0·2 M borate pH 8·75 buffer, containing 1·0 M sodium sulphate and 10 ml. of copper phosphate reagent, and make up to the mark. Shake the reaction mixture, allow it to stand for a half-hour but shake every 5 min. Place portions of the reaction mixture in two 35-ml. centrifuge tubes (28 mm outer diameter borosilicate glass tubing, tapered toward the bottom to about 4 mm inner diameter, below which a small 2–3 ml. bulb is blown) and centrifuge out all the unreacted copper phosphate. Without disturbing the precipitate, carefully remove a 25-ml. aliquot of centrifugate from each of the two tubes, and combine together with 5 ml. of 1·1 M ethylene-diaminetetraacetate pH 8·3. Add 0·1 ml. of a 0·5 per cent gelatin solution, deoxygenate the reaction mixture and record the polarographic wave for the copper-EDTA complex at −0·4 V.

*Notes.* (1) The principles given above can be applied to the continuous analysis of amino acids in chromatographic column effluents.[84]
(2) Other materials which form stable complexes with copper can be determined by this method in exactly the same way. The method can be, for example, used for determination of ethylenediaminetetraacetic acid.

### 6.1.8. *Other Reactions*
*Malic acid* can be determined after conversion to fumaric acid:

*Procedure.* Treat the sample containing malic acid with solid sodium hydroxide, evaporate to dryness and heat in a porcelain dish to 130–140°C for 4 hr. Dissolve in 0·5 N HCl and record the wave corresponding to the sum of concentrations of maleic and fumaric acids.[85, 86]

*Note.* The wave of fumaric acid formed from malic acid is lowered by the presence of lactic acid. However, by treatment with barium chloride[87] this interference is removed, provided that the concentration of lactic acid in the sample is less than 0·1 per cent. The method was used for the determination of malic acid in wines, ciders and fruit juices.

For the determination in sweet and fermented beverages a fractionation on an ion exchange column was suggested.[88] All the acids were first collected on an ion-exchange resin, tannic acid was eluted first with ethanol and the malic acid together with other acids with ammonia. The determination of malic acid in the eluate was effected as above.

*Pentoses* and *pentosans* can be determined[89] after conversion to polarographically active furfural in acidic media. Xylose, for example, is heated with hydrochloric acid ($d = 1·06$) for 2–3 hr at 160°C and, after cooling, the wave in 0·2 M KOH is recorded. This method was used for the determination of pentosans in cellulose.[90]

*Rodenticide Warfarin* is determined[91] as follows:

*Procedure.* React the acetyl group in Warfarin [3(α-phenyl-β-acetyl-ethyl)-4-hydroxycoumarine] with iodine in alkaline solution (as hypoiodite) to form iodoform. Filter off the precipitated iodoform, dissolve in methanol and add one part of this solution to nine parts of a supporting electrolyte consisting of 40 ml. of acetone, 20 ml. of ethanol and 40 ml. of 0·5 N sulphuric acid. Deoxygenate and record the polarographic curve.

*Note.* The unreacted benzalacetone content must be determined polarographically beforehand in the analysis of technical Warfarin.[91]

*m-Aminophenol*, present as a toxic impurity in *p*-aminosalicylic acid, is determined after diazotisation of the reaction mixture in a sulphuric acid medium. Diazotized *p*-aminosalicylic acid decomposes quickly and, after the solution is made alkaline, the wave for diazotized *m*-aminophenol is recorded.[92] Similarly, after diazotization, the biologically inactive 5-aminosalicylic acid can be determined in the presence of *p*-aminosalicyclic acid.[93]

## 6.2. CONCENTRATION CHANGE OF POLAROGRAPHICALLY ACTIVE SUBSTANCES

Both inorganic and organic polarographically active substances can react with a wide variety of organic compounds, and the organic compound can be determined by measuring the change in the height of the wave of the reagent. Such reactions are usually common for a functional group or a group of substances, and are not selective for a given compound. Thus, such techniques when applied are usually non-specific. The same classification will be used, as in the previous section for the arrangement of examples. i.e. according to the type of chemical reaction involved.

### 6.2.1. *Condensations*

The determination of *acetone* is made possible by measuring the decrease in the wave of sulphurous acid.[94] Acetone forms in an acidic media with sulphurous acid an addition compound which does not undergo reduction at the dropping mercury electrode. The curve is recorded in acid solutions in the presence of sodium sulphite before and after additions of acetone. The decrease in wave-height after addition of acetone is proportional to the concentration of acetone in the sample. Calibration is carried out by recording a curve from a solution containing a known amount of acetone. The decrease, due to the sample, should be smaller than 50 per cent of the decrease resulting from the addition of the standard solution. The addition of the standard solution should decrease the wave of sulphurous acid by about 80 per cent.

In a similar manner numerous other carbonyl compounds, e.g. cyclanones, dialkylketones, alkyl aryl ketones or even benzaldehydes, can be determined.[95] For water-insoluble carbonyl compounds, aqueous ethanol or dioxane is suggested as a solvent.

*Amino acids*[96] as well as ammonia,[97] and probably also other primary amines can be determined from the decrease in the wave for phthalaldehyde. In the presence of an excess of phthalaldehyde a nonreducible compound is formed after the addition of amino compounds. Condensation occurs in most instances in a ratio 1 phthalaldehyde: 1 amino acid; histidine, lysine and ammonia react in the ratio 3 : 2. The time necessary for completion of the reaction is between 0·3 hr. (for lysine) and 2–3 hr (for glycine, alanine and ammonia). Because the decrease of the phthalaldehyde wave changes according to the amino acid used, it is necessary in a mixture to separate first the individual amino acids and to use a separate calibration curve for each amino acid. A reaction involving the amino groups of *gelatin* has also been observed.

### 6.2.2. *Additions*

The possible method of following the concentration of bromine as a measure of the total amount of unsaturation has not yet been very widely used (see amperometric titration on p. 163), but rather a method which involves a reaction with maleic anhydride.

For the determination of *butadiene* in gaseous mixtures[98] a known volume of gas is placed in contact with a known amount of maleic anhydride. Butadiene reacts with maleic anhydride with the formation of tetrahydrophthalic anhydride. After dissolution, the amount of unreacted maleic anhydride can be determined polarographically.

In a similar way *styrene* and *vinylacetate* monomers can be determined in polymerization reactions.[99] In the determination of styrene the reaction mixture containing maleic anhydride is boiled under reflux for 3 hr. The unreacted maleic anhydride is hydrolysed to maleic acid and determined (in the determination of styrene) in aqueous solutions of pH 3·0 or (in the determination of vinylacetate) in benzene solutions.

### 6.2.3. Oxidations

The Malaprade reaction can be applied when aldehyde waves are measured (p. 132). The decrease of the first wave of periodic acid, which increases directly from the potential of the dissolution of mercury, can also be measured. This wave corresponds to the electrochemical reduction of periodic acid to iodic acid; in the Malaprade reaction periodic acid is reduced chemically by the glycol to the iodic acid. In the course of the Malaprade reaction the first wave decreases, but the height of the second wave, corresponding to polarographic reduction of iodic acid, remains unchanged (Fig. 45)* because the total concentration of iodate (formed electrochemically at the mercury drop and formed chemically in the bulk of solution) remains unchanged (unless a side reaction, so called over-oxidation, takes place in which also iodic acid is reduced).

The method is unspecific, but allows the determination of α-*diols*, *polyols*, and α-*amino alcohols* in the presence of simple alcohols (e.g. methanol or ethanol). Ethyleneglycol,[72] glycerol[72] or sugars[72, 101] and serine[102] can be determined using either an acetate pH 4·7 buffer[72] or a phosphate pH 7 buffer,[101] or solutions simply acidified with periodic acid,[102] both as a reaction medium and as a supporting electrolyte.

---

* The small wave at negative potentials increasing with time in Fig. 45 corresponds to the reduction of the benzaldehyde formed.

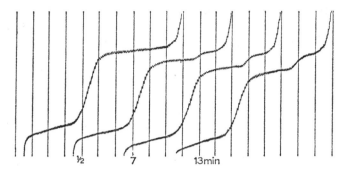

FIG. 45. Oxidation of *threo*-1-phenylpropane-1,2-diol by periodate. 1 M Acetate buffer pH 4·7, $1 \times 10^{-5}$ M 1-phenylpropane-1,2-diol, 25°C. The curves were recorded after elapsing of the time marked on the beginning of the curve on polarogram, starting at 0·0 V, mercurous sulphate electrode, 200 mV/absc., 325 mV/min, $t_1 =$ 2·8 sec; $m = 1·9$ mg/sec, full scale sensitivity 3·2 $\mu$A.

The method was used in the study of the mechanism of the Malaprade reaction,[72, 103] and for the estimation of the number of vicinal hydroxy groups in structural determinations,[72] e.g. for the structures of laserpitin, artabsin or ascorbigene. Owing to the difference in the oxidation rates of threo- and erythro epimers of 1,2-diols, measurements of the wave-heights of periodic acid at two time-intervals made possible the determination of the amount of the particular epimer in the mixture. This technique was used for determination of the ratio of epimers prepared by various methods.[72] The change in the height of the wave of periodic acid was also applied to the determination of *blood sugar*, by the direct reaction of plasma solution with periodate solutions at pH 7 without deproteination.[104]

When irradiated with an ultraviolet lamp even simple alcohols react with periodic acid. Methanol reacts substantially faster than ethanol, and this fact could be used in their simultaneous determination.[72] The decrease of periodic acid by a spontaneous photochemical reaction is negligible for an irradiation time of 30 min. In the photo-catalysed reaction of periodic acid and methanol, not only periodate, but also iodate is consumed.

The method for the determination of *diglycols* in a mixture of ethylene and propylene glycols involves the technique of successive specific oxidation.[105]

*Procedure.* First oxidize the monoglycols with periodic acid to aldehydes and distil off the resulting aldehydic compounds. Remove the excess of periodic acid by reduction with hydrogen peroxide in alkaline solutions, and destroy the excess hydrogen peroxide by boiling. Acidify the resulting solution, oxidize with dichromate and in alkaline solution measure polarographically the decrease of dichromate.

For the determination of *ethanol* in blood, the alcohol is oxidized with potassium dichromate in nitric acid. The excess of dichromate is measured polarographically.[100] The method is claimed to determine 2–3 per cent ethanol with an accuracy of 0·05–0·3 per cent in the presence of less than 0·6 per cent acetone, provided that the excess of dichromate is not too large.

### 6.2.4. *Complex Formation*

*Cardiazole*, (pentamethylenetetrazole) forms a slightly soluble compound with cuprous ions, and the precipitate can be separated and dissolved in an ammoniacal medium. The wave of copper is recorded and its height is proportional to the concentration of Cardiazole.[106]

The wave of copper ions can be also used in the determination of reducing sugars.[107] Briefly the procedure is:

Treat the sugar with Fehling's solution and heat in the usual way. Remove the precipitate of cuprous oxide by filtration and record the wave of the remaining cuprous copper in the solution after the addition of ammonia.

The decrease in the copper wave is proportional to the sugar content. Calibration curves can be prepared with standard glucose solutions.

### 6.3. POLAROMETRIC (AMPEROMETRIC) TITRATIONS OF ORGANIC COMPOUNDS

Polarometric and amperometric titrations* are based on measurements of the current, flowing at a chosen potential between

---

* The terminology here is not strictly unified: Often the same titrations are called "polarometric", "amperometric", "polarographic" or "limiting current titrations". In this section the term "polarometric" will

an indicator and reference electrodes, placed in the solution to be titrated and dependent on the volume of titrant added. The equivalence point is determined by the point of intersection of two lines, showing the dependence of the current on the volume of titrant. The lines connect points corresponding to the current measured before and after the equivalence point. Usually two or three points before, and two or three points after, the equivalence point are sufficient, and the points obtained in the neighbourhood of the equivalence point are neglected. If this method is used for the determination of the equivalence point, it is sufficient that only one of the reacting substances, i.e. either the titrated substance or the titrant, need be polarographically active. The current is usually measured at potentials corresponding to the limiting current.

According to the polarographic behaviour of the titrated substance and titrant, several types of titration curves can be obtained.

When only the titrated substance is polarographically active at the potential chosen, the change of polarographic curves and resulting titration curve is as given in Fig. 46. The arrows show the potential at which the current is measured. The small waves observed when the equivalence point is surpassed are due to incomplete reaction caused by, for example, solubility. On the other hand, when the titrated substance shows no reduction current at the chosen potential at which the current is measured (Fig. 47, arrows), the product is inactive, but the volumetric reagent gives a reduction wave, the changes of the polarographic curve and the type of titration curve follow from Fig. 47.

When both the titrated substance and the titrant are polarographically active at a chosen potential, a V-shaped titration curve is observed (Fig. 48). When the titrated substance shows an anodic wave and the titrant a cathodic wave, the anodic wave decreases and the cathodic wave increases during the titration, and a titration curve crossing near the galvanometer zero line is observed (Fig. 49).

---

be used, in accordance with the view of Professor Heyrovský, as a general description for titrations with a dropping mercury electrode. When solid electrodes are employed, "amperometric" will be used.

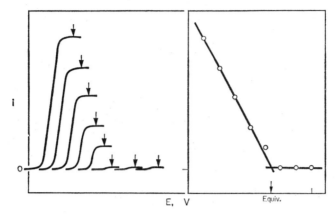

FIG. 46. Polarometric titration, electroactive substance titrated with an electroinactive reagent.
Left, polarographic curves after addition of increasing amount of reagent; right, dependence of the limiting current, measured at points marked with arrows, on the volume of the titrant.

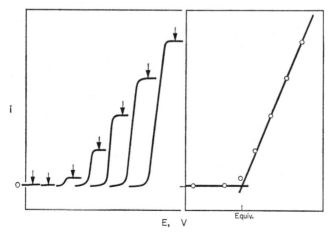

FIG. 47. Polarometric titration, electro-inactive substance titrated with an electroactive reagent.
Left, polarographic curves after addition of increasing amount of reagent; right, dependence of the limiting current, measured at points marked with arrows, on the volume of the titrant.

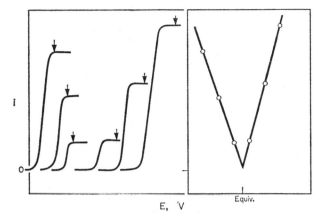

FIG. 48. Polarometric titration, electroactive substance titrated with an electroactive reagent.
Left, polarographic curves after addition of increasing amount of reagent; right, dependence of the limiting current, measured at points marked with arrows, on the volume of the titrant.

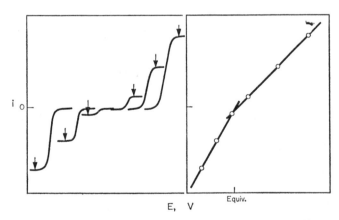

FIG. 49. Polarometric titration, substance showing an anodic wave titrated with a substance showing a cathodic wave.
Left, polarographic curves after addition of increasing amount of reagent; right, dependence of the limiting current, measured at points marked with arrows, on the volume of the titrant.

The above four types of titration curves are those most frequently observed. In special examples, the dependence of the limiting current on the volume of titrant added, possesses another form. Of these we shall show here only that which (Fig. 50)

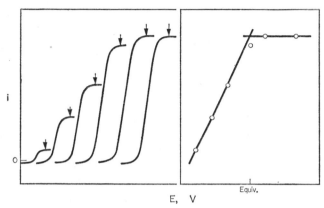

FIG. 50. Polarometric titration, an insoluble salt titrated with a complex-forming reagent.
Left, polarographic curves after addition of increasing amount of reagent; right, dependence of the limiting current, measured at points marked with arrows, on the volume of the titrant.

results when an insoluble compound is titrated by a complex-forming agent (or another agent that dissolves the precipitate) or when a complex, nonreducible at the given potential, is transformed into a polarographically active species. The deviations from the linear course around the equivalence point are given by the solubility product or the complex stability constant.

The equipment consists of the e.m.f., the indicator and reference electrode, the galvanometer or microammeter, the titration cell and the burette (Fig. 51). As indicator electrodes, the dropping mercury electrode and the rotating platinum electrode are the most frequently used. Reference electrodes are either the mercury pool electrode, or separated electrodes such as the calomel electrode, or some special types of reference electrodes. The titration cell is usually a simple beaker (25–100 ml.) with a plug through which all necessary parts are inserted. If the titration

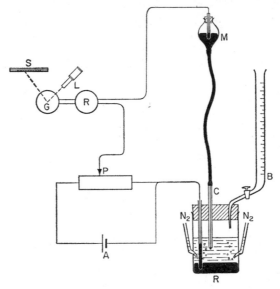

FIG. 51. Equipment for a polarographic titration.
(A) Storage cell, accumulator; (P) potentiometer; (G) galvanometer; (R) sensitivity reductor; (L) lamp; (S) scale; (M) mercury
reservoir; (C) capillary; (B) burette; (R) reference electrode;
(N₂) nitrogen inlet.

agent is sensitive to atmospheric oxygen, an inert gas can be
introduced into and over the solution in the burette. The circuit
of the polarograph or, alternatively, a simple potentiometer and a
galvanometer of the Multiflex type, can be used as a source of
the e.m.f. and as a current indicator. Some titrations can be performed with a "short circuit system", i.e. without an external
e.m.f. and the current can be measured at the potential of the
reference electrode. For some systems, reduced or oxidized at
positive potentials, the potential of the usual calomel electrode is
sufficient, but other reference electrodes with more negative
potentials (such as mercuric iodide or sulphide electrode, zinc
amalgam electrode etc.) have also been suggested.

In polarometric titrations, as in most polarographic measurements, it is desirable to work nearly always in the absence of
oxygen. The inert gas used to deaerate the solution, also stirs the
solution in a simpler way than most mechanical or magnetic

stirrers. Only when the concentration of the titrated substance is larger than about 0·005 M is the limiting current of oxygen negligible. However, the oxygen need not be removed if the current is measured at potentials more positive than those at which oxygen is reduced. Sometimes the addition of surface active agents to suppress a maxima is also necessary. The precautions in using these additives are the same as in classical polarography.

A correct choice of the supporting electrolyte and the applied voltage is of a fundamental importance in perfecting the performance of the polarometric titration. For this purpose also it is recommended that one records the whole polarographic curve, and only uses the limiting currents of well developed waves. During the titration, the current deflection is read after each addition of titrant and the solution is mixed by stirring. The observed current values are plotted against the volume of titrant and the equivalence point determined as in Figs. 46–50. As already mentioned, two or three measurements before, and two or three after, the equivalence point are usually sufficient.

To avoid great changes in the volume of the titrated solution, it is preferable to use a more concentrated titrating agent than the solution. When the total volume of the titrated solution is changed during the titration by more than about 5 per cent, the observed current must be corrected for the volume change before plotting the graph according to the relation:

$$i_{corr} = i_{meas} \frac{V + v}{V}$$

where $V$ is the volume of the titrated solution before titration and $v$ the volume of titrant added.

Polarometric titrations are usually more accurate than polarographic analysis (0·1 per cent reproducibility is claimed), and they are less dependent on the factors influencing limiting currents (such as capillary characteristics, composition of supporting electrolyte, temperature etc.), because only the relative changes of the limiting current are measured. The main limitation is the same as in polarography, i.e. other substances giving limiting currents at the same chosen potential as the compound to be determined, must not be present in a large excess. Furthermore,

L

only the total amount of related substances which react with the titrant in the same manner can usually be determined.

Selected examples of polarometric and amperometric titrations, given in the following paragraph, are arranged according to the type of reaction occurring in solution (similar to the preceding sections). The most important are the precipitation and oxidation-reduction reactions, but some other methods based on coupling, addition and substitution reactions, soluble complex formation and even condensation and acid-base reactions have also been described.

### 6.3.1. *Precipitation Reactions*

The most frequently used titrating agents in polarometric and amperometric titrations are silver and mercury compounds and some heteropoly acids. It should be stressed once more that little selectivity, especially for precipitation reactions, can be expected and thus in the analysis of mixtures the application of polarometric titrations must be preceded by separation techniques.

The type of precipitation will be normally discussed according to the reagent used, but because among the precipitation titrations a great deal of research was carried out with *compounds bearing a thiol group*, and as various precipitation or even oxidizing reagents were used with these methods, this group of determinations will be discussed first.

Compounds bearing a sulfhydryl group react with most heavy metals: the products of these reactions depend on the metal, on the structure of the organic compound and on the conditions (pH, buffer, solvent) used. Silver salts, mercuric salts, and *p*-chloromercuribenzoate are the most frequently used precipitating agents, and cupric ions and iodine the oxidizing agents.

With mercaptans and other compounds bearing isolated thiol groups, the situation is relatively simple: practically any of the reagents named can be used, the most frequently used being silver nitrate. Accurate results can be obtained with pure solutions when both the titrated solution and the standard solution of the titrant are deaerated. In an ammoniacal medium, the determination is not influenced by chloride, sulphate, phosphate and small amounts of bromide; but iodide, cyanide, heavy metals such as zinc, cadmium, cobalt and copper and reducing substances such as ascorbic acid do interfere. An attempt has been made to reduce these interferences by carrying out the titration in 90 per cent ethanolic solutions.

When the substance bears an amino and carboxy group in addition to a sulfhydryl group the situation is more complex. The metal used as titrant can either form chelate complexes involving two or three groups, or form salts with one particular group. Often this type of behaviour changes according to reaction conditions. Such complex behaviour is the more important as the important amino acids, cysteine and glutathione, belong to this group. The behaviour of the latter substance is additionally complicated by the presence of further amino and carboxy groups, and by the tendency of this tripeptide to form cyclic structures.

Under such conditions, even though the reaction with the isolated amino-groups has little effect, owing to the competitive reaction with the excess of ammonia in the medium used, the use of silver salts is questionable for the titration of these compounds which bear several groups, for they tend to bind silver ions in addition to the thiol group. Thus mercuric salts were suggested for the amperometric titration of glutathione with a mercury coated platinum electrode. According to the conditions the formation of one $[Hg_2(GS)_2$ in borate at pH 9·2] or two compounds $[Hg(GS)_2$ and $Hg_2(GS)_2$ at pH 3] was observed and the composition of the resulting salt was even affected by the presence of neutral salts. In contrast to the determination of glutathione, the results in the titrations of cysteine were greatly influenced by the state of the electrode and thus, after each titration the electrode must be cleaned by immersion in hot nitric acid.

Thus the most promising titrations appear to be with cupric copper and p-chloromercuribenzoate (in the latter example it is possible that the existing favourable opinion is due to the fact that so far, no thorough basic study has been carried out on the reactions of this compound under the conditions used in the titrations). The determination of cysteine with a standard solution of cupric copper is carried out in ammoniacal media. In contrast to argentometric titrations, there is no interference from iodide, cadmium and zinc (only cobalt interferes, forming a coloured complex with cysteine). In comparison with the mercurimetric technique there is, in this amperometric titration, no contamination of the platinum electrode surface, because only reduction of the divalent copper to cuprous copper is involved. The titration with $p$-chloromercuribenzoate is carried out in pH 7 buffer or in an alkaline medium. Large amounts of iodide or sulphite interfere, but there is no interference from bromide and chloride.

These titrations are often applied to the determination of low-molecular thiol compounds in biological materials. Here, three additional problems arise: (i) the metals of the standard solution can be bound on proteins, (ii) proteins and other high-molecular components present can affect the limiting current of the metal and can be involved in electrode processes (mainly due to their adsorbability) in a similar way to other surface active substances and finally, (iii) the reaction medium used for the titration can denaturate the proteins in the biological material, or involve other factors through which the amount of the compound to be studied is changed. It frequently happens that not only the so-called soluble thiol compounds are present in the sample before handling, but also, in the course of the titration, additional thiol compounds are formed and are co-determined in the titrations of biological materials.

The ideal procedure allows a specific determination of the soluble thiol compounds, under conditions in which a change of state of the biological material is prevented. However, no such method exists as yet and the material is either handled carefully, or the conditions for the selective determination of the soluble thiol compounds are firmly fixed. These two conditions are never fulfilled simultaneously in any existing method. Using ammoniacal or ethanolic solutions undoubtedly represents a large change in the biological conditions. Thus from this point of view, titrations with $p$-chloromercuribenzoate give the nearest approximation to the ideal state, but even here it has been shown[131] that the reagent (even under the mild conditions used) causes a denaturation of proteins.

From the above discussion, it can be deduced that the results of the determinations of soluble thiol compounds can be substantially influenced by the titrant and the conditions used. Only results obtained by the same method under identical conditions are thus strictly comparable.

The situation is even more complicated when the thiol group content is determined in proteins. All the methods given above were used for such a determination and the complications given were: complex-formation with other functional groupings, adsorption of proteins, denaturation and other changes of structure of the second or even first order structure of proteins. Proteins in aqueous solutions, when extremely carefully treated, contain almost no free titratable groups. It is, for instance, questionable, whether or not, after denaturation with ethanol on the one hand and with an aqueous ammoniacal medium on the other, the same thiol groups are liberated for the reaction with heavy metals. Thus the above deduction can also be applied here: the results should be treated as relative values, and only those obtained under identical conditions should be compared.

It can be concluded that for the analysis of biological systems more thorough fundamental work is still necessary, and at present greater caution is required in interpreting the results of these titrations for the content of free or bound thiol groups.[108]

6.3.1.1. *Argentometric methods* were used, as mentioned above, in the determination of thiol compounds. The amperometric determination of mercaptans[109] can be carried out as follows.

*Procedure.* Titrate 5 mg of thiol sulphur in 100 ml. of 95 per cent ethanol, containing 0·25 N ammonia and 0·1 N ammonium chloride, at the potential of a saturated calomel electrode (a short circuit system) with an aqueous solution of 0·005 M silver nitrate. Deoxygenate both solutions.

For the determination of primary and tertiary *mercaptans*[110] two aliquot portions are titrated, one argentometrically and the other iodometrically. In the first titration the total amount of mercaptans present is determined, as all react in the ratio 1 : 1. When titrated with a standard iodine solution, primary mercaptans react with 0·5 mole, and tertiary with 1·0 mole of iodine. To prevent the formation of disulphides, an excess of a lead salt is added during the iodometric titration.

The disulphides, in the determination of *disulphides* in the presence of mercaptans,[111] are reduced first to mercaptans with zinc amalgam. The titration before and after reduction gives the quantity of mercaptans and the sum of mercaptans and disulphides respectively. For the determination of traces of disulphides in mercaptans, the mercaptans are separated before reduction as silver mercaptans. The methods were used in polymer[112, 113] and petroleum[114] chemistry.

The method was also used for the determination of *cysteine*[115] and *glutathione*,[116] but its application presents, mainly in biological materials, the doubts expressed in the previous paragraphs. For the determination of cystine a method is employed based on the reduction of cystine in an acidic medium with sodium amalgam or on the reaction with sulphite at pH 8–12 according to equation:

$$RSSR + SO_3^{2-} \longrightarrow RS^- + RSSO_3^-$$

and subsequent amperometric titration of the cystein formed in the aqueous ammoniacal medium.[117] The method was applied for the determination of cystine in proteins after hydrolysis,[118] and even for the determination of sulphides in blood proteins after reaction with sulphite.[119]

The sodium salt of 5-ethyl-5(1-methylbutyl)-thiobarbituric acid (*Pentothal*, Thiopental) was determined[120] with silver nitrate as titrant and either a dropping mercury or rotating platinum electrode.

Some organic bases, e.g. *alkaloids*, can be determined by titrating the anion portion (usually chloride or bromide) argentimetrically with amperometric control. Similarly sulphates are titrated with lead nitrate, and even mixtures can be analysed.[121, 122]

6.3.1.2. *Mercurimetric methods* have no advantage over the argentimetric methods for the titration of cysteine, but they are more suitable for the determination of *glutathione*.[123] The method has been used for the determination of soluble thiols in flour.[124]

Differences in the rates of the reactions of disulphides and hydroxyl ions, can be used for the analysis of a mixture of *oxidized glutathione and cystine.*[125] The oxidized form of glutathione undergoes hydrolytic cleavage:

$$2\ GSSG + 3\ OH^- \longrightarrow 3\ GS^- + GSOOH + H_2O$$

and GS⁻ formed can be titrated mercurimetrically. Cystine does not undergo hydrolytic cleavage. The procedure is as follows:

Deaerate the solution containing 0·1 M sodium nitrate, 0·1 M ammonia and 0·01 M sodium hydroxide with a stream of ammonia-saturated nitrogen and add a sample containing oxidized glutathione ($2 \times 10^{-5}$ to $1 \times 10^{-4}$M in the resulting solution). Carry out the titration at a platinum electrode with 0·001 M mercuric chloride at an applied voltage of $-0·3$ V to $-0·4$ V.

In the mercurimetric titration of *thiol compounds in proteins*[123] the flat titration curves became steep after the addition of chloride ions. The titration can be carried out in acetate pH 5·6 buffer with 0·5 M potassium chloride, phosphate pH 7·3 buffer with 0·5 M potassium chloride or borate pH 8·8 buffer with 0·5 M ammonium nitrate. In the presence of ammonia the curves were steep, even in the absence of chlorides. It has been suggested[123] that ammonia prevents the bonding of mercury to groups other than the thiol grouping.

Several pharmaceuticals can be determined with mercuric perchlorate as a volumetric agent, e.g. salicylates, [126] *antipyrine,*[127] *Irgapyrin*[127] (3,5-diketo-1,2-diphenyl-4-butylpyrazolidine) and *barbiturates.*[128, 129] In the latter example the ratio mercury: barbiturate should be revised.

**6.3.1.3.** *p-Chloromercuribenzoate* is recommended for the titrations of *cysteine* and *glutathione*[130–132] as a specific reagent for thiol groups. Standard solutions of this reagent, which permits titrations at pH 7, were used for the determination of thiol groups in proteins.[130–133]

**6.3.1.4.** *Halogenide complexes of heavy metals* such as mercury bismuth, cadmium and antimony can be used in the titration of some *basic heterocyclic nitrogen compounds*[134, 135] and among others, *thiamine.*[136] In this latter example, thiamine was titrated with $BiI_4^-$ and the limiting current of bismuth was measured. Alternatively the precipitate formed in the reaction of thiamine with $BiI_4^-$ was separated, dissolved in sodium potassium tartrate and the iodide content determined polarographically.[137]

**6.3.1.5.** *Lead nitrate* can be used for the titration of *tartrates*[138] or *glycerol phosphates*[139] in addition to sulphates already mentioned. A standard solution of lead nitrate is also used for the final titration in an indirect determination of *morphine.*[140] The method consists of treatment of the sample containing morphine with an excess of a standard solution of potassium dichromate in acid solution. Morphine is oxidized and the chromate reduced to the chromic state. The excess of dichromate is determined by titration with a standard solution of a lead salt at pH 4·2. The method was used for the analysis of *Tinctura Opii*.

**6.3.1.6.** *Solutions of heavy metals* can be used in the determination of substances which are generally used in analytical chemistry as organic reagents. Thus, for example, solutions of salts of several heavy metals can be used in the determination of mercaptobenzthiazole,[141] of various oximes (e.g. α-benzoinoxime, salicylaldoxime etc.), α-nitroso-β-naphthol etc.

**6.3.1.7.** *Chromates* have been used in the precipitation titration of *acridine*[142] and other organic bases.

**6.3.1.8.** *Heteropolyacids* have proved as useful (even when unselective) as titrating agents for different types of organic nitrogen containing bases. Of the heteropolyacids studied, the most universal seems to be silicotungstic acid. The second reduction wave of this acid is used in polarometric titrations with a mercury dropping electrode. In 0·05–0·2 N hydrochloric acid the current is measured at an applied voltage of −0·65 V, and the readings can be made some 15–30 sec after addition as the precipitates are formed very rapidly. The reactions proceed in steady and simple stoichiometric relationships; according to the structure of the base 1 mole of the reagent usually reacts with two or four moles of the organic base.

Several *alkaloids*, when present as single pure substances, can be determined by this method[143–146] in the same way as some dyestuffs[147] and several pharmaceuticals,[148–151] e.g. phenthiazine derivatives, xanthen-9-carboxylic acids, anti-histaminics and spasmolytics.

6.3.1.9. *Reinecke salt* has also recently been used for the precipitation titration of alkaloids[134] and thiamine,[152] even though the solution of this reagent is not very stable.

6.3.1.10. *Organic titrants.* Among the organic substances the *aromatic nitro derivatives* can be used as reagents for the titrations of organic substances such as *alkaloids* and other organic bases.[153] However these derivatives are less useful than the heteropolyacids and halogenide complexes of heavy metals. Of the acids, only picric acid and flavianic acid are used. The titration is carried out at pH 4·7, and the current is measured at −0·4 V. *Alizarin sulphonate* precipitates some *alkaloids*[153] and this compound has also been used for the titration of *diamidines*.[154]

*Procedure.* Dissolve 10 mg of diamidine salt in 10 ml. of a phosphate pH 7 buffer and after deaeration titrate with a 0·08 M standard solution of alizarin sulphonate. Follow the diffusion current of the alizarin sulphonate, and plot the graph which has the form of the titration curve shown in Fig. 47.

The hydrolysis of amidine pharmaceuticals have been followed with this method.

Finally, *streptomycin* can be determined by titrating with a dye formed by coupling diazotized *p*-rosaniline with 1-naphthol-4-sulphonic acid.[155] A sample, containing 1–3 mg of streptomycin, was titrated in 10 ml. of triethylamine citrate buffer at −0·8 V with a 0·01 M solution of the dye.

6.3.2. *Oxidation-reduction Reactions*

As mentioned above, mixtures of primary and tertiary *mercaptans* can be titrated *iodometrically* with amperometric detection of the end-point[110] in the presence of an excess of lead nitrate or perchlorate. The determination of *thiosinamine*[156] and *thiourea*[156] was carried out similarly. The latter is claimed to give a reversible oxidation-reduction system, whereas in all other instances the oxidation of the thiol form proceeds irreversibly. Iodometric titrations with standard solutions of iodine or *o*-iodosobenzoate were also carried out with the biological materials mainly in milk.[157] The titration with *o*-iodosobenzoate indicated[158] about twice the equivalent concentration of thiols, from that found with argentimetric titration in aqueous medium. The method evidently lacks specificity.

Amongst the other more frequently used *oxidizing agents* for the oxidation of ascorbic acid are permanganate,[159] ferricyanide,[160] iodate[161] and bromate.[162] The latter was also recommended for the titration of *p*-aminosalicylic acid:[163]

*Procedure.* Dissolve 1–2 mg of the compound in 100 ml. of a solution containing 0·05 M potassium bromide and 0·08 M acetic acid in 1·0 M hydrochloric acid, and titrate with 0·02 M potassium bromate at a rotating platinum electrode on which the liberated bromine is reduced. The titration curve is as given in Fig. 47.

Easily brominated compounds interfere; *m*-aminophenol can be determined as above.

Dichromate is used as a standard solution in the determination of *dialkyl peroxides*[164] by the following procedure:

Dissolve the sample in 70–80 per cent acetone–water mixture, and after acidifying with sulphuric acid, reduce the peroxide with an excess of a ferrous salt. Titrate the unconsumed ferrous ions with a dichromate solution.

Among the more common oxidizing agents are the cerium salts. These are used for example in the titrations of substituted *phenols and anilines*[165] which are used as developers in photography. Anodic waves of the phenolic and similar substances were followed from +0·75 to 1·0 V with a rotating platinum electrode.

It is possible to titrate *oxalic acid* with a ceric salt dissolved in glacial acetic acid. In the reaction, accelerated by the presence of perchloric acid, one mole of oxalic acid reacts with two moles of the ceric salt with the formation of carbon dioxide.[166] Tartaric acid, citric acid[167] and sugars such as *glucose* and *fructose*[168] can also be oxidized with an excess of ceric perchlorate in 1 N HClO$_4$ at 60°C. The excess of oxidant is titrated, after cooling, with sodium oxalate solution. The current is measured with a platinum indicator electrode and a saturated calomel reference electrode at the potential of the reference electrode (short circuit system).

A *less familiar volumetric agent* is gold chloride; it is used for the titration of α-tocopherol.[169] However it is not specific enough to be recommended for the analysis of such complicated materials as fats.

A more successful reagent which is used for the analysis of thiols is a standard solution of cupric copper. The titration, performed in ammoniacal solution, is more selective than argentimetric procedures, and it is possible by this titration (which is dependent on the reduction of divalent copper with *cysteine* to cuprous copper) to analyse mixtures of cysteine and cystine.[170]

*Procedure.* Deoxygenate 25–100 ml. of 0·05 N ammonia in the titration cell and add a sample of $4 \times 10^{-4}$ M to $1 \times 10^{-5}$ M cystine or cysteine. Make the solution 0·1 M to sodium sulphite and carry out the titration with a 0·01 M solution of divalent copper which is preferably prepared from metallic copper. Measure the current at −0·4 V with a rotating platinum electrode. The titration curve obtained should be of the form given in Fig. 47.

Because the reaction takes place according to the following reaction:

$$2\,Cu^{2+} + RS^- + SO_3^{2-} \rightarrow 2\,Cu^+ + RSSO_3^-$$

each mole of cysteine requires two moles of copper. If cystine is present, it reacts with sulphite according to the reaction:

$$RSSR + SO_3^{2-} \rightarrow RS^- + RSSO_3^-$$

and hence one mole of cystine gives one mole of cysteine, and thus consumes also two moles of the standard copper solution.

If both cysteine and cystine are to be determined in a mixture, the cystine is first reduced with a sodium amalgam. In this reaction two moles of cysteine are formed from one mole of cystine. Thus one mole of cystine after reduction with the sodium amalgam consumes four moles of copper.

Finally, among the *organic oxidative reagents*, the possibility has been reported of the application of 2,6-dichlorophenol-indophenol for the titration of *ascorbic acid*.[170a] When the current is measured at the potential of the limiting current of ascorbic acid in an acetate pH 4·7 buffer, a titration curve is obtained of the type given in Fig. 49. The equivalence point is given by passing the current through the null point of the galvanometer (after subtracting the capacity current, when necessary). This point can be detected with a high galvanometer sensitivity; hence the method is very sensitive (even when non-selective, as are all titrations with this reagent) and especially useful for the determination of small amounts of ascorbic acid. As the equilibrium in solution is established very quickly, and as it is unnecessary to wait until the potential of the electrode becomes constant, the time required for this polarometric titration is a fraction of the time necessary for a potentiometric titration.

### 6.3.3. *Coupling Reactions*
The azocompound formed in the coupling reaction between a phenol or aniline derivative and a diazonium salt, is reduced at more negative potentials than the corresponding diazonium salt. If the current is measured at potentials corresponding to the limiting current of the diazonium salt, but more positive than the reduction of the azocompound, it is possible to measure the excess of the diazonium salt from the equivalence point. The resulting titration curve possesses the form given in Fig. 47.

The scope of this technique is given by the reactivity of the hydroxy group in phenols, and the amino-group in anilines and related compounds. The method was originally devised for the determination of *naphthols* and *pyrazolons*,[171] but was later used for the determination of several *alkaloids*[172, 173] (morphine, cephaeline, emetine), *phenolic compounds*[172] (phenol, catechol, orcinol, guaiacol etc.), *sulpha drugs*,[172, 174] *oxine*[175] and *capsaicine*.[176] The most widely used titrant is *p*-diazobenzene sulphonic acid. The standard solutions of this acid can be easily prepared and are relatively stable.

For the determination of most substances the following procedure was applied:

Dissolve the sample in 25 ml. of a Clark Lubs pH 9·3 buffer and make up to 50 ml. Cool the solution so that the temperature is below 10°C, deoxygenate and after addition of 0·5 ml. of a 0·5 per cent solution of gelatin, titrate with 0·025 M *p*-diazobenzene sulphonic acid at −0·4 V.

Most of the determinations were carried out with pure substances or in pharmaceutical materials; capsaicine was determined in plant materials by this method.

## 6.3.4. *Addition and Substitution Reactions*

The number of *unsaturated bonds* can be determined by a titration with a standard solution of bromine dissolved in glacial acetic acid. The sample is also dissolved in glacial acetic acid to which sodium and ammonium acetate are added, so as to give a final concentration of 0·5 and 0·1 M respectively. The cathodic current of bromine is measured with a short circuit system using a rotating platinum indicator, and a calomel or chloranil reference electrode at the potential of the reference electrode. Several unsaturated open chain compounds and terpenes have been titrated in this way.[177] Other modifications of this technique have been used to determine the amount of unsaturation in fats in methanolic solutions. The standard solution of bromine is prepared in methanol, saturated with sodium bromide, and the methylester of stearic acid is added to suppress the maxima.[178] If the methanolic solution is acidified, 0·1 M potassium bromate with 0·1 M sodium bromide can be used instead of bromine. The bromine generated in homogeneous solution can be used to analyse xylenol and cresol fractions of coal-tars.[179] Other phenolic compounds may be similarly determined.[180] The method was used for the determination of small concentrations of *styrene*.[181]

*Procedure.* Add to 75 ml. of methanol, 5 ml. of concentrated hydrochloric acid and 1 g of potassium bromide. Cool the solution to 5–10°C and add to it a sample containing no more than 10 mg of styrene.

Titrate with a standard solution containing 0·002 N potassium bromate in 0·1 N potassium bromide, using a platinum electrode at the potential of a saturated calomel electrode.

*Oxine*[182, 183] can be titrated as the other phenolic compounds, mentioned above.

## 6.3.5. *Soluble Complex Formation*

The decrease of the anodic wave of ethylenediaminetetraacetic acid (EDTA), at 0·2 V in pH 6·4 buffered solutions, with standard solutions of heavy metals which form stable complexes with EDTA (e.g. Mn, Co, Ni, Cd, Mg and Zn), can be used for the polarometric titration of EDTA.[184] The titration curve is of the form given in Fig. 46. In acetate pH 5 at $-0.45$ V the amperometric titration of EDTA can be done with a standard solution of divalent copper.[185]

The polarometric determination of *histidine*[186] is based on an ingenious principle. The method utilizes the formation of an anodic wave of the polarographically active bihistidinatocobaltous ion which is produced by the addition of standard solutions of cobaltous salts to buffered histidine solutions. In the presence of histamine, protein hydrolysates and other amino acids, a phosphate pH 8·0 buffer is used when the interferences are at the minimum. In solutions, where only histidine is present, a Britton–Robinson pH 9·1 buffer is preferred in which the formation of the bihistidinatocobaltous ion is favoured.

*Procedure.* Add a sample of histidine to 10–25 ml. of a pH 8·0 (or 9·1) buffer so that the final concentration of histidine is about $6 \times 10^{-4}$ to $2 \times 10^{-3}$ M. Deoxygenate the solution, titrate with the standard solution of cobaltous sulphate and measure the current at $-0.04$ V.

The titration curve has the form* shown in Fig. 50. Owing to the formation of monohistidinatocobaltous complexes, a small decrease in the limiting current beyond the end-point was observed at pH 8·0. This consequently caused a negative error of $-6$ per cent.

The above method, contrary to the methods of estimation of amino acids based on copper complexes, is selective. A threefold excess of several common amino acids (including histamine) does not interfere. The method thus enables free histidine to be determined in protein hydrolysates, provided that the histidine concentration is sufficiently high. Tryptophane deforms the polarographic waves when present in an amount corresponding to half that of histidine (above 1 mg/10 ml.). Mercaptoamino acids also interfere, but most of the types of compounds are destroyed during the protein acidic hydrolysis. Glycine affects the end-point if present in amounts larger than 10 mg/10 ml. of the sample.

A similar titration curve (Fig. 50) is observed, when a suspension of *lead tannate* is titrated with dilute nitric acid in 20 per cent ethanol. By measuring the limiting current, lead can be determined in this complex.[187] In a similar way insoluble precipitates can be analysed after the addition of complex-forming reagents, e.g.

---

* If the anodic current is plotted, as on polarograms, in the negative direction below the x-axis, a mirror image of the curve in Fig. 50 is obtained.

bismuth hydroxide, or its basic salts can be titrated with tartaric acid.

The composition of the nonreducible boric acid-fructose complex was determined by a polarometric titration.

The increase of the fructose wave, after addition of fructose to different concentrations of boric acid solutions, was dependent on the fructose concentration in the form given in Fig. 47. The mole ratio of boron to fructose was found[188] to be 1 : 1.

### 6.3.6. Condensations

The reaction of 2,4-dinitrophenylhydrazine with carbonyl compounds has been made the basis of a volumetric method.[189] The wave of the reagent in excess after passing the equivalence point was measured at $-0.76$ V in $0.01$ N sulphuric acid, in the presence of 50 per cent ethanol.

REFERENCES

(1) ŠKRAMOVSKÝ, S. and TEISINGER, J., Časopis lekařů českých 82, 621 (1943).

(2) SRBOVÁ, J., Pracovní lékařství 4, 47 (1952); see also Anal. Chem. 24, 917 (1952).

(3) BEZUGLYJ, V. D. and OGDANEC, N. D., Trudy Komissii po analitičeskoj chimii, Akad. Nauk SSSR 7, 149 (1956).

(4) LANDRY, A. S., Anal. Chem. 21, 674 (1949).

(5) ŠEDIVEC, V., Collect. Czechoslov. Chem. Commun. 23, 57 (1958); Chem. průmysl 8, 180 (1958).

(6) ROUBAL, J. and ZDRAŽIL, J., Pracovní lékařství 2, 187 (1950); 3, 148 (1951).

(7) ROUBAL, J. and ZDRAŽIL, J., Proc. 1st Internat. Polarograph. Congr., Prague 1951, Pt. I, 724 (1951), Pt. III, 542 (1952).

(8) BERGEROVÁ-FIŠEROVÁ, V., ŠKRAMOVSKÝ, S. and MENŠÍKOVÁ, J., Pracovní lékařství 6, 229 (1955).

(9) MATSUMOTO, K., J. Pharm. Soc. Japan 73, 1375 (1953); Leybold polarograph. Ber. 2, 87 (1954).

(10) NOVOTNÝ, B., Československ. farmacie 3, 302 (1954); Chem. Tech. (Berlin) 6, 662 (1954).

(11) MONNIER, D. and RUSCONI, Y., Helv. Chim. Acta 34, 1297 (1951).

(12) RUSCONI, Y., MONNIER, D. and WENGER, P. E., Helv. Chim. Acta 34, 1943 (1951).

(13) MONNIER, D. and RUSCONI, Y., Anal. Chim. Acta 7, 567 (1952).

(14) MONNIER, D. and BESSO, Z., Helv. Chim. Acta 35, 777 (1952).

(15) BESSO, Z., MONNIER, D. and WENGER, P. E., Anal. Chim. Acta 7, 286 (1952).

(16) MONNIER, D. and GUERNE, R., *Anal. Chim. Acta* **19**, 90 (1958).
(17) WENGER, P. E., MONNIER, D. and VOGEL, J., *Microchim. Acta* **3–4**, 406 (1957).
(18) MONNIER, R. D., VOGEL, J. and WENGER, P. E., *Anal. Chim. Acta* **22**, 369 (1960).
(19) KALVODA, R., *Českoslov. farmacie* **3**, 300 (1954).
(20) BAGGESGAARD-RASMUSSEN, H., HAHN, C. and ILVER, K., *Dansk. Tidskr. Farm* **19**, 41 (1945).
(21) BAGGESGAARD-RASMUSSEN, H., *Bull. federation intern. pharm.* **21**, 233 (1947).
(22) LUND, H., *Acta Chim. Scand.* **12**, 1444 (1958).
(23) NOSEK, J. and KRESTÝNOVÁ, O., *Časopis českého lékárnictva* **63**, 49 (1950).
(24) VOLKE, J., Private communication.
(25) NOVOTNÝ, B., RUBEŠ, T. and STEJSKAL, Z., Private communication.
(26) NOVOTNÝ, B., *Českoslov. farmacie* **3**, 199 (1954).
(27) SMALES, A. A. and WILSON, H. N., *J. Soc. Chem. Ind.* **67**, 210 (1948).
(28) ENGLISH, F. L., *Anal. Chem.* **23**, 344 (1951).
(29) LECLERCQ, M., *Mem. Poudres* **35**, 365 (1953).
(30) GRY, O., *Dansk. Tidsskr. Farm.* **23**, 139 (1949).
(31) DAVÍDEK, J. and MANOUŠEK, O., *Českoslov. farmacie* **7**, 399 (1958).
(32) DAVÍDEK, J. and MANOUŠEK, O., *Českoslov. farmacie* **7**, 73 (1958).
(33) JINDRA, A., JUNGR, V. and ZÝKA, J., *Českoslov. farmacie* **1**, 177 (1952).
(34) KALVODA, R. and ZÝKA, J., Unpublished results.
(35) NOVOTNÝ, B., *Českoslov. farmacie* **3**, 12 (1954).
(36) NOVOTNÝ, B., *Českoslov. farmacie* **3**, 85 (1954).
(37) ZUMAN, P., *Collect. Czechoslov. Chem. Commun.* **15**, 839 (1950).
(38) ZUMAN, P. and BŘEZINA, M., *Chem. listy* **46**, 599 (1952).
(39) BŘEZINA, M. and ZUMAN, P., *Chem. listy* **47**, 975 (1953).
(40) VAN ATTA, R. E. and JAMIESON, D. R., *Anal. Chem.* **31**, 1217 (1959).
(40a) RŮŽIČKA, V., MATUŠŮ, Z. and MEDONOS, V., Sci. Papers from Inst. Chem. Technol. Prague, 633 Fac. Inorg. Org. Technol. (1958).
(40b) HALL, M. E., *Anal. Chem.* **31**, 2007 (1959).
(41) ZUMAN, P. and ŠANTAVÝ, F., *Chem. listy* **46**, 393 (1952); *Collect. Czechoslov. Chem. Commun.* **18**, 28 (1953).
(42) ZUMAN, P., *Chem. listy* **46**, 521 (1952).
(43) WASA, T., TAKAGI, M. and ONO, S., *Bull. Chem. Soc. Japan* **34**, 518 (1961).
(44) ZUMAN, P., Unpublished results.
(45) SOUCHAY, P. and GRAIZON, M., *Chimie analytique* **36**, 85 (1954).
(46) COULSON, D. M., *Anal. Chim. Acta* **19**, 284 (1958).
(47) WOLFE, J. K., HERSHBERG, E. B. and FIESER, L. F., *J. Biol. Chem.* **136**, 653 (1940).

(48) PRELOG, V. and HÄFLIGER, O., *Helv. Chim. Acta* **32**, 2088 (1949).
(49) BŘEZINA, M., VOLKE, J. and VOLKOVÁ, V., *Collect. Czechoslov. Chem. Commun.* **19**, 894 (1954).
(50) HERSHBERG, E. B., WOLFE, J. K. and FIESER, L. F., *J. Biol. Chem.* **140**, 215 (1941).
(50a) NEISH, W. J. P., *Rec. Trav. chim. Pays-Bas* **72**, 105, 1098 (1953).
(51) KEMULA, W., Chromatopolarography, in *Progress in Polarography* (P. Zuman, I. M. Kolthoff, editors), Vol. 2, p. 397, Interscience, New York (1962).
(52) LUPTON, J. M. and LYNCH, C. C., *J. Amer. Chem. Soc.* **66**, 697 (1944).
(52a) HAAS, J. W. and LYNCH, C. C., *Anal. Chem.* **29**, 479 (1957).
(52b) WHITNACK, G. C., YOUNG, J. E., SISLER, H. H. and GANTZ, E. S. C., *Anal. Chem.* **28**, 833 (1956).
(53) ZAHRADNÍK, R. and JENŠOVSKÝ, L., *Chem. listy* **48**, 11 (1954).
(54) ZAHRADNÍK, R., *Collect. Czechoslov. Chem. Commun.* **21**, 447 (1956).
(55) ZAHRADNÍK, R., MANSFELD, V. and SOUČEK, B., *Českoslov. farmacie* **4**, 119 (1955); *Pharmazie* **10**, 364 (1955).
(56) ZUMAN, P., ZUMANOVÁ, R. and SOUČEK, B., *Collect. Czechoslov. Chem. Commun.* **18**, 632 (1953).
(57) ŠEDIVEC, V. and VAŠÁK, V., *Chem. listy* **48**, 19 (1954).
(58) RJABOV, A. V. and PANOVA, G. D., *Dokl. Akad. Nauk SSSR* **99**, 547 (1954).
(59) MEDONOS, V., *Collect. Czechoslov. Chem. Commun.* **23**, 1465 (1958).
(60) ELVING, P. J. and VAN ATTA, R. E., *Anal. Chem.* **26**, 295 (1954).
(61) WARSHOWSKY, B. and RICE, M. W., *Anal. Chem.* **20**, 341 (1948).
(62) HEYROVSKÝ, J. and HASSELBACH, H., *Z. Pflanzenzucht* **25**, 443 (1943).
(63) FILOV, V. A., *Gigiena Truda i professionalnyje zabolevanija* **54** (1960).
(64) WENGER, P. E., MONNIER, D. and FARAGGI, S., *Anal. Chim. Acta* **13**, 89 (1955).
(65) ZAPLETÁLEK, A., *Collect. Czechoslov. Chem. Commun.* **11**, 28 (1939).
(66) ŠŤASTNÝ, J., *Chem. Obzor* **19**, 119 (1944).
(67) SCHMIDT, O. and MANZ, R., *Klin. Wochschr.* **33**, 857 (1955).
(68) KUBIS, J., *Časopis lékařů českých* 852 (1959); *Pracovní lékařství* **9**, 465 (1959).
(69) WARSHOWSKY, B. and ELVING, P. J., *Ind. Eng. Chem., Anal. Ed.* **18**, 253 (1946).
(70) CANNON, W. A., *Anal. Chem.* **22**, 928 (1950).
(71) ELVING, P. J., WARSHOWSKY, B., SHOEMAKER, E. and MARGOLIT, J., *Anal. Chem.* **20**, 25 (1948).
(72) ZUMAN, P. and KRUPIČKA, J., *Collect. Czechoslov. Chem. Commun.* **23**, 598 (1958).
(73) BOYD, M. J. and BAMBACH, K., *Ind. Eng. Chem., Anal. Ed.* **15**, 314 (1943).

(74) DIRSCHERL, W. and BERGMEYER, H. U., *Biochem. Z.* **320**, 46 (1949).
(75) BISTER, F. and WOLFF, J. H., *Arzneimittel-Forsch.* **3**, 481 (1953).
(76) GREENBERG, L. A., *J. Biol. Chem.* **147**, 11 (1943).
(76a) HENDERSON, J. and FREEDBERG, A. S., *Anal. Chem.* **27**, 1064 (1955).
(77) HORTON, A. D., THOMASON, P. F., and KELLEY, M. T., *Anal. Chem.* **27**, 269 (1955).
(78) HALL, M. E., *Anal. Chem.* **31**, 1219 (1959).
(79) DANIEL, R. L. and LEBLANC, R. B., *Anal. Chem.* **31**, 1221 (1959).
(80) HOYLE, W. and WEST, T., *Talanta* **2**, 158 (1959); **3**, 47 (1959).
(81) HOYLE, W., SANDERSON, I. P. and WEST, T. S., *J. Electroanalyt. Chem.* **2**, 166 (1961).
(82) JONES, T. S. G., *Biochem. J.* **42**, 59 (1948).
(83) MARTIN, A. J. P. and MITTELMANN, R., *Biochem. J.* **43**, 353 (1948).
(84) BLAEDEL, W. J. and TODD, J. W., *Anal. Chem.* **32**, 1018 (1960).
(85) HEYROVSKÝ, J., SMOLEŘ, I., and ŠŤASTNÝ, J., *Věstník Československ. akad. zemedělské*, **9**, 599 (1933).
(86) HENNIG, K. and BURKHARDT, R., *Z. Lebensm. Unters. u. Forsch.* **92**, 245 (1951).
(87) GROHMANN, H. and GILBERT, E., *Z. Lebensm. Unters. u. Forsch.* **98**, 186 (1954).
(88) TANNER, H. and RENTSCHLER, R. H., *Schweiz. Z. Obst. Weinbau* **62**, 74 (1952); *Leybolds polarograph. Ber.* **1**, No. 4, 26 (1953).
(89) TACHI, I., *J. Agric. Chem. Soc. Japan* **16**, 161, 1057 (1940); *Chem. Abstr.* **35**, 6827 (1941).
(90) DOMANSKÝ, R., *Proc. 1st Internat. Polarograph. Congr. Prague 1951.* Pt. I, p. 740, Prague (1951).
(91) KOVÁČ, J., *Chem. zvesti* **8**, 342 (1954).
(92) KALVODA, R. and ZÝKA, J., *Časopis českého lékárnictva* **63**, 219, 222 (1950).
(93) KALVODA, R. and ZÝKA, J., *Československ. farmacie* **1**, 21 (1952).
(94) NOVÁK, J. V. A. cf. HEYROVSKÝ, J., *Polarographie*, p. 368, Springer, Vienna (1941).
(95) STRNAD, F., *Chem. listy* **43**, 16 (1949).
(96) NORTON, D. R. and FURMAN, N. H., *Anal. Chem.* **26**, 1116 (1954).
(97) NORTON, D. R. and MANN, C. K., *Anal. Chem.* **26**, 1180 (1954).
(98) WARSHOWSKY, B., ELVING, P. J. and MANDEL, J., *Anal. Chem.* **19**, 161 (1947).
(99) WHITNACK, G. C., *Anal. Chem.* **20**, 658 (1948).
(100) MONNIER, D. and RUEDI, W. F., *Helv. Chim. Acta* **38**, 402 (1955).
(101) TAKIURA, K. and KOIZUMI, K., *J. Pharm. Soc. Japan* **78**, 961 (1958).
(102) LADIK, J. and SZÉKÁCS, I., *Nature*, **184**, 188 (1959).
(103) ZUMAN, P., SICHER, J., KRUPIČKA, J. and SVOBODA, M., *Nature* **178**, 1407 (1956); *Collect. Czechoslov. Chem. Commun.* **23**, 1237 (1958).
(104) TAKIURA, K. and KOIZUMI, K., *J. Pharm. Soc. Japan* **79**, 809 (1959).

(105) FRANCIS, C. V., *Anal. Chem.* **21**, 1238 (1949).
(106) PARRÁK, V., *Československ. farmacie* **3**, 42 (1954).
(107) DLEZEK, J., *Proc. 1st Internat. Polarograph. Congr. Prague 1951*, Pt. I, p. 740, Prague (1951).
(108) BŘEZINA, M. and ZUMAN, P., *Polarography in Medicine, Biochemistry, and Pharmacy*, Interscience, New York (1958) p. 500–506, 662–670, where the references are extensively quoted.
(109) KOLTHOFF, I. M. and HARRIS, W. E., *Ind. Eng. Chem., Anal. Ed.* **18**, 161 (1946).
(110) KOLTHOFF, I. M. and HARRIS, W. E., *Anal. Chem.* **21**, 963 (1949).
(111) KOLTHOFF, I. M., MAY, D. R., MORGAN, P., LAITINEN, H. A. and O'BRIEN, A. S., *Ind. Eng. Chem. Anal. Ed.* **18**, 442 (1946).
(112) KOLTHOFF, I. M., GRUSS, L. S., MAY, D. R. and MEDALIA, A. I., *J. Polymer. Sci.* **1**, 340 (1946).
(113) KOLTHOFF, I. M. and MILLER, I. K., *J. Amer. Chem. Soc.* **73**, 3055 (1951); **74**, 4419 (1952).
(114) GRIMES, M. D., PUCKETT, J. E., NEWBY, B. J. and HEINRICH, B. J., *Anal. Chem.* **27**, 152 (1955).
(115) KOLTHOFF, I. M. and STRICKS, W., *J. Amer. Chem. Soc.* **72**, 1952 (1950).
(116) BENESCH, R. E. and BENESCH, R., *Arch. Biochem.* **28**, 43 (1950).
(117) KOLTHOFF, I. M. and STRICKS, W., *J. Amer. Chem. Soc.* **72**, 1951 (1950).
(118) HATA, T., *Bull. Research Inst. Food Sci. Kyoto Univ.* **4**, 451 (1951).
(119) STRICKS, W. and KOLTHOFF, I. M., *J. Amer. Chem. Soc.* **73**, 1728 (1951).
(120) ČIHALÍK, J., DOLEŽAL, J., SIMON, V. and ZÝKA, J., *Československ. farmacie* **2**, 43 (1953).
(121) BOZSAI, I., *Acta Pharm. Hung.* **24**, 49 (1954); *Acta Chim. Hung.* **9**, 265 (1956).
(122) KALVODA, R. and ZÝKA, J., *Časopis československ. lékárnictva* **63**, 219 (1950).
(123) KOLTHOFF, I. M., STRICKS, W. and MORREN, L., *Anal. Chem.* **26**, 366 (1954).
(124) SULLIVAN, B., *J. Agric. Food. Chem.* **2**, 1231 (1954).
(125) STRICKS, W. and KOLTHOFF, I. M., *Anal. Chem.* **25**, 1050 (1953).
(126) KALVODA, R. and ZÝKA, J., *Československ. farmacie* **1**, 515 (1952).
(127) KALVODA, R. and ZÝKA, J., *Chem. listy* **46**, 56, 57 (1952).
(128) KALVODA, R. and ZÝKA, J., *Časopis českého lékárnictva* **63**, 36 (1950).
(129) HEYNDRICKX, A., *Pharm. Belgique* 132 (1954).
(130) IWAKI, G., *J. Physiol. Soc. Japan* **13**, 351 (1951); *Chem. Abstr.* **46**, 1606 (1952).
(131) MATOUŠEK, L. and LAUČÍKOVÁ, O., *Chem. listy* **47**, 1062 (1953).
(132) PIHAR, O., *Chem. listy* **47**, 1647 (1953).
(133) HATA, T., *Bull. Research Inst. Food Sci., Kyoto Univ.* **5**, 42 (1951).
(134) ČIHÁKOVÁ, M. and ZÝKA, J., *Československ. farm.* **5**, 572 (1956).

(135) SCHILLEROVÁ, V. and ZÝKA, J., *Československ. farm.* **6**, 93 (1957).
(136) MATSUO, M., *J. Sci. Hiroshima Univ.* **20A**, 157 (1957).
(137) PLETICHA, R., *Pharmazie* **8**, 987 (1953).
(138) KALVODA, R. and ZÝKA, J., *Československ. farm.* **2**, 14 (1953).
(139) KALVODA, R. and ZÝKA, J., *Československ. farm.* **1**, 98 (1952).
(140) KALVODA, R. and ZÝKA, J., *Časopis českého lékárnictva* **62**, 134 (1949).
(141) DOLEŽAL, J. and ZÝKA, J., *Polarometrické titrace (Polarometric titrations),* SNTL, Prague 1961, p. 98 where further references can be found.
(142) BLAŽEK, A., KALVODA, R. and ZÝKA, J., *Časopis českého lékárnictva* **63**, 138 (1950).
(143) SOUČKOVÁ, M. and ZÝKA, J., *Československ. farmacie* **4**, 181 (1955).
(144) OGAWA, T., *J. Electrochem. Soc. Japan* **24**, 476 (1956); **25**, 377 (1957).
(145) OGAWA, T., *J. Chem. Soc. Japan, Pure Chem. Sect.* **76**, 739 (1955); **77**, 535 (1956).
(146) YOSHINO, T., *J. Pharm. Soc. Japan* **78**, 1303 (1958).
(147) OGAWA, T., *J. Electrochem. Soc. Japan* **25**, 613 (1957); **26**, 134 (1958).
(148) KRÁČMAR, J., BLAŽEK, J. and STEJSKAL, Z., *Pharmazie* **12**, 803 (1957).
(149) KRÁČMAR, J. and STEJSKAL, Z., *Československ. farmacie* **6**, 139 (1957).
(150) BLAŽEK, J., *Československ. farmacie* **5**, 210 (1956).
(151) BLAŽEK, J. and STEJSKAL, Z., *Pharmazie* **12**, 409 (1957); *Pharm. Zentralhalle* **17**, 255 (1958).
(152) MARUYAMA, M., *Polarography* **2**, 117 (1954); *Chem. Abstr.* **50**, 7013 (1956).
(153) ZÝKA, J., *Československ. farmacie* **4**, 301 (1955).
(154) CONN, J. B., *Anal. Chem.* **20**, 585 (1948).
(155) CONN, J. B. and NORMAN, S. L., *J. Clin. Invest.* **28**, 837 (1950).
(156) LIBERTI, A. and CERVONE, E., *Ann. Chim. (Roma)* **42**, 491 (1952); **41**, 95 (1951).
(157) LARSON, B. L. and JENESS, R., *J. Dairy Sci.* **33**, 890, 896 (1950).
(158) HURTON, J. T. and PATTON, S., *J. Dairy Sci.* **35**, 699 (1952).
(159) DESHPANDE, S. M. and NATARJAH, R., *J. Amer. Pharm. Assoc., Sci. Ed.* **47**, 633 (1958).
(160) HUBICKA, K., *Ann. Univ. M. Curie-Sklodowska Lublin,* **10AA**, 35 (1955).
(161) COULSON, D. M. and CROWELL, W. R., *Anal. Chem.* **22**, 525 (1950).
(162) ROUBALOVÁ, D. and DOLEŽAL, J., *Chemist-Analyst* **49**, 76 (1960).
(163) LIBERTI, A., *Atti Acad. Lincei, Cl. fis. mat.* **8**, 608, 613 (1950).
(164) KOLTHOFF, I. M. and MEDALIA, A. I., *Anal. Chem.* **23**, 595 (1951).
(165) BOGDANOV, S. G. and SUCHOBOKOVA, N. S., *Ž. anal. Chim.* **6**, 344 (1951).
(166) HINSWARK, O. N. and STONE, K. G., *Anal. Chem.* **28**, 334 (1956).

(167) MICHALSKI, E. and CZARNECKI, K., *Chem. analit.* (*Warzaw*) **4**, 83 (1959).
(168) MICHALSKI, E., CZARNECKI, K. and IGNACZAK, M., *Talanta* **5**, 137 (1960).
(169) SMITH, L. I., KOLTHOFF, I. M. and SPILLANE, L. J., *J. Amer. Chem. Soc.* **64**, 646 (1942).
(170) KOLTHOFF, I. M. and STRICKS, W., *Anal. Chem.* **23**, 763 (1951).
(170a) ZUMAN, P. and PROCHÁZKA, Ž., *Collect. Czechoslor. Chem. Commun.* **18**, 442 (1953); *Chem. listy* **47**, 357 (1953).
(171) ELOFSON, R. M. and MECHERLY, P., *Anal. Chem.* **21**, 565 (1949).
(172) JINDRA, A., KALVODA, R., and ZÝKA, J., *Časopis českého lékárnictva* **63**, 106 (1950); *Collect. Czechoslov. Chem. Commun.* **15**, 797 (1950).
(173) JINDRA, A., JUNGR, V., and ZÝKA, J., *Českoslov. farmacie* **1**, 177, 185 (1952).
(174) ENOKI, T. and MORISAKA, K., *J. Pharm. Soc. Japan* **78**, 432 (1958).
(175) JINDRA, A., JUNGR, V. and ZÝKA, J., *Českoslov. farm.* **1**, 316 (1952).
(176) SPANYAR, P., KEVEI, J. and KISZEL, J., *Élelmiszervizsgálati Közlemények* **2**, 257 (1956).
(177) BLAŽEK, A., *Proc. 1st Internat. Polarograph. Congr.*, *Prague 1951*, Pt. III, p. 563, Prague (1952).
(178) BALTES, J. and HILLER, A., *Fette u. Seifen* **56**, 371 (1954).
(179) VOROBJEV, V., *Chem. průmysl* **8**, 50 (1958).
(180) HASLAM, J., WHETTON, S. M. A., and NEWLANDS, G., *Analyst* **78**, 340 (1953).
(181) KOLTHOFF, I. M., and BOVEY, F. A., *Anal. Chem.* **19**, 498 (1947).
(182) DUYCKAERTS, G., *Bull. soc. roy. sci. Liege* **18**, 152 (1949); *Proc. 1st Internat. Polarograph. Congr.*, *Prague 1951.* Pt. I, p. 51, Prague (1951).
(183) FERNANDO, Q., *Analyst* **79**, 713 (1954).
(184) MICHEL, G., *Anal. Chim. Acta* **10**, 87 (1954).
(185) KNIGHT, W. S. and OSTERYOUNG, R. A., *Anal. Chim. Acta.* **20**, 481 (1959).
(186) JASELSKIS, B., *Anal. Chem.* **30**, 1968 (1958).
(187) DREWES, S. E., *Analyst* **86**, 104 (1961).
(188) ISHIBASHI, M., FUJINAGA, T., and NAGAI, T., *Bull. Inst. Chem. Research, Kyoto Univ.* **36**, 134 (1958).
(189) ZOBOV, E. V. and LJALIKOV, J. S., *Žurn. Anal. Chim.* **11**, 459 (1956).

# CHAPTER VII

# SEPARATION TECHNIQUES

Usually in the analysis of mixtures, an attempt is made to eliminate the possible interferences by the choice of composition of the solution to be polarographed, or by a change in the polarographic instrumentation. In some instances, especially if the mixtures are complex, or if the analyses of a series of chemically related compounds are required, the application of separation techniques becomes necessary. In these operations, which precede the proper polarographic analysis, either the interfering substances are separated from the mixture, or the substance to be determined is isolated, or finally the mixture is fractionated and the polarographic analysis is made on particular fractions. With a few exceptions the separation methods used are techniques which are not specific for polarography, but are operations generally used in organic chemistry. Strictly speaking, these approaches fall outside the domain of polarographic analysis. However, as the steps needed to obtain a sample in which the desired constituents can be determined without interference, are often more involved and time-consuming than the actual measurement, at least the enumeration of the technique and some haphazardly selected examples will be given.

The most important separation techniques used in the polarographic analysis of organic substances are: precipitation and complex formation, extraction, distillation (including steam distillation), dialysis, electrolysis and chromatography.

## 7.1. PRECIPITATION AND COMPLEX FORMATION

The interfering substance can be sometimes removed by precipitation. Thus, for example, the interfering wave of formaldehyde can be eliminated by dimedone.[1] Lead acetate is sometimes suitable for the separation of interfering substances in the analysis of biological materials. Trichloroacetic acid and phosphomolybdic acid cannot be recommended for the deproteination, as they both give waves. Deproteination can be achieved by sulphosalicylic or perchloric acids, and by organic solvents such as acetone or alcohol. The latter agents possess the additional advantage of being volatile, and they can be removed by evaporation. In this way the concentration of the substance under study can be increased many times.

Among the complex-forming reagents it is primarily boric acid which causes profound changes in the polarographic curves of α-diketones or α-hydroxyketones. In some instances, in the presence of borates, the waves are shifted to such negative potentials that the wave does not appear before the discharge of the supporting electrolyte. Such behaviour is observed for e.g. benzil[2] and erythrose.[3]

## 7.2. EXTRACTION

The simplest extraction methods can be demonstrated by the determination of *ether autoxidation products*.[4] When ether is extracted by an equal volume of 0·01 N lithium hydroxide, the polarographic curve recorded in the aqueous phase shows the presence of aldehydic and peroxydic compounds, which are formed during the course of oxidation (Fig. 52). Once the partition coefficients of the particular compounds have been determined for aqueous and ether phases, the original concentrations of aldehydes and peroxides in ether can be determined.

Another application of extraction techniques occurs in the determination of 2-methyl-1,4-naphthoquinone (*vitamin* $K_3$, menadione) in poultry feed.[5] The sample of poultry feed is extracted in the absence of light in an extraction apparatus devised by Berntrop. The sample solution should be exposed to as little light as is possible, to avoid the photochemical decomposition of naphthoquinones. 10 ml. of the extract is then mixed with 25 ml. of 0·08 N ammonia, 0·08 N ammonium chloride (pH 9) in isopropanol containing 10 per cent of water. An aliquot is finally subjected to polarographic electrolysis.

In hydrolysates of iodinated casein, an excess of 3,5-diiodotyrosine is present in addition to thyroxine. The procedure for the determination of *thyroxine* is:

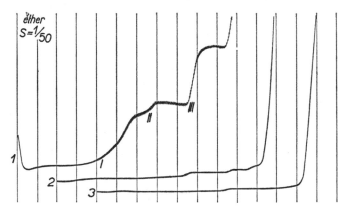

Fig. 52. Purity of ether.
Ether extracted with equal volume of lithium hydroxide, aqueous phase polarographed. (1) Ordinary ether; (2) distilled ether; (3) ether for narcosis. I and II peroxides, III aldehydes. Curves starting at 0 V, Hg-pool electrode, 200 mV/absc., full scale sensitivity 20 $\mu$A.

Extract with *n*-butanol, in slightly acidic solution, and wash the extract with a solution containing 16 per cent sodium hydroxide and 5 per cent sodium bicarbonate. The excess of 3,5-diiodotyrosine is thus removed by these operations.[6] Distil off the butanol and dissolve the residue in a solution containing 0·5 N sodium carbonate, 5 per cent tetramethylammoniumbromide and 20 per cent isopropanol. Determine the content of thyroxine from the most positive wave at −1·2 V. The two other waves at −1·4 V and −1·7 V coincide with the reduction waves of 3,5-diiodotyrosine.

The extraction of *santonine* from *Flores Cinae* can be carried out using chloroform as a solvent[7] at laboratory temperatures. The extract is filtered, chloroform distilled off, the residue dissolved in ethanol and polarographed after diluting with a twofold volume of an aqueous solution of 0·2 N lithium sulphate.

Extraction with 90 per cent ethanol precedes the determination of *fructose* in fruit.[8] The ethanol is distilled off, and from the resulting aqueous solution the excess of acids is removed on an anion-exchange column. The fructose wave is recorded in the effluent after the addition of calcium chloride.

Extraction, however, has not only been used as a preliminary separation technique but also as a fractionation process, aimed at separating mixtures of compounds of similar polarographic and chemical properties. Substances possessing similar half-wave potentials, such as the members of a homologous series, can be fractionated on the basis of their different partition coefficients using two immiscible solvents.[9] Partition chromatography, discussed later, is based on these same principles. The principles of "partition polarography" can be described as follows:

The total limiting current of the mixture is measured. If the mixture contains $n$ components then $(n - 1)$ extractions are carried out with an immiscible solvent. After each extraction the remaining total limiting current is measured. These $n$ values enable the construction of $n$ simultaneous equations, correlating the measured limiting currents with the concentrations and involving the "diffusion current constants" (proportionality constants between limiting current and concentration for particular components of the mixture) and partition coefficients. The solution of these simultaneous equations gives the concentration of the individual components. Application of this principle to the determination of *acetaldehyde*, in the presence of *propionaldehyde* and *butyraldehyde*, using a water–benzene extraction gave good results for binary mixtures, but the results for ternary mixtures were unsatisfactory.

### 7.3. DISTILLATION AND STEAM DISTILLATION

*Acetaldehyde* in alcohol and in spirits can be determined after distillation.[10]

*Procedure.* Mix the sample with 9 volumes of water and distil off one-tenth of this solution. Condense this portion by cooling the receiver. (It contains practically all acetaldehyde.) Make an aliquot portion of the distillate slightly alkaline by the addition of lithium hydroxide, and add for increased conductivity some lithium chloride to make the final concentration about 0·1 M. Record the reduction wave of acetaldehyde shortly after the preparation of the solution, so that the aldol formation does not have a pronounced effect on the wave-height of acetaldehyde (cf. p. 134).

The volatility of *diacetyl* can be used for its determination in butter and fats.[11] The diacetyl is distilled off from an ethanolic solution of the fat and the distillate is polarographed in a pH 6 buffer.

The procedure for the determination of *cuminaldehyde* in Roman caraway seeds, *Semen Cumini Cymini*[12] is:

Crush and grind 1 g of the sample with the same amount of sea sand, moisten the mixture with 0·5 ml. of ethanol and treat with about 40 ml. of water. Steam distil this mixture, and dilute the first 40 ml. of the distillate with the same volume of ethanol. Polarograph the resulting solution after mixing with a phosphate pH 6·8 buffer.

Different volatilities at laboratory temperatures can be used for the fractionation of a mixture of *aliphatic aldehydes*.[13] Under well defined conditions (mainly at controlled flow-rates of the gas stream, but also for a given inlet and cell geometry) the decrease of every component of the mixture, with time, can be measured when a stream of an inert gas is introduced into the solution. The decrease of the wave-height, observed with a solution of the sample under identical conditions (when all the aldehydes are reduced at practically the same potential) allows one to obtain information as to the composition of the sample.

The volatility of the analysed component was used for transferring volatile compounds, such as benzene (p. 113), or carbon disulphide (p. 128), into the reaction mixture. In a similar manner it was possible, from the mixture formed in the electrolysis of ω-piperidinoacetophenone, to transfer the acetophenone with a stream of nitrogen into the polarographic vessel.

## 7.4. DIALYSIS

The presence of proteins, polymers and other substances with high molecular weights sometimes affects the polarographic waves of the substance to be analysed. These effects are often caused by the formation of an adsorbed layer at the dropping mercury electrode. Thus it is sometimes preferable to separate first the high-molecular components before the solution is polarographed.

An example of such a sample preparation is the determination of *thiol-substances* in serum proteins.[14] In this example the low molecular weight substances were separated.

*Procedure.* Dialyse about 10 ml. of human serum against 1000 ml. of distilled water at 4°C for 48 hr, and then for 1 hr against 1000 ml. of physiological solution. Measure the increase in volume after dialysis, in order to enable a calculation of the results upon the basis of the original serum. Dilute 3 ml. of the dialysate with water, and after the addition of ammonia, ammonium nitrate, and ethanol to make up the total volume to 30 ml., amperometrically titrate the solution with a standard silver nitrate solution.

## 7.5. ELECTROLYSIS

Electrolysis at a controlled potential has been so far used in organic polarography mainly for the identification of electrolysis products, and for the determination of the number of the electrons transferred during the electrode process. The application, used sometimes in inorganic polarographic analysis, for the elimination of excess of interfering substances which are reduced at more positive potentials than the substances to be investigated, is rarely used in organic polarography though its application is both logical and advantageous.

An important example of this type of separation process is the *purification of the supporting electrolyte* by controlled potential electrolysis. Thus by electrolysis at −2·35 V, the alkali metals (and the lower amines) can be separated from 0·1 M tetraethyl-ammonium hydroxide in 50 per cent ethanol after 45 min.[15]

## 7.6. CHROMATOGRAPHY

Applications of the three main techniques used at present in chromatography, i.e. adsorption chromatography, partition chromatography, and ion-exchange techniques, sometimes even combined with electrophoresis, have been successfully used in conjunction with polarography. The main reasons for the success of this combination can be ascribed to the fact that for both polarography and chromatography, only small amounts of the analysed substance are required. In addition, chromatography enables the separation of complicated mixtures which cannot be resolved by polarography alone, and polarography offers a quantitative evaluation of the fractions separated by chromato-graphy. Such quantitative methods are usually needed in chromato-graphy. Several examples of the applications of chromatography have already been mentioned, dealing with either the removal of the interfering substances, or the separation of the substance to be investigated, e.g. separation of acids in the determination of fructose with an anion-exchange column (p. 174), fractionation of tannic acid in the determination of malic acid using the same technique (p. 141), separation of amino acids (p. 140) or of 2,4-dinitrophenylhydrazones (p. 126) using paper chromatography, or separations of histidine and histamine (p. 128) and copper aminopolycarboxylates (p. 137) by paper electrophoresis. Only a few further examples will be added here.

Thus alumina column chromatography was used[16] for the separation of *caroten from chlorophyll* in the determination of the former based on the reaction with iodine (cf. p. 131). Carotene is eluted from the alumina column with a petroleum ether–benzene mixture, whereas chlorophyll and other carotenoids remain on the column.

Paper chromatography was used for the separation of *morphine* in analysis of blood.[17]

*Procedure.* Deproteinize about 10 ml. of blood, containing more than 100 $\mu$g of morphine, with acetone or ethanol. Centrifuge off the precipitate, distil off the acetone and dissolve the residue in 0·3 ml. of 0·1 N hydrochloric acid. Place an aliquot portion of this solution on a paper strip, and prepare a one-dimensional chromatogram using a butanol-acetic acid mixture. Detect the position and area of the spots from the fluorescence after irradiation by a u.v. lamp. Cut a square of paper, about 2 cm broad, around the spot and place it in a test tube. Elute the paper with 2 ml. of 1 N hydrochloric acid for 12 hr, then with another 2 ml. of 1 N hydrochloric acid for 2 hr and finally with 1 ml. of 1 N hydrochloric acid for 1 hr. Nitrate and carry out the determination in the joint eluates by the procedure given on p. 118.

*Notes.* (1) The evaluation is preferably carried out by the standard addition method, i.e. in a parallel run 100 $\mu$g of morphine are added either at the start of the chromatogram or into the sample of blood. Errors can be minimized in this way, as all factors which influence the results, such as adsorption during the course (wandering) of the spot or incomplete elution, similarly affect the substance to be analysed and the standard.

(2) *Pyruvic acid* was determined[18] similarly in blood.

Not only the determination, but also the detection and identification of unknown spots on paper chromatograms can be achieved by polarography. The unknown spot is cut out and the polarographic behaviour of the eluate studied. In this way the spot of so called "overglycine" in the chromatography of blood has been identified as corresponding to pyruvic acid.[19] In a similar way impurities in $\beta$-piperidinopropiophenone[20] were identified. The complicating characteristic pattern of the oscillographic d$E$/d$t$–$E$ curves can also be used in the identification of unknown spots on chromatograms, e.g. of nucleotides and nucleosides.[21] On the other hand paper chromatography also proved useful for the identification of the products of electrode reactions,[22] as mentioned on p. 54.

The analysis of blood proteins using paper electrophoresis is discussed on p. 198.

Even though there has been no systematic study on the problem, ion-exchange methods offer promising opportunities for the resolution of mixtures containing charged particles.

Because polarography is most suitable for continuous analysis, successful attempts have been made to analyse continuously effluents from chromatographic columns and paper strips. This combination of polarography and chromatography, called "chromato-polarography", has been recently investigated and exploited by W. Kemula and his co-workers.[23]

In the conventional arrangement used (Fig. 53), the current flowing is measured at a constant applied voltage (corresponding to the limiting current of the substance to be analysed). The chromatographic column (1) is joined to a polarographic vessel (2); a cell with a small volume is preferable. The volume of the effluent from the chromatographic column is measured by a graduated cylinder (3), and the current flowing through the electrolysis cell is plotted against the volume of the effluent. This graph is called a chromatopolarogram (Figs. 54–56). If a recorder with a constant scanning rate and a fast response is available, chromato-polarograms can be recorded instead of plotting graphs point by point.

The chromatography can be carried out using either an elution method, where the analysed mixture is placed on the top of the chromatographic column and the separation is arrived at by additions of a suitable solvent at the top of the column, or by using the frontal method, where the sample is dissolved first in the solvent and the solution of the sample in the solvent is added to the top of the column.

The chromato-polarogram corresponding to the elution method

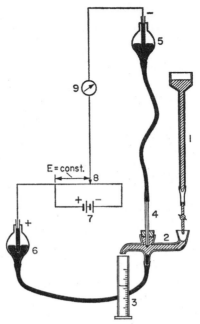

FIG. 53. The chromato-polarographic arrangement.
(1) Column with stopcock; (2) electrolytic vessel; (3) calibrated
receiver; (4), (5) dropping mercury cathode with capillary;
(6) mercury anode; (7) accumulator battery; (8) potentiometer;
(9) galvanometer; according to W. Kemula.

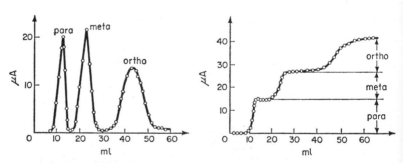

FIG. 54. The chromato-polarographic analysis of isomers of nitro-
anilines by elution (left curve) and frontal (right curve) methods.
Partition system (on rubber): benzene – 0·2 N potassium iodide
in 30 per cent methanol – water solution. According to W. Kemula.

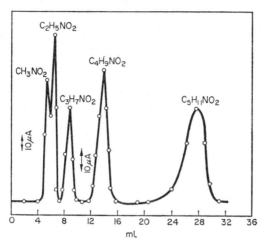

Fig. 55. The chromato-polarographic analysis of an homologous
series of nitro-alkanes.
Partition system (on rubber): heptane – 0·2 M potassium iodide in
50 per cent methanol–water solution. According to W. Kemula.

is given in Fig. 54, left. A single peak corresponds to the elution
of each component from a zone on the column. The area covered
by this peak is a function of the concentration of the compound.

The chromato-polarogram obtained with the frontal technique is
given in Fig. 54 right. Owing to their different partition coefficients,
the particular components of the mixture pass the column at
different rates. This causes a step-wise elution, the height of
each step being proportional to the concentration of a given component. The steps are additive, i.e. when sufficient effluent has
left the column, so that not only the first but also the second
substance is eluted, the limiting current measured corresponds to
the sum of first and second substance.

More precise results can be obtained by measurement of the
step-height in the frontal method, than by measurement of the
surface under a peak in the elution method. However, a greater
amount of substance is required for the former method. In elution
techniques 0·1–0·5 mg sample is usually sufficient. When a
differential method is used for compensating the effect of oxygen
dissolved in the polarographed effluent, as low as 0·004 mg to

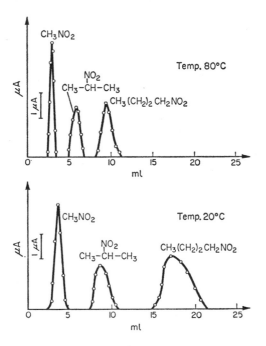

FIG. 56. The influence of temperature on partition.
The chromato-polarographic analysis of a mixture of nitro-aliphatic
compounds on Dowex 50. The percolating liquid is 1 M ammonium
sulphate. According to W. Kemula.

0·01 mg are used, and the error even at these extreme conditions
is no greater than about 10 per cent.

Powdered rubber swollen by a suitable solvent has proved useful
in most separations as a filler for the chromatographic column.
The use of ion-exchange resins, cellulose acetate, some cross-
linked polymers and clathrates has been recently suggested.

The solvent mixtures used consisted most frequently of benzene
or heptane and an aqueous moving phase composed of water, an
organic water-soluble solvent (e.g. methanol, acetone, dioxane or
dimethylformamide) and a 0·1 M to 1·0 M salt (e.g. potassium
iodide or chloride, eventually containing buffer). The presence of
the salt serves two purposes: it plays the role of a supporting

electrolyte for the polarography of the effluent, and it influences adsorption isotherms in such a way that peaks in the elution method are symmetrical, and steps in the frontal method are strictly additive, showing no interaction of the single components. Acidity always plays a role, if the separated substances undergo a proton transfer. Hence, for example, by changing the acidity of the moving phase, even the order of elution of the components of the mixture can be reversed. When ion-exchange resins are used as fillers, separation is affected by salting out and temperature effects (Fig. 56).

The chromato-polarographic technique can be applied successfully to the analysis of mixtures of compounds of identical or very similar half-wave potentials, e.g. position isomers (Fig. 54), straight chain-branched chain isomers (Fig. 56) or homologues (Fig. 55).

In addition to diffusion limiting currents, catalytic currents can also be used for chromato-polarographic separations. Moreover, the surface activity effects which result in the suppression of streaming maxima can also be utilized, for example in the analysis of a mixture of strychnine and brucine.

Indirect methods of polarographic analysis (p. 112) can also be applied. Thus in the separation of amino acids, the chromatographic column was filled with copper phosphate, and the current of the dissolved copper complexes of amino acids was used for the detection of the amino acids in mixtures.

2,4-dinitrophenylhydrazones of aliphatic aldehydes can be separated with rubber as a filler, and by using the system iso-octane – 70% dimethylformamide – 30% water with 0·2 M potassium chloride. The current is measured at −1·3 V.

Chromato-polarography can also be used for the analysis of the effluents from paper chromatograms. Another method[24] used for the evaluation of paper chromatograms, recommends that the paper is placed on a drum of porous material, soaked with potassium chloride and connected to a reference electrode. The indicator electrode is a golden wire and it is placed around a wheel. The moistened chromatographic paper moves slowly between the drum and the wheel, and the current is measured at different positions of the paper.

N

REFERENCES

(1) NEIMAN, M. B. and GERBER, M. I., *Žh. analit. Chim.* **2**, 135 (1947).
(2) PASTERNAK, R., *Helv. Chim. Acta* **30**, 1984 (1947).
(3) ZUMAN, P. and ZINNER, H., *Chem. Ber.*, **95**, 2089 (1962).
(4) GOSMAN, B. A., *Collect. Czechoslov. Chem. Commun.* **7**, 467 (1935).
(5) ONRUST, H. and WÖSTMANN, B., *Recueil Trav. Chim. Pays-Bas* **69**, 1207 (1950).
(6) BORROWS, E. T., HEMS, B. A. and PAGE, J. E., *J. Chem. Soc.* 1949, 204.
(7) ŠANTAVÝ, F., *Collect. Czechoslov. Chem. Commun.* **12**, 422 (1947).
(8) WILLIAMS, K. T., McCOMB, E. A. and POTTER, E. F., *Anal. Chem.* **22**, 1031 (1950).
(9) GORDON, B. E. and JONES, L. C., *Anal. Chem.* **22**, 981 (1950).
(10) SMOLEŃ, I, *Collect. Czechoslov. Chem. Commun.* **2**, 699 (1930).
(11) PROSKE, G., *Z. Unters. Lebensmittel* **71**, 385 (1936).
(12) SAPARA, V. and BITTER, B., *Chem. listy* **43**, 140 (1949).
(13) GNJUBKIN, V. I., DOBRINSKAJA, A. A. and NEIMAN, M. B., *Acta Physicochim. U.S.S.R.* **10**, 701 (1939).
(14) BENESCH, R. and BENESCH, R. E., *Arch. Biochem.* **19**, 35 (1948).
(15) MEITES, L., *Anal. Chem.* **27**, 416 (1955).
(16) HEYROVSKÝ, J. and HASSELBACH, H., *Z. Pflanzenzucht.* **26**, 443 (1943).
(17) ZUMAN, P. and ERBEN, J., Unpublished results.
(18) ZUMAN, P., Unpublished results.
(19) KOŠTÍŘ, J. and RÁBEK, V., *Biochem. Biophys. Acta* **8**, 210 (1950).
(20) MICHL, J., Unpublished results.
(21) ZUMAN, P. and HORÁK, V., *Collect. Czechoslov. Chem. Commun.* **26**, 176 (1961).
(22) PALEČEK, E., *Collect. Czechoslov. Chem. Commun.* **25**, 2283 (1960).
(23) KEMULA, W., Chromato-Polarography, in *Progress in Polarography* (P. Zuman, I. M. Kolthoff, editors), Interscience, New York (1962), where previous references are given.
(24) LANGER, A., *Anal. Chem.* **28**, 426 (1956).

# CHAPTER VIII

# PRACTICAL APPLICATIONS

POLAROGRAPHY has been successfully applied to both basic research and practical analysis. The possibilities of application to the solution of problems of theoretical interest are treated in Chapters IX–XI. This Chapter gives selected examples to show how polarography has been successfully used for practical problems. Limited space, however, prevents an exhaustive survey to be made. The number of papers devoted to practical applications of organic polarography increased substantially recently, as can be seen from the fact that an exhaustive description of applications of polarography in medicine, biochemistry and pharmacy needed already a substantial volume[1]. A selection was thus necessary, and subjectivity of choice was inevitable. The aim of the choice was to give the analyst an insight as to how his particular problem could perhaps be solved, although similar problems have yet to be investigated. The subject matter has been arranged according to the field of application and the material to be analysed.

## 8.1. PHARMACY[1-4]

The greatest percentage of papers devoted to applied organic polarography describe applications to the problems of pharmaceutical analysis. This is due to several factors: (i) Numerous physiologically active substances are polarographically active, or so chemically reactive that they can be transformed into electroactive substances. (ii) Pharmaceutical preparations are in most instances relatively simple, pure, well-defined mixtures of an approximately known composition. (iii) The preparation of the sample in a great number of examples consists of simply diluting a liquid sample with an appropriate supporting electrolyte, or of dissolving a tablet in a solution. (iv) Insoluble portions of tablets and other additives do not usually interfere. Often filtration or other separation techniques are unnecessary and, after settling of the fillers, the supernatant liquid is pipetted off. (v) Active substances are in the dispensing forms often present in low concentrations. (vi) Detection of traces of impurities, often toxic, is of importance. (vii) The sensitivity of the method allows small samples of expensive drugs to be used. (viii) The speed of analysis enables production control. (ix) Major constituents can sometimes be determined in the absence of other methods.

A great number of examples of the applications of organic polarography to pharmacy have already been quoted,* viz. determinations of nicotinamide, dulcin, phenacetin, Neoeserine, phenobarbital, morphine, estrone, heroin, codeine, rutin, quercetin, cephaeline, antipyrine, Intercain, procainpenicillin, cardiac glycosides, ascorbic acid, pyridoxal, ketosteroids, carotene, m-aminophenol in p-aminosalicylic acid, cardiazole, thiobarbiturates, alkaloids, salicylate, Irgapyrin, barbiturates, thiamine, tartrates, glycerol-phosphates, diamidines, streptomycin, p-aminosalicylic acid, tocopherol, sulpha-drugs, unsaturated terpenes, peroxides in ether, santonine, cuminaldehyde etc. Thus only a few more examples will be quoted.

*Purity of chloramphenicol.*[5] The analysis of technical chloramphenicol (I) for the ketocompound (II) concentration is of importance because II possesses some physiological side effects.

$$O_2N-\langle\phantom{x}\rangle-CH-CH-CH_2OH$$
$$\phantom{O_2N-\langle\phantom{x}\rangle-}OH\phantom{x}NHCOCHCl_2$$

(I)

$$O_2N-\langle\phantom{x}\rangle-CO-CH-CH_2OH$$
$$\phantom{O_2N-\langle\phantom{x}\rangle-CO-}NHCOCHCl_2$$

(II)

---

* The examples are quoted in the same sequence as they were discussed in Chapters VI and VII. Exact location can be found in the index.

In the determination 20 mg of chloramphenicol are dissolved in 10 ml. of a phosphate pH 7·0 buffer containing 10 per cent of ethanol. In this solution the wave of ketone II, which is about 150 mV more positive than the wave of chloramphenicol I, is best separated by employing the derivative circuit of Vogel and Říha (Fig. 57).

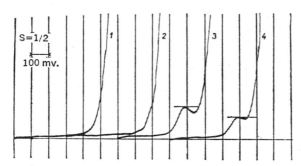

FIG. 57. Determination of traces of the toxic ketone analogue in chloramphenicol.
10 ml. phosphate buffer pH 7·0, 20 mg sample of: (1) D-chloramphenicol (Parke, Davis); (2) racemic chloramphenicol recrystallized from water; (3) and (4) samples of racemic chloramphenicol before crystallization. Derivative circuit according to J. Vogel and J. Říha: measuring resistance 400 $\Omega$, derivative condenser 2500 $\mu$F, damping condenser 500 $\mu$F. Curves starting at —0·1 V, S.C.E., 100 mV/absc., 70 mV/min, full scale sensitivity 1·2 $\mu$A. After E. Knobloch and E. Svátek.

*Thiomersalate.*[6] Phenylmercury and its derivatives are reduced in two one-electron steps. These waves can be used for the analysis of Thiomersalate (ethylmercurithiosalicylate).

*Procedure.* Add the sample containing 0·1–1·0 mg of Thiomersalate to 1 ml. of concentrated hydrochloric acid and 1 ml. of 0·1 per cent solution of gelatin. Dilute the solution to 10 ml. with water, deoxygenate and record the curve at about —0·5 V.

*Phenolphthalein.* There are two methods for the determination of phenolphthalein in emulsions.
The first[7] procedure is:

Mix 10 ml. of emulsion containing 30 mg of phenolphthalein in a 50 ml. flask with 30 ml. of 96 per cent ethanol. After the two layers have separated make up the solution to the mark with ethanol and mix. After settling add

25 ml. of the clear ethanol solution, containing the phenolphthalein extracted from the emulsion, to 55 ml. of 25 per cent solution of hydrochloric acid. After the addition of 1 ml. of an aqueous 0·1 per cent solution of basic fuchsine, dilute the solution to 100 ml. with water and obtain a polarogram.

### Procedure for the second method[8]:

Add the same amount of emulsion in a separatory funnel to 20 ml. of warm glacial acetic acid. Shake the mixture for 5 min, separate the lower layer and transfer to a 50-ml. flask and further extract the remaining oil and emulsifier with two 10-ml. portions of warm glacial acetic acid. Make up the combined extracts to 50 ml. with acetic acid, and transfer an aliquot corresponding to 1–5 mg of phenolphthalein into another separatory funnel. Make up with glacial acetic acid to 2·5 ml., add 3·0 ml. of 5 M sodium acetate and dilute with water to 20 ml. Extract the solution with 20 ml. of petroleum ether to separate the oil dissolved in acetic acid. Separate the lower aqueous phase and, after deaeration, record the polarographic curve.

The determination in tablets or in chocolates can be carried out in a similar way.

*Barbiturate* preparations can be determined[9–11] by employing a dropping mercury electrode with $1 \times 10^{-4}$ to $1 \times 10^{-5}$ M solutions* in 0·05 M borax. The anodic waves corresponding to the formation of a salt with mercury are recorded. A 100-fold excess of chloride ions did not interfere in this determination.

Barbital and other 5,5-dialkylbarbituric acids gave the well-developed waves, whereas the wave of phenobarbital is ill-developed. The determination of barbiturates is prevented by substitution of hydrogen in the NH group as in N-methyl-5,5-phenylethylbarbituric acid.

The same electrode process was used in oscillographic polarography for the analysis of biological materials, mainly in toxicology.[12] Because the detection of barbiturates is carried out after extraction and paper chromatography, the speed of the final examination is not the limiting factor, and it seems that application of classical polarography would be at least equivalent to the suggested method.

---

* With a streaming electrode in 0·05 M borax and 1 M potassium nitrate the range can be extended to $1 \times 10^{-3}$ to $1 \times 10^{-5}$ M.

*Thiobarbiturates* such as Pentothal or Nesdonal are best determined[13] by dissolving the sample directly in 0·1 N sodium hydroxide without heating, so that the final concentration is below $7 \times 10^{-4}$ M. The anodic wave of the mercury salt formation is recorded (Fig. 58).

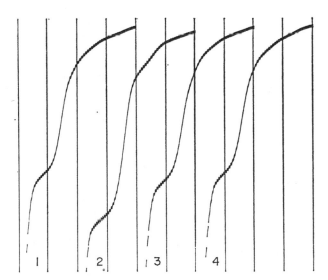

FIG. 58. Anodic waves of thiobarbiturates.
0·1 N NaOH, different pharmaceutical preparations: (1) Trapanal; (2) Thiogenal 16·5 mg/100 ml.; (3) Baytinal 12 mg/100 ml.; (4) Inactin 11·0 mg/100 ml. Curves recorded from negative to positive potentials, mercurous sulphate electrode, 200 mV/absc, $t_1 = 2·4$ sec, $m = 2·6$ mg/sec, full scale sensitivity 2·3 $\mu$A.

*Multivitamin preparations.* Most water-soluble vitamins are polarographically active and can be determined in simple preparations without any difficulties. Difficulty is given, however, with complex multivitamin preparations. In a preparation containing in 1·0 g (in addition to fillers) 2500 I.U. of vitamin A, 200 I.U. of vitamin D, 1 mg of vitamin $B_1$, 1·5 mg of vitamin $B_2$, 1 $\mu$g of vitamin $B_{12}$, 0·5 mg of pteroylglutamic acid, 0·5 mg of calcium pantothenate, 10 mg of niacinamide, 37·5 mg of vitamin C, 1 mg of vitamins E and 0·2 mg of vitamins K, the analyses were carried out by preparing, in a phosphate pH 6·8 buffer, a 1·0 per cent solution of the preparation.[14] The anodic wave at −0·05 V corresponds to ascorbic acid, the cathodic wave at −0·47 V to riboflavine and the cathodic wave at −1·2 V to pteroylglutamic acid. As the wave of the latter is sometimes affected by the filler, the analysis of pteroylglutamic acid can be repeated in a solution containing 5 per cent of the preparation in 0·1 N hydrochloric acid. The cathodic wave at −0·41 V is measured.

In the determination of 2-methyl-1,4-naphthohydroquinone-diacetate a hydrolysis must precede the polarographic electrolysis. Under the conditions used for hydrolysis, the naphthohydroquinone formed is further decomposed and the conditions of hydrolysis must be strictly controlled. A 10 per cent solution of the preparation in a 0·025 M borate pH 8·5 buffer, is heated for 20 min at 100°C and the oxidation-reduction wave at −0·33 V is measured.

Thiamine is determined by employing a catalytic wave in an ammoniacal cobaltous solution. Because the height of the catalytic wave decreases with time (about 1 per cent per minute), the curve is either recorded after a short constant period after mixing, or after several time intervals and extrapolated to zero time. The height of the catalytic wave reaches a limiting value with increasing concentration, and it is consequently important to work within the suggested concentration range. In the suggested procedure, 2 ml. of a 10 per cent solution of the preparation is added to 1 ml. of each of 0·01 M cobaltous chloride, 1 M ammonium chloride and 1 M ammonia, and made up to 10 ml. with water. The reagents are deoxygenated in advance and the catalytic wave at −1·5 V is measured.

To determine niacinamide, a polarogram is obtained of a 2 per cent solution of the preparation in 0·1 N sodium hydroxide. In all determinations the evaluation is carried out by using the "added standard" method.

*Strychnine.* In addition to the numerous alkaloids that can be directly or indirectly determined polarographically, an indirect method based on nitration has been recently described for strychnine.[15] The resulting 2,4-dinitrostrychnine is reduced in alkaline media in two waves at −0·64 V and −0·79 V, which correspond to a reduction of one nitro-group to the hydroxylamino, and of the other to an amino group.

*Procedure.* Dissolve 0·01–0·5 mg of strychnine in 1 ml. of nitric acid ($d$ = 1·41), add 2 ml. of water and warm the mixture in a closed test tube on a boiling water-bath for 20 min. Cool the solution, make alkaline with 8 ml. of 2·5 M potassium hydroxide and after deoxygenation record the reduction waves of the dinitroproduct.

*Note.* In brucine mixtures a preliminary separation with paper chromatography is necessary.

*Ascaridol.* Several ketonic and aldehydic terpenes have been determined polarographically in ethereal oils, seeds, drug portions and in other materials. Recently, interest has been shown in the determination of the terpene peroxide, ascaridol. The determination[16] consists of dissolving 100 mg of the oil in 100 ml. of ethanol, and mixing an aliquot portion with the same volume of 0·2 N lithium sulphate. The wave at −0·9 V gives the content of ascaridol, e.g. in *Oleum Chenopodii* or in *Oleum Boldo.*

*Glycyrrhizic acid.* The glycoside, composed of glycyrrhetic acid (III) as an aglycone linked to two molecules of hexuronic acid, can be determined in *Succus liquiritae.*[17]

III

*Procedure.* Dissolve 1 g of sample by boiling in a 50 per cent water–dioxane mixture. Add 80 ml. of 3 per cent sulphuric acid and reflux the solution for 3 hr. Upon cooling, a precipitate of glycyrrhetic acid (III) forms. Add 50 ml. of chloroform and reflux the mixture for another 15 min. Then transfer the mixture to a percolator and continue the extraction for 1·5 hr. Cool, separate the chloroform layer and dilute to 100 ml. with chloroform. Evaporate a 25-ml. aliquot to dryness and dissolve the residue in ethanol and adjust the volume of ethanol to 25 ml. Mix a 3 ml. aliquot with 7 ml. of ethanol, 5 ml. of 0·5 M acetate pH 5·0 buffer and 1 ml. of a saturated solution of potassium chloride. Dilute to 25 ml., deaerate and record the waves at −1·5 V.

*Pollen allergens* can be determined[18] from the catalytic wave which these proteins give in ammoniacal cobaltic solutions. To express the content of pollen allergens in different preparations it is necessary to choose, as a standard, the allergen from one plant.

## 8.2. MEDICINE AND BIOCHEMISTRY[1, 19]

Other fields in which polarography has found numerous and successful applications are medical research, medical practice and several branches of pure and applied biochemistry. In addition to research studies, it is mainly clinical chemistry,* toxicology and industrial hygiene, where polarography is most frequently used. The medical research and biochemical studies were devoted to the mechanisms of biochemically important reactions, both *in vivo* and *in vitro*, to the studies of metabolism and the administration of drugs etc.

Several examples of the applications of polarography in these fields have been already mentioned in Chapters VI and VII, viz. determinations of benzene, toluene, naphthalene and phenols in the atmosphere, breath, blood or urine, of amino acids (with particular interest to tyrosine, tryptophane, phenylalanine, histidine and histamine), of ketoacids, ketosteroids, carbon disulphide in air and blood, ethanol, acetoin, sugars and morphine in blood, of lactic acid, mandelic acid in bile and urine, adrenaline and thyroxine in iodinated proteins and last, but not least, of thiol compounds, both soluble and bound in biological materials. A few further examples will be given here.

*Drugs in biological fluids.* An example of the determination of drugs in biological fluids, is the analysis of the anti-tubercular drug 2-ethyl-4-thiocarbamidopyridine.[20] In the blood serum of rats, rabbits, horses, and humans, and in cerebrospinal fluid it

---

* It may be noted that in Czechoslovakia the application of polarography to clinical methods is probably much more common than in other countries. Routine polarographic examinations are regularly carried out in most of the larger hospitals of that country.

is possible without the addition of any supporting electrolyte, to record directly the waves of the drug at −0·8 V. The concentration range available was 0·2 μg/ml. to 5·0 μg/ml. Urine was acidified with a 5 per cent solution of glacial acetic acid. The concentration range here was 5–30 μg/ml. In this instance the presence of proteins did not affect the reduction wave, but it has already been mentioned (p. 177) that interference is given with other substances.

*Toxic substances.* Among other toxic substances, several nitro-compounds and nitrosamines have been determined in the blood and urine of individuals exposed to such toxic substances. As an example, the determination of 2,4-dinitrophenol[21] in the urine of humans working in the production of picric acid can be mentioned.

*Procedure.* Acidify 1 ml. of urine with 5 ml. of a 2 per cent solution of hydrochloric acid and extract with 5 ml. of ether. Shake for 5 min and separate the extract. Treat the extract with 5 ml. of 0·5 N sodium hydroxide and remove the ether on a steam bath. Cool the solution and carry out a polarographic electrolysis, but bear in mind the changes of polynitrobenzenoid substances in alkaline media.

*Proline and hydroxyproline* present together in amino acid mixtures obtained from the acidic hydrolysis of proteins, were analysed during an investigation into the role of hydroxyproline in the synthesis of collageneous proteins.[22]

*Procedure.* Treat the mixture of amino acids formed in the hydrolysis of proteins with nitrous acid. In this treatment the amino acids with a primary nitro-group are transformed into hydroxyacids, but proline and hydroxyproline are transformed into corresponding nitrosamines. Remove the excess of nitrous acid by the addition of urea. In one aliquot, and after diluting, determine the sum of nitrosamines polarographically. In another aliquot carry out a hydrolysis with 10–11 N hydrochloric acid at 25°C. Under these conditions N-nitrosohydroxyproline is hydrolysed about 30 times faster than N-nitrosoproline, and thus it is possible after 30 min to record a wave predominantly proportional to N-nitrosoproline. From the difference determine the content of hydroxyproline (Fig. 59).

*Adenine* shows in 0·1 N perchloric acid-potassium perchlorate, a reduction wave at −1·1 V. This enables the determination of

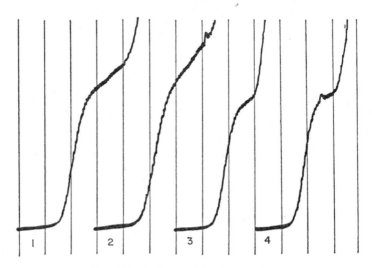

FIG. 59. Proline and hydroxyproline.
$4 \times 10^{-4}$ M depolarizer, excess of nitrites removed by addition of urea. (1) and (2) nitroso hydroxyproline, (3) and (4) nitrosoproline. (1) and (3): the nitroso derivative prepared by nitrosation of the aminoacid; (2) and (4): curves obtained with solutions prepared from synthetic samples. N.C.E., 200 mV/absc., $t_1 = 3\cdot5$ sec, full scale sensitivity 6 $\mu$A.

this purine derivative in hydrolysates from ribo- and deoxy-ribonucleic acids.[23] Guanine, guanosine, guanylic acid, cytidine and cytidylic acid are not reducible under these conditions and do not interfere. In the determination in tissues, such as pancreas, the adenine must be separated from interfering compounds in the hydrolysate by precipitation with silver oxide.[24] Blood must be deproteinated with trichloroacetic acid before the treatment with silver oxide.[25]

*Ketosteroids.* Several methods for the determination of different steroid hormones in biological materials have been described.[1] A simple method for the determination of 17-ketosteroids in urine[26] will be given here.

*Procedure.* Hydrolyse 10 ml. of urine with 3 ml. of concentrated hydrochloric acid on a boiling water-bath for 10 min. Cool the solution rapidly and shake twice for 3 min with 20 ml. of freshly distilled ether. Wash the combined extracts with 40 ml. of 2 N sodium hydroxide and twice with 40 ml. of distilled water. Evaporate the mixture to dryness on a water-bath, and to the residue add a 10 per cent solution of Girard's reagent D in glacial acetic acid, in an amount corresponding to 0·1 ml. for each milli-gram of the 17-ketosteroids present. Heat the mixture on a steam bath for 3 min. Cool and add 0·5 ml. of aldehyde-free ethanol and 0·25 N sodium hydroxide (in an amount corresponding to 3·2 ml. for each 0·1 ml. of the previously added Girard's reagent D). Regulate the pH-value to 4·7 and dilute the solution to 5 ml. with water. Deoxygenate and record the wave (Fig. 60).

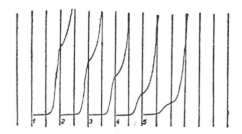

Fig. 60. Dehydroisoandrosterone dimethylglycylhydrazone. Preparation of the electrolysed solution described in text. Con-centration of dehydroisoandrosterone: (1) $2·4 \times 10^{-4}$ M; (2) $1·8 \times 10^{-4}$ M; (3) $1·2 \times 10^{-4}$ M; (4) $0·6 \times 10^{-4}$ M; (5) $0·3 \times 10^{-4}$ M. Curves starting at $-1·0$ V, S.C.E., 200 mV/absc., $t_1 = 3·3$ sec, $m = 1·9$ mg/sec, full scale sensitivity $3·4 \mu A$.

*Note*. Occasionally a wave appears for some other compound in the urine at a more positive potential than that for the dimethylglycylhydrazone of the 17-ketosteroids. This compound can be removed by permanganate oxidation, but the procedure is lengthy and a measurement of the hydrazone wave from the inflexion point between the two waves is advocated. An accuracy of within 5 per cent can be obtained by this empirical method of measurement.

*Acetaldehydogenic* and *formaldehydogenic steroids*, on the $C_{21}$ hydroxygroups in the side chain, can be determined after oxidation with periodic acid to acetaldehyde or formaldehyde,[27] as with other polyols (p. 132). The aldehydes formed are determined in the oxidized urinary extracts, either after microdistillation or after reducing the excess of periodic acid with lithium bisulphite.

*Brdička catalytic wave.* The Brdička protein reaction is perhaps one of the most important among the polarographic methods used

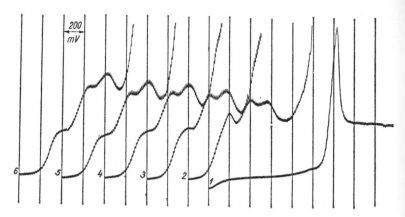

FIG. 61. Catalytic double-wave of proteins.
0·1 M Ammonium chloride, 0·1 M ammonia, 0·001 M hexamo-cobaltichloride, human blood serum added in concentration: (1) 0; (2) 0·1%; (3) 0·2%; (4) 0·3%; (5) 0·4%; (6) 0·5%. Curves starting at −0·8 V, mercury pool electrode, 200 mV/absc., $t_1 = 3·0$ sec, $m = 2·2$ mg/sec, full scale sensitivity 60 μA.

in practical clinical analysis.* It is based on a catalytic wave which is observed when a protein solution is added to a buffered ammoniacal solution of cobalt salts (Fig. 61). The wave has been obtained in materials containing usually sulphur, low-molecular weight compounds, peptides (such as oxytocine) or proteins. As the presence and the state of thiol groups in blood and other biological materials often reflects the pathological changes in organisms, the wave has been frequently used for diagnostic purposes, even though the mechanism of the hydrogen evolution is not yet fully understood. Of the various test forms which enable one to follow changes in different fractions of serum proteins, the following modification was recommended[28] as the most sensitive to the pathological changes in serum.

*Procedure.* Add at room temperature 1 ml. of 0·1 N potassium hydroxide to 0·4 ml. of serum, obtained by centrifuging non-hemolysed blood taken from the vein after fasting (in the morning). Allow the mixture to stand for 45 min. The denaturation occurs during this time. Then deproteinate

* At least in Czechoslovakia.

the solution by the addition of 1 ml. of a 20 per cent solution of sulpho-salicylic acid, to precipitate the high-molecular weight albumin and globu-lin fractions. Shake the mixture vigorously in order to obtain a homogen-eous suspension. After 10 min separate the precipitated blood proteins from the solution containing low-molecular weight proteins, by filtering through a hardened filter paper.

The duration of the filtration should be approximately constant for all samples compared, say 10 or 20 min and the resulting filtrate must be clear.

Add 0·4 ml. of the filtrate to 4 ml. of cobaltic solution, consisting of 0·001 M $Co(NH_3)_6Cl_3$, 0·1 N ammonium chloride and 0·1 N ammonia. After mixing, transfer the solution to a simple electrolysis vessel (test tube) and polarograph the solution, open to the atmosphere, from −0·8 V against the mercury pool electrode.

*Notes.* (1) The sensitivity of the recording system should be chosen so that the height of the wave corresponding to the reduction of cobaltous ions (the second step, at −1·0V) is about one fifth of the full scale deflection.

(2) The height of the catalytic double wave is measured from the diffusion current, corresponding to the reduction of divalent cobalt, to the highest point of the double-wave. In some instances however, especially at higher concentra-tions of proteins, the surface active substances present suppress not only the streaming maximum, but also the limiting current of divalent cobalt. Therefore, for each series of serum analyses, it is always better to record separately the curve for the blank cobaltic solution without protein, and to take the limiting diffusion current of the cobalt wave as the zero line for all subsequently recorded protein curves.

(3) For each polarographic equipment, i.e. capillary, galvanometer, mer-cury pressure etc. a standardization must be first carried out by the analysis of at least 30 sera of clinically healthy individuals. From the measurement of heights of particular catalytic waves a mean value can be determined for the height of normal serum. The same procedure, the same filter paper and filtering arrangements must be used for all measurements that are compared because different filter papers adsorb proteins differently.

(4) The height of the catalytic wave of a clinical case is compared with the height obtained for normal sera. The pathological increase of the filtrate double wave is best expressed by the ratio of its height, to the height of the double wave for the average normal serum.

(5) Hemolysed blood interferes in the determination and older sera give low values for the height of the catalytic wave. When smaller volumes of blood (e.g. 0·1 ml.) are analysed, filtration is replaced by centrifugation.

It was at first assumed that an increase of the catalytic double-wave in this so called "Brdička filtrate test" is characteristic of cancer diseases. Later, however, it was recognized that the situa-tion was complicated by the fact that whereas about 90 per cent of the cancer cases studied showed an elevated catalytic wave (only small nonmetastatic skin tumors give invalid results), several other diseases, mainly accompanied with fever and inflammatory diseases, also showed an increased reaction. Hepatitis and some diseases of the liver cause a decrease in the filtrate reaction.

When other diseases are eliminated by clinical observations, the filtrate reaction together with other tests can point to malignancy. If an increase in the filtrate reaction, repeated at definite time intervals, is observed, suspicion of cancer is more likely. Advantages of the Brdička filtrate reaction are simplicity, objectivity, the small amount of the sample used and the independence on biological standards. On the other hand, the reaction is sometimes positive only in an advanced stage of the disease. This prevents the detection in early stages when the patient can be easily treated. Thus the main importance of the Brdička filtrate reaction is in the control of the course of the disease, and of the effectivity of the treatment when cancer is once diagnosed. After an operation or irradiation, a decrease in the height of the catalytic wave shows if the treatment has been successful.

In general medicine the Brdička filtrate reaction possesses another important function: every substantial increase above or decrease below the normal level shows pathological changes in the organism (Fig. 62). For diagnosis it is thus of the utmost importance, comparable with the classical sedimentation test but more specific.

The increase of the filtrate reaction is, according to our present state of knowledge, due to the multiplication of certain fractions of serum proteins, called mucoproteins and possible others.

In a serum, fractionated by paper electrophoresis, the electropherogram can be evaluated using a polarographic method if a separate calibration is constructed for each of the separated protein fractions.[29]

## 8.3. AGRICULTURAL AND FOOD CHEMISTRY

Another field where the advantages of polarography have been exploited, viz. that its techniques are often undisturbed by the presence of biological material, is in agricultural and food chemistry. This includes also the analysis of insecticides, fungicides and rodenticides, and recently also of antibiotics both in commercial preparations and in residues. The possibilities of determinations of several vitamins, of acetoin and diacetyl in butter, malic

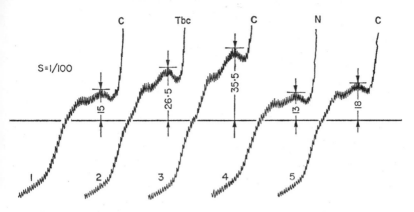

FIG. 62. Brdička filtrate reaction for human serum of five persons. 0·1 N Ammonia, 0·1 N ammonium chloride, 0·001 M hexamocobaltichloride, filtrate after treatment with sulphosalicyclic acid (see text) added. Serum of people ill with: (1) *Carcinom portionis vaginalis;* (2) *Fungus genus sinistri* (tuberculosis); (3) and (5) *Carcinom ventriculi;* (4) normal serum. Curves starting at —0·8 V, mercury pool electrode, 200 mV/absc., full scale sensitivity 76 μA. After R. Brdička.

acid in alcoholic beverages, of rodenticide Warfarin, of capsaicine, fructose in fruit, and acetaldehyde in spirit have already been discussed in Chapters VI and VII. Some additional examples are given here:

*Carbonyl compounds in beverages.* Several aldehydes and ketones have been determined in various beverages, e.g. benzaldehyde in alcoholic beverages (mainly fruit wines) during fermentation processes.[30]

*Procedure.* Dilute 50 ml. of wine with 25 ml. of water, steam distil, and collect the first 50 ml. of the distillate. Add to a 15-ml. aliquot portion, 1·0 ml. of a 0·1 per cent solution of gelatin and 14·0 ml. of phosphate pH 7·0 buffer and record the curve at —1·3 V.

*Saccharin in foods* can be determined[31] after homogenizing the sample in a Waring Blendor with water and excess of lead acetate to remove oxalates.

o

*Procedure.* Filter off the precipitate, acidify the filtrate with hydro-chloric acid and extract the saccharin with three portions of 80 ml. of ether. Wash with 10 ml. of water and evaporate the combined extracts to dryness. Take up the residue in 50 ml. of a 0·1 per cent solution of sodium carbonate, and add a 5-ml. aliquot of this solution to 10 ml. of 0·05 M hydrochloric acid and 0·05 M potassium chloride.

*Note.* If ethanol or sugar is present, but not an excess of organic acid, the extraction is unnecessary and the sample can be analysed directly after acidifying with hydrochloric acid.[32]

*Ascorbic acid in fruit and vegetables* has been determined success-fully in the juice.[33,34]

*Procedure.* Simply strain the juice[33] in soft juicy fruits such as tomatoes, currants, gooseberries, raspberries, strawberries, melons and citrus fruits through a hydrophilic gauze into a 25-ml. beaker. Deoxygenate 5 ml. of 1 M acetate pH 4·7 buffer in a Kalousek vessel and add 5 ml. of the juice. Remove the rest of the oxygen and record the anodic wave of ascorbic acid.

*Note.* Juice strained from fruit that is easily spoilt, as for example that from raspberries, must not be allowed to stand longer than 10 min. In some instances a wave at more negative potentials is observed, but this is caused by thiol compounds and does not interfere.

For the determination in hard fruits and vegetables, such as cauliflower, kohlrabi, carrots and cabbage grinding is unavoidable.

*Procedure.* Pipette 100 ml. of 3 per cent meta-phosphoric acid into a Waring Blendor and remove the oxygen. Add 20 g of the sample and homogenize for 1–2 min in a carbon dioxide atmosphere. Deoxygenate 6 ml. of a 1 M acetate pH 4·7 buffer in a Kalousek vessel and add 4 ml. of the liquid homogenate. Finally record the anodic wave of ascorbic acid.

*Note.* The recorded waves of ascorbic acid (Fig. 63) are sometimes ill-developed. This is often due to the surface active substances (proteins etc.) present in the juice or homogenate. A greater dilution (smaller sample) is recommended, as the effect of these surfactans is often dependent on their absolute concentration and not on the ratio of concentrations of surfactans and ascorbic acid. Excess of chlorides, if present, can be removed with thallous sulphate.

*Thiol substances in fruit and vegetables.* Soluble thiols, usually denoted as glutathione, are determined[33] in soft, juicy, fleshy fruits by pressing through surgical gauze, and are polarographed either directly (because the juice is usually well buffered and

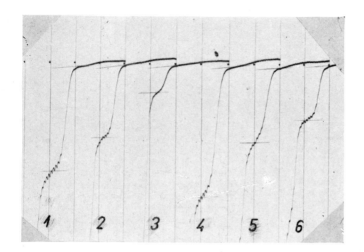

FIG. 63. Changes in ascorbic acid concentration during preservation process.
10 ml. Acetate buffer pH 4·7, 0·5 g sample of reddish paprika.
Paprika: (1) Before preservation; (2) crushed fruits; (3) crushed
fruits extracted; (4) extracted juice evaporated (thickened) under
reduced pressure (at 600 mm Hg) in the carbon dioxide atmosphere;
(5) fruits instead of crushing were treated with steam in carbon
dioxide atmosphere at 100°C for 15 min; (6) these fruits were
extracted and pressed and the juice analysed. (1) The fruits were
ground with buffer and with quartz sand; (2) and (5) the mass was
extracted with buffer; (3), (4) and (6) the extract or juice was
diluted with buffer. The process used in (5) and (6) is superior
to that used in (2) and (3). During heating in (4) ascorbic acid-like
substances are formed. Curves recorded from negative to positive
potentials, mercurous sulphate electrode, 200 mV/absc., full scale
sensitivity, 7·2 μA.

conducting) or after mixing with an acetate pH 4·7 buffer. The wave at potentials about 0·3 V more negative than that for ascorbic acid is recorded (Fig. 64).

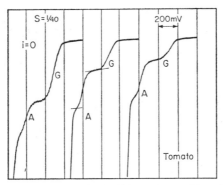

FIG. 64. Determination of thiols (G) and ascorbic acid (A) in the tomato juice.
The juice obtained from different parts of one tomato mixed with equal volume of acetate buffer pH 4·7. Curves recorded from negative to positive potentials, mercurous sulphate electrode, 200 mV/absc., full scale sensitivity 8·0 $\mu$A.

For the determination in hard fruits and vegetables a careful grinding procedure is necessary.

*Procedure.* Transfer 1–10 g of the sample to a small mortar and mix with the same amount of quartz sand. Place the mortar at the bottom of a deep vessel and during the grinding sweep out with carbon dioxide. Add to the mortar 20 ml. of 3 per cent deoxygenated metaphosphoric acid and grind the sample for 2–3 min. Allow the mixture to settle down for 1 min under a constant stream of carbon dioxide. Deoxygenate, in a Kalousek vessel, 6 ml. of an acetate pH 4·7 buffer and add 4 ml. of the supernatant liquid from the mortar. Record the anodic wave.

*Note.* The homogenizer could not be used owing to the ease of oxidation, even in a carbon dioxide atmosphere.

*Fat oxidation.* Peroxides formed in fats can be followed by dissolving 0·01–0·40 g of the oil (so as to give complete solution) in 100 ml. of 0·3 M lithium chloride in a methanol–benzene 1 : 1 mixture.[35–37]

*Insecticides, pesticides, fungicides, rodenticides and antibiotics.*[38] Several compounds belonging to these groups have been analysed polarographically. Perhaps the greatest attention was paid to the determination of γ-hexachlorocyclohexane (Gammexane, HCH, BHC, Hexachlorane, Lindane etc.). From the various methods suggested, the analysis of Lindane-Kerosene[39] will be given here. In this example a suitable detergent such as polyethylene glycol or sorbitol esters must be used.

*Procedure.* Add the sample of Lindane-Kerosene to 5 ml. of a detergent solution consisting of 16 g of the detergent, 4 g of cyclohexanol and 2 g of sodium sulphite in 100 ml. of water. Shake the mixture in a closed flask until a homogeneous solution is obtained. Mix the resulting solution with 5 ml. of 0·2 M potassium chloride and again shake for 1 min. After 20 min analyse an aliquot portion polarographically and record the wave at −1·4 V.

Technical benzene hexachloride contains in addition to γ-hexachlorocyclohexane, the other isomers of hexachlorocyclohexane (which do not interfere, as their half-wave potentials are about 0·5 V more negative), heptachlorocyclohexanes, and octachlorocyclohexane. These latter compounds interfere because they are reduced in indistinct waves at potentials more positive than that for the gamma isomer. The measurement of the wave-height of Gammexane is thus made difficult. The solution of this problem has been attempted, either by using empirical methods of measurement of the wave-height (graphical extrapolations, measurements at two selected potentials etc.) or by using the different rates of dehydrochlorination in alkaline media. An original solution of the problem[40] suggests a correction obtained from a polarographic comparison of two saturated solutions of γ-hexachlorocyclohexane. One solution is saturated with the pure isomer and the other solution contains a known amount of a technical sample, to which sufficient pure γ-hexachlorocyclohexane was added to saturate the solution. This solution contains the impurities in a known quantity of the technical sample and the current of these impurities can be measured and subtracted in analysed samples.

Another insecticide, *o,o*-dimethyl-2,2,2-trichloro-1-hydroxy-ethylphosphonate, currently known as Bayer L 13/59 or Dipterex, can be determined in fly bait formulations.[41]

*Procedure.* Dissolve a sufficient amount of the sample in water so that 1 ml. of the solution contains about 1 mg of the insecticide. Shake the solution intermittently for 1 hr and centrifuge if necessary. Transfer 20 ml. of the clear solution to a 100 ml. flask, add 20 ml. of 0·1 M potassium chloride and 2 ml. of a 0·1 per cent gelatin solution and dilute to the mark. Record the wave at −0·68 V in an aliquot of the solution.

In the determination of the fungicide pentachloronitrobenzene in forage[42] the chemical is extracted using Skellysolve B. The extract is filtered and dried, and part of the extractives are removed by freezing and absorption on Attaclay. Chromatography of the concentrated extract on Florisil removes the remainder of the interfering substances. After chromatography, the solvent is evaporated and the residue dissolved in propyl alcohol. An equal volume of 0·04 M acetate buffer is added and the wave at −0·47 V is recorded.

Parathione (o,o-diethyl-o,p-nitrophenylthiphosphate) similarly can be determined[43] by using the wave of the nitro-group (at −0·39 V in 0·1 N acetic acid), in commercial powders after extraction with acetone.

Nitrofurazone (5-nitro-2-furanaldehyde semicarbazone) is added as a bacteriostaticum to chicken feeds.

*Procedure.* For feeds[44] containing more than 10 mg of nitrofurazone in 100 g, extract overnight 1 g of the sample with 5 ml. of ethanol. Filter the mixture and extract twice more with 3 ml. ethanol portions for 5–10 min. Dilute the combined ethanol extracts to 10 ml. with ethanol. Dilute a 3-ml. aliquot to 10 ml. with an acetate pH 4·7 buffer and polarograph the solution. Filter turbid solutions on a Schleicher & Schuel No. 589² filter paper. For samples containing less than 10 mg of nitrofurazone in 100 g partly distil off the ethanol from the combined extracts, so that the final volume is 3 ml. Dilute to 10 ml. with an acetate pH 4·7 buffer and record the polarographic curve.

## 8.4. PURITY OF TECHNICAL PRODUCTS

Relatively little attention has been paid to the possibilities of utilizing polarography for the analysis of organic technical products. It must be mentioned that the scarcity of the published data is added to by the relative reluctance of industrial chemists to publish. The analysis of mixtures of amines, determination of nitrilotriacetic acid and other amines in technical ethylenediaminetetraacetic acid, and of pentoses and pentosans in cellulose have already been described in Chapter VI. A few other examples are given here.

*Unsaturated hydrocarbons.* Styrene is determined in styrene fractions of crude benzene[45] by dissolving about 0·1 ml. of the fraction in 1 ml. of 15 per cent ethanol. After the addition of 1 ml. of a 7·4 per cent solution of tetrabutylammonium iodide in 75 per cent ethanol the wave at $-2·0$ V is recorded.

Anthracene and phenanthrene can be determined in coal tars.[46] The supporting electrolyte consists of 0·75 ml. of dioxane, and 0·25 ml. of water to which 0·037 g of tetrabutylammonium iodide is added. In this solution a sample of coal tar is dissolved and the polarographic curve recorded. The anthracene wave is at $-2·09$ V and the phenanthrene waves are at $-2·55$ V and 2·82 V (potential drop probably causes such extremely negative values).

*Carbonyl compounds.* Crotonaldehyde in technical acetaldehyde can be determined in an acidic media.[47] A small wave observed in pure acetaldehyde under these conditions can be suppressed with gelatin.

*Procedure.* Add to 5 ml. of a solution containing 0·12 N hydrochloric acid 0·12 N lithium chloride, 0·03 per cent of gelatin and 0·5 ml. of the sample of technical acetaldehyde. Deoxygenate and record at 10°C the crotonaldehyde wave at $-1·05$ V (Fig. 65).

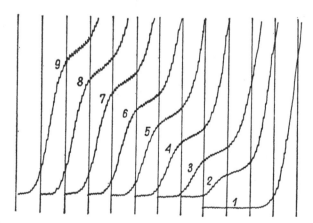

Fig. 65. Crotonaldehyde in the presence of acetaldehyde. 0·25 N Hydrochloric acid, 0·25 N lithium chloride, 9% acetaldehyde, 0·03% gelatine. Concentration of crotonaldehyde: (1) 0; (2) 0·03%; (3) 0·06%; (4) 0·09%; (5) 0·11%; (6) 0·14%; (7) 0·16%; (8) 0·18%; (9) 0·20%. $t_1 = 2·6$ sec, $m = 4$ mg/sec, full scale sensitivity 52 $\mu$A. After J. Paściak.

In a similar way acrolein was determined in technical glycerol.[48] One millilitre of the analysed glycerol was added to 4 ml. of 0·1 to 0·5 N hydrochloric acid, and the polarographic curve recorded.

For the determination of anthraquinone, added as a stabilizer in capacitor dielectrics (using chlorinated diphenyls, chlorinated naphthalenes and mineral oils as impregnants) a solvent consisting of a 3 : 2 mixture of chloroform and methanol with magnesium chloride and hydrochloric acid was able to dissolve all materials used.[49] Owing to the presence of the strong acid, the reduction of anthraquinone is shifted to potentials near 0·0 V. At these potentials the waves of the chlorinated products do not interfere.

The determination of benzanthrone in technical products can be carried out in the presence of anthraquinone:[50]

*Procedure.* Dissolve 0·3–0·5 g of the sample in 100 ml. of sulphuric acid ($d = 1·84$). Transfer a 2-ml. aliquot portion into a 50-ml. flask, add 40 ml. of methanol and dilute with water. Deoxygenate an aliquot portion of this mixture and record the reduction wave of benzanthrone at −0·96 V.

*Note.* Anthraquinone is reduced at −0·36V and does not interfere when present in normal quantities. The same solution can be used for the determination of anthraquinone, using greater sensitivities of the galvanometer.

*Nitrocompounds.* Polarography was successfully used for the determination of traces (to 0·0001 per cent) of nitrobenzene in aniline:[51]

*Procedure.* Mix a 1–2 ml. sample in the ratio 4:1 with concentrated (37 per cent) hydrochloric acid. Mix, cool and record the polarographic curve directly in the mixture open to the atmosphere.

The wave of nitrobenzene is situated between the two oxygen waves.

The determination of mixtures of *p*-nitrotoluene and *p*-aminobenzaldehyde is possible in 0·1 N acetic acid containing 10 per cent ethanol.[52] The waves of *p*-nitrotoluene (−0·46 V) and of *p*-aminobenzaldehyde (−1·18 V) are well separated and allow the simultaneous determination of both components.

*Quinoline and isoquinoline* in the quinoline fractions of coal tar are determined by treating the sample with phthalic anhydride to remove quinaldine as quinophthalone.[53]

*Procedure.* Extract the remaining bases containing quinoline and quinaldine, with ether. Then distil off the ether, dry the residue and dissolve in 0·5 ml. of ethanol. Add 10 ml. of a supporting electrolyte (consisting of 0·1 N ammonium chloride, 0·1 N ammonia, 0·1 per cent gelatin and 0·1 N sodium sulphite in 50 per cent ethanol) and subject to electrolysis at a dropping mercury electrode. The wave at −1·3 V corresponds to quinoline and the wave at −1·5 V to isoquinoline.

*Xanthates* may be determined in flotation liquids[54] by utilizing a stock solution consisting of 0·05 N sodium hydroxide, 0·1 N potassium chloride and 0·001 M eosin. The presence of eosin counteracts the adsorption and extends the useful concentration range of 0·05 mM to 2·5 mM solutions. The anodic waves of the xanthates, corresponding to a mercury salt formation are recorded at −0·3 to −0·4 V.

Finally in the *purity of reagent grade chemicals* field there have been surprisingly few polarographic methods described. Thus in a preparation of 5,8-dihydroxynaphthoquinone about 20 per cent of the labelled substance[55] was found, and in a preparation of erythrose less than 5 per cent of the substance.[55] In pyridoxal-5-phosphate preparation about 1·5 per cent of pyridoxal could be detected.[56] These are only a few examples of compounds produced by well-known companies. It is doubtless that the specific properties of polarographic analysis would make the method very suitable as a control technique in this field.

## 8.5 PETROLEUM AND FUELS

During the last decade the quantity of literature describing the applications of polarography in petroleum chemistry has greatly increased. Most papers described the applications to the determination of sulphur derivatives, mainly mercaptans and disulphides (the argentometric-amperometric methods for the determination of these substances have already been described in Chapter VI), sulphides, sulphones and thiophene derivatives. Oxygen-containing oxidation products were also analysed.

*Sulphur derivatives.* A preliminary polarographic scan is recommended to provide sufficient information as to the presence or absence of hydrogen sulphide, elemental sulphur, mercaptans (thiols), disulphides and organic polysulphides. This preliminary test is used as a starting point for the Humble Scheme[57] which enables a systematic analysis of sulphur compounds in petroleum naphtha.

*Procedure.* Add 1 ml. of the sample to 23 ml. of an acidic solvent, prepared by dissolving 13·7 g of sodium acetate trihydrate in 500 ml. of absolute methanol, and adding 6 ml. of glacial acetic acid and diluting to 1 l. with benzene. Add 1 ml. of a 0·02 per cent nigrosine black solution in benzene to suppress the maxima, deaerate an aliquot and subject it to polarographic electrolysis.

The reduction wave at $-0·6$ V indicates the presence of elemental sulphur, the reduction waves at $-0·35$, $-0·6$ and $-1·2$ V of polysulphides, and the anodic wave at $-0·3$ V indicates the presence of mercaptans (methyl mercaptan however may be lost during the purging).

*Mercaptans* can be determined in gasoline by using the anodic wave, which corresponds to a mercury compound formation at the surface of the dropping mercury electrode.

*Procedure.*[58] Dilute 1–2 ml. of gasoline 20 to 50 times with ethanol. Add sulphuric acid so as to make the final concentration 0·025 N, and add 0·05 ml. of a 3 per cent solution of cadmium nitrate (to remove the sulphide ions present). Then dilute the solution to a certain volume with water and ethanol so as to make the final concentration of ethanol 85–90 per cent. Finally, measure the anodic wave at $-0·02$ V.

*Note.* The simultaneous determination of hydrogen sulphide may be made from the difference in the total height of the waves obtained before and after addition of cadmium nitrate.

The argentometric titration of mercaptans, described in Chapter VI, can also be used for the determination of mercaptanes in hydrocarbons.[59] Liquid samples are dissolved in ammoniacal acetone and titrated with a standard solution of silver nitrate; gaseous samples are absorbed in a solution containing excess of silver nitrate and the unreacted silver is titrated with standard dodecyl mercaptan.

The reduction potentials of *disulphides* strongly depend on the nature of the groups bound to the disulphide bond.* For the

* The reaction constant $\rho^*$ has the value 0·8 V,[60] and a shift of the order of 1·0 V for the difference in half-wave potentials of dimethyl- and diphenyldisulphide can be predicted.

determination in petroleum products[61] the sample is dissolved in 85 per cent ethanol containing 0·02 M tetramethylammonium iodide. For the determination of the sum of elemental sulphur, diphenyldisulphide and dialkyldisulphides, the total limiting current at −2·15 V is measured. The dialkyldisulphide content is estimated from the difference of limiting currents at −1·0 V and −2·15 V, and the current at −1·0 V is proportional to the concentration of elemental sulphur and diphenyldisulphide. Sulphur is removed by a treatment with metallic mercury for the diphenyldisulphide estimation.

The anodic waves of dialkylsulphides, obtained with a stationary platinum electrode,[62] do not look very promising from the analytical point of view, owing to the properties of the stationary solid electrodes and to the peak-shaped form of the resulting currents. An indirect method is therefore now being investigated in our laboratory.

On the other hand the determination of aromatic sulphides and thiophene derivatives, after oxidation to the sulphones with hydrogen peroxide[63], appears to be very promising.

*Procedure.* Dissolve 2 ml. of Kuwait No. 2 fuel oil in 10 ml. of thiophene-free benzene. To this solution add 20 ml. of glacial acetic acid and 0·188 ml. of hydrogen peroxide (corresponding to three times the molar quantity of the total sulphur in the sample) and reflux the mixture for 2 hr. Cool and transfer the reaction mixture quantitatively, using several small portions of benzene, to a 125 ml. separatory funnel. Extract the benzene layer, avoiding vigorous shaking, with five 75-ml. portions of distilled water to remove acetic acid and unreacted hydrogen peroxide. Filter the benzene solution through a Whatman No. 30 filter paper and dilute to 25 ml. with benzene. Mix 2 ml. of this benzene solution with 10 ml. of 0·2 M tetrabutylammonium iodide in methanol and dilute to 25 ml. with benzene.

*Note.* In this supporting electrolyte, alkyl thiophenes and benzothiophenes, converted to the corresponding dioxides, produce waves between −1·0 V and −1·3 V, sulphones derived from diarylsulphides produce waves at −1·7 V, aryl-alkylsulphones produce waves at slightly more negative potentials, but sulphones, resulting from the oxidation of dibenzyl- or dialkylsulphides, show no waves up to −2·4 V. The method has been employed for the analysis of the molecular distillates of chromatographic fractions derived from crude oil, of straight-run kerosene and fuel oil distillates.

*Oxygen derivatives.* A methanol–benzene (1 : 1) mixture containing 0·3 M lithium chloride as supporting electrolyte, was first used[35] to detect peroxides formed in the autoxidation of fats and petroleum products. The same supporting electrolyte was used[64] for the determination of *hydroperoxides* in gasoline.

For the determination of *hydrogen peroxide, formaldehyde and acetaldehyde* in mixtures formed during the low-temperature oxidation of hydrocarbons, the hydrogen peroxide wave is recorded in an acidic buffer solution (in which the aldehydes do not interfere). The formaldehyde wave is measured in a solution to which titanium tetrachloride is added to eliminate the interference of hydrogen peroxide in acidic media, and which is brought to pH 12·2. The acetaldehyde wave is recorded in a similar solution to which dimedone is added before making alkaline, to remove the excess of formaldehyde.[65] The application of dimedone, for the analysis of mixtures of formaldehyde and higher aliphatic aldehydes in the oxidation products of ethane and cracking gases, has already been recommended.[66]

*Antioxidants* in gasoline, derived from aniline, have been determined using the anodic oxidation waves at a wax-impregnated graphite electrode directly in an alcoholic solution of the sample.[67]

*Naphthalene* in coke gas can be determined by using the reduction wave at −2·2 V in 0·02 N tetrabutylammonium iodide containing 55 per cent ethanol, 37 per cent xylene and water.[68]

Quinoid, as well as other carbonyl compounds (predominantly strongly conjugated aromatic ketones), in *coal extracts* have also been detected polarographically.[69, 70]

## 8.6. PLASTICS[38]

The remarkable growth of interest in polarographic applications among polymer chemists can be easily understood, because the polarographic methods enable one to follow the analysis of monomers, of catalysts (both initiators and inhibitors) and even certain reactive groupings in polymers. Several compounds belonging to the first two classes, e.g. halogenated-ethylenes, 1,2-diaminocyclohexane in hexamethylenediamine, butadiene, styrene, vinylacetate, mercaptans and peroxides have already been discussed in Chapter VI. As in other sections of this Chapter, several other examples are now mentioned.

### 8.6.1. *Monomers*

The reduction wave of alkylmethacrylates, observed in the presence of tetraalkylammonium salts at $-1.9$ V, can be used for the determination of monomers in the presence of polymers. [71-74]

In the study of the kinetics of block polymerization of butyl methacrylate catalysed by benzoyl peroxide[71], the samples, taken during the course of reaction, were dissolved in the minimum amount of dioxane and precipitated with methanol. The turbid solution was filtered into a volumetric flask, the polymer washed repeatedly with methanol, and the combined filtrates diluted to the mark with methanol. An aliquot was then transferred into 20 ml. of 0·1 M tetramethylammonium bromide in 50 per cent ethanol and polarographed. A portion of the monomer remained adsorbed on the polymer.

Free butylmethacrylate can be determined in polybutyl-methacrylate. [73, 74]

*Procedure.* Dissolve 1–1·5 g of the product over a period of 3–4 hr in 10 ml. of benzene. Add sufficient methanol containing 0·02 N tetramethyl-ammonium iodide to make the final concentration 96 per cent.

*Notes.* (1) Two waves are observed on the polarographic curve: the wave at $-1.77$ V corresponds to the dibutylphthalate present as plasticizer, and the wave at $-2.0$ V corresponds to the sum of the second wave of dibutylphthalate and butylmethacrylate. Because the ratio of the two dibutylphthalate waves is known,[73] it is possible to determine from the increase of the second wave the concentration of butylmethacrylate.

(2) In copolymers of methylmethacrylate and styrene[72, 73] the former is determined from a wave at $-1.9$ V, and the latter from a wave at $-2.3$ to $-2.4$ V in tetrabutylammonium iodide.

*Acrylonitrile* can be determined during polymerization in solution, catalysed by hydrogen peroxide and ferrous sulphate. [71] The samples of the solution are added to tetramethylammonium hydroxide, containing galactose, to bind the ferric ions into stable complexes.

The determination of residual acrylonitrile in a styrene-acrylo-nitrile copolymer is carried out[75] directly in a N,N-dimethyl-formamide solution of the polymer.

*Procedure.* Dissolve 2·5 g of copolymer in 50 ml. of N,N-dimethyl-formamide. Dilute the solution to 100 ml. with a solution containing 0·2 M tetrabutylammonium iodide and 10 per cent water in N,N′-dimethyl-formamide. Record the acrylonitrile wave at −1·63 V (vs. Hg-pool).

*Note.* Among the products of the persulphate-initiated oxidation of acrylonitrile, formaldehyde, cyanide and glycolonitrile did not interfere with the wave in 0·02 M tetramethylammonium iodide.[76] Excess of persulphate reacts with the added hydroquinone. When the concentration of acrylonitrile is determined from a measurement of the current at −1·5 V and −2·0 V, potassium ions in the sample interfered and thus a numerical correction based on a known concentration of potassium ions was introduced.

*Styrene* can be determined[77] in polystyrene, by extracting a 10 per cent solution of polystyrene in benzene with a solution of tetrabutylammonium iodide in 75 per cent ethanol. The wave at −2·4 V is recorded in the ethanolic phase. In the modified method,[78] the use of a 20 per cent solution of styrene in benzene and extraction with pure ethanol, later mixed with an ethanolic solution of tetrabutylammonium bromide, was recommended and the nonlinearity of the calibration curve stressed.

When 0·5 ml. of a 2·5–5 per cent benzene solution of polystyrene are added to 2 ml. of 0·1 M tetrabutylammonium iodide in N,N′-dimethylformamide, a wave at −2·46 V is observed which is strictly linearly proportional to the styrene concentration.[78]

Finally the procedure for the third method[79] is:

Shake 0·5 g of polyester resin for 1 hr with 50 ml. of 95 per cent ethanol on a shaker. Dilute to the mark with 95 per cent ethanol, and add a 5-ml. aliquot to a polarographic vessel containing 10 ml. of 95 per cent ethanol and 5 ml. of 0·1 M tetrabutylammonium chloride. The wave at −2·5 V is uninfluenced by diethylphthalate, maleic anhydride and maleate and fumarate esters.

*Vinyl acetate* gives a well-defined reduction wave in methanolic solutions containing mercuric acetate.[80] The wave is attributed to the reduction of a mercury addition compound. It was thus possible to determine vinyl acetate in the presence of acetic acid, acetaldehyde and crotonaldehyde. The same principle can be utilized for the determination of allyl alcohol, vinyl butyrate or styrene.

*Maleic anhydride* can be determined[81] in technical phthalic anhydride.

*Procedure.* Dissolve 1 g of the sample in 20 ml. of acetone. Add 50 ml. of 0·2 N hydrochloric acid and boil the mixture until most of the acetone is distilled off. Maleic anhydride is hydrolysed to maleic acid and the greater part of phthalic anhydride and 1,4-naphthoquinone is precipitated, and can be filtered off. Dilute the solution to 100 ml. with water and extract the remaining quinone with two portions of 25 ml. of benzene. The wave at −0·68 V in the aqueous phase is proportional to the maleic anhydride concentration.

In the elaboration of a method for the determination of maleic anhydride (together with maleate esters), homogeneous alkaline hydrolysis is prevented by the dimerization of these species. A two-phase saponification was recommended.[82]

*Procedure.* Dissolve the polyester in benzene and shake with 1 N potassium hydroxide (aqueous) at room temperature. Then neutralize the water phase with sulphuric acid, and add the sample to a supporting electrolyte, consisting of 0·05 N sulphuric acid and 0·2 N tetramethylammonium bromide, and measure the current at −0·40 V and −0·90 V.

*Phthalic anhydride* in alkyl resins was first saponified, precipitated as potassium phthalate, the alcoholate was dissolved in sulphuric acid and the curve was recorded in the presence of tetramethylammonium bromide.[83] However, the application of the two-phase saponification, mentioned in the previous paragraph, seems to be more convenient.[82]

*Alkylphthalate esters* have been determined in plastics, resins and explosives.[84] Terephthalic acid can be determined in the presence of other phthalic acid isomers, at concentration levels as low as 0·1 per cent, by using the first wave of terephthalic acid at −1·93 V in 1·0 M lithium hydroxide.[85] A substantially better developed wave was observed in the presence of calcium ions.[85a]

### 8.6.2. *Catalysts and Other Substances present in Polymers*

Products from the oxidation of methacrylates, e.g. *peroxides and pyruvate*, can be determined[86], both in monomers and polymethacrylates, by dissolving the sample (1:1 for monomer, 1: 25 for polymer) in a methanol–benzene (1:1) mixture containing 0·3 M lithium chloride. Pyruvate, which is the final product in the methacrylate oxidation, shows in this medium a wave at $-1.2$ V and the peroxides are reduced at $-0.8$ V. The method has been applied to the study of the kinetics of autoxidation of butyl-methacrylate.[87]

*Benzoylperoxide* in polymethylmethacrylate emulsions or in the above final product can also be determined.[73]

*Procedure.* Dissolve 1.5–1.8 g of the material in 20 ml. of benzene in a 100-ml. flask. Dilute the solution with methanol until the polymer precipitates, add 2 g of ammonium nitrate and 1 ml. of a 0.2 per cent solution of methyl red, and dilute the solution to the mark with methanol. Shake occasionally, allow the solution to stand for 20 min and in an aliquot record the benzoylperoxide wave at $+0.2$ V.

Benzoylperoxide can be determined similarly in the liquor after polymerization.

The determination of *hydroquinone* in vinylic monomers and polymers, can be carried out in a methanol–benzene (1:1) mixture containing 0.1 M ammonium acetate as a supporting electrolyte.[88] Monomers can be mixed with the solvent in a 1:1 ratio and 0.00004 per cent of hydroquinone can be detected. In polymers, the solubility of which is about 0.2 g in 100 ml. of solvent, 0.03 per cent of hydroquinone is the lowest level. The method has been applied to methacrylates, vinylacetate, acrylonitrile, styrene and divinyl-benzene. For monomeric acids, such as methacrylic, the acid is first neutralized to phenolphthalein, and the anodic wave of hydroquinone is recorded in a phosphate–borate pH 7.0 buffer.

*Salol* can be determined in plastics[73] after dissolving 1–2 g of the sample in 20 ml. of benzene, adding 10 ml. of 0.2 N tetra-methylammonium iodide and diluting with methanol to 100 ml. The half-wave potential is $-1.91$ V.

### 8.6.3. *Polymers*

Conjugated unsaturated bonds in unsaturated polyester resins are reduced at the dropping mercury electrode and the height of the wave, resembling maleic acid esters, is a measure of the *maleate unsaturation* in polyesters.

*Procedure.*[89] Dissolve 1 g of the sample in 100 ml. of ethyl acetate. Treat a 5-ml. aliquot with 25 ml. of pure ethanol, 25 ml. of 1.0 N hydrochloric acid and dilute to 100 ml. with ethylacetate. Subject a portion of this solution to polarographic electrolysis, and measure the wave which occurs between $-0.55$ V and $-0.97$ V.

*Note.* Phthalic acid, styrene, and several other compounds, often present in unsaturated ester resins, cause no interference. The effect of chain-length and the number of polymerized maleic acid residues on the limiting current has also been studied.[90]

Indirect methods have been suggested for polymers which do not bear groups that are directly reducible at the dropping mercury electrode. Thus the *carbonyl group* content was determined in polyvinyl alcohol[91, 92] by using the formation of hydrazones with *p*-nitrophenylhydrazine in acetate buffers. The reaction mixture was allowed to stand for two days, and the polymer bearing the hydrazone groups was isolated, washed with methanol and the dried polymer dissolved in water. After hydrolysis, in strong acid solutions, the *p*-nitrophenylhydrazine is determined from the reduction wave of the nitro-group.

*Carboxy groups* present in polyvinyl alcohol are transformed into calcium salts and isolated. After hydrolysis, the calcium ions can be determined by using the zinc ethylenediaminetetraacetate complex. The current of the liberated zinc ions is then measured.

Finally, a decrease of the periodic acid concentration can be a measure of 1,2-*glycol groups* and of 'head to head' bonds in polyvinyl alcohol.

### 8.6.4. *Identification of Polymers*

The direct polarography of pyrolyzed polymer products, together with polarographic electrolysis after bromination and nitration, can lead to the characterization of several polymers.[93]

*Procedure.* Pyrolyze 1–1.5 g of polymer under controlled conditions, and trap the volatile products in 10 ml. of methanol. When the methanolic solution is neutral or alkaline (to neutral red), transfer 0.1–1.0 ml. to a polarographic vessel containing 0.05 N tetramethylammonium iodide in 50 per cent methanol and record the curve. Acidic solutions are first neutralized with tetraalkylammonium hydroxide.

To another portion (2–3 ml.) of the methanolic solution add small quantities of methanolic 1.0 N bromine to the first stable yellow colouration. Detect the excess of bromine in coloured solutions with a potassium iodide paper. Neutralize the solution with 5 per cent ammonia in 80 per cent methanol, and polarograph the resulting solution of the brominated products in 0·1 N lithium chloride containing 50 per cent methanol.

As the bromides complicate the measurement of the half-wave potentials of positive waves, separate the brominated products by extraction into ether. Distil off the ether, dissolve the residue, and polarograph in 0·1 N lithium sulphate and 50 per cent methanol.

Nitrate the third portion (5 ml.) of the methanolic solution with 4·5 ml. of the nitration mixture (5 parts of concentrated sulphuric acid, 4 parts of concentrated nitric acid). Slowly dilute the mixture, while cooling in ice, with 25 ml. of distilled water. Extract the nitro-products with ether, separate the ether phase and wash with a 5 per cent solution of potassium hydroxide and three times with water. Distil off the ether, dissolve the residue in methanol and polarograph in 0·1 N lithium chloride containing 50 per cent methanol.

The materials tested, and the half-wave potentials measured, are given in Table 4. If the final polarographic analysis of the pyrolysis products and the corresponding nitro-compounds is carried out in three different buffered solutions, this interesting method would gain additional selectivity.

## 8.7. EXPLOSIVES

The basis of the application of polarography to the chemistry of explosives are the reducibility of the nitro-group at the dropping mercury electrode to hydroxylamino or amino derivatives, of organic nitrates in which the N–O bond is reduced to form the nitrate ion and the possibility of the determination of amines.

*Determination of nitroglycerine* has attracted considerable interest recently.[94–97] The analysis of propellants was first carried out[94, 95] by extracting nitroglycerine with ethanol, and recording a curve in a medium consisting of 0·5 M tetramethylammonium chloride in 50 per cent ethanol. A drawn out wave in the voltage range −0·2 V to −1·5 V was observed[94] on classical polarographic curves, but a higher resolution is possible with the single-sweep method (cf. pp. 44 and 50).[95] Three peaks were observed at −0·25 V, −0·45 V and −0·75 V. As dinitroglycol gives two peaks at −0·45 V and −0·75 V, and as the isomers of mononitrotoluene give peaks which occur near to the third of nitroglycerine (−0·75 V), the measurement of the first peak at −0·25 V is recommended[95] for the analysis of mixtures. The form of this peak is

P

TABLE 4. HALF-WAVE POTENTIALS OF PYROLYSIS PRODUCTS OF POLYMERS AND THEIR BROMINATED AND NITRATED DERIVATIVES (ACCORDING TO REFERENCE [93]).

| Polymer | Suspected products of pyrolysis | Product $N(CH_3)_4Cl$ | Brominated 0·1 N Li Cl | Nitrated 0·1 N Li Cl |
|---|---|---|---|---|
| Polyethylene | — | — | —1·06 | —1·11 |
| Polyisobutylene | $CH_2=C(CH_3)_2$ | — | —1·06 | —1·15 |
| Natural rubber | $CH_2=CH—C(CH_3)=CH_2$ | — | —0·6; —1·18 / —1·42 | —1·20 |
| Polycaprolactam | $CH_2CH_2CH_2\diagdown CH_2$ / NH CO CH$_2$ | — | | —1·0 |
| Polyvinylchloride | HCl, chloroderivatives | +0·30 | | |
| Igelit | HCl, chloroderivatives | +0·30 | | —0·88 |
| Methylacrylate (monomer)[d] | $CH_2=CH\ COOCH_3$ | —1·81[a] | —0·15[b] | |
| Polymethylmethacrylate | $CH_2=C(CH_3)COOCH$ | —1·91[a] | —0·02 | —1·05[b] |
| Polybutylmethacrylate | $CH_2=C(CH_3)COOC_4H_9$ | —2·00[a] | +0·02 | |
| Polystyrene | $CH_2=CH—C_6H_5$ | —2·34[c] | +0·14 | —1·2[b] |
| Copolymer of methyl methacrylate and styrene | $CH_2=C(CH_3)COOCH_3$ / $CH_2=CH\ C_6H_5$ | —1·91[c] —2·34[c] | +0·14[b] | |
| Aminoplast | — | —2·0[a] | | —1·0 |
| Phenoplast | — | — | —1·78 | —0·90 |
| Polyvinylalcohol | — | —1·48[a]; —2·06[a] | —1·18; —1·70 | —1·2 |
| Polyvinylbutyral | — | —1·48[a]; —2·06[a] | —1·18; —1·70 | —1·32 |
| Ethylcellulose | — | —1·90[a] | —1·78 | — |

[a] 0·05 N N$(CH_3)_4$ I;  [b] 0·1 N Li$_2$SO$_4$;  [c] N$(C_4H_9)_4$ I  [d] Product of decomposition of polymethylacrylate.

further improved by the presence of pyridine.[96] This is either due to the mechanical properties of the adsorbed film formed, or due to the change in composition of the electrical double layer. In the determination a supporting electrolyte is used, consisting of 100 ml. of pyridine, 90 ml. of 1·0 N potassium chloride and 450 ml. of 2 N ammonium chloride made up to 1000 ml. with water.

Double-base powder[96] is analysed as follows:

*Procedure.* Introduce 0·1 g of the sample into a 20-ml. flask and add 10 ml. of pyridine. Immerse the flask in a water-bath at a temperature of 40–45°C, and shake until the sample is fully dissolved (about 5 min). Cool the solution, dilute to the mark with ethanol and transfer 0·5 ml. of this mixture to a 10-ml. flask which is made up with supporting electrolyte. Record the wave in an aliquot with a peak potential at −0·27 V.

*Notes.* (1) In the analysis of blasting explosives, 0·2 g of the sample is dissolved in 20 ml. of an ethanol–pyridine (1 : 1) mixture. The rest of the procedure is the same as in the previous instance.
(2) In the presence of pyridine, dinitroglycol (ethyleneglycol dinitrate) shows no peak on oscillographic tracing with the single sweep method at potentials more positive than −0·5 V, and thus does not interfere in the determination of nitroglycerine. Dinitrotoluene which gives a peak at −0·45 V in the pyridine-containing supporting electrolyte does not interfere either. On the other hand the peaks of trinitrotoluene, pentaerythritol tetranitrate and cyclotrimethylene-trinitramine (Cyclonite) interfere in the analysis of mixtures. In any of the above mentioned methods[94–96] neither nitrocellulose, or ethylcentralite or dibutylphthalate interfere.

In mixtures of *dinitroglycol and nitroglycerine*, the determination of the former can be carried out in aqueous solutions containing 0·1 N potassium chloride and 1 N ammonium chloride. The application of a derivative circuit for a better resolution of particular waves is also recommended[97] (at −0·35 V, −0·44 V and −0·62 V for nitroglycerine and at −0·44 V and −0·62 V for dinitroglycol).

*Pentaerythritol trinitrate* can be determined in nitrocellulose propellants containing, as major constituents,[98] nitroglycerine, nitrocellulose, 2-nitrodiphenylamine and dibutylphthalate. As nitrocellulose and dibutylphthalate do not interfere, but the waves of the other three compounds coincide, it was necessary to use a special technique. The sample of the propellant is first dissolved in acetone. An aliquot is added to a supporting electrolyte, so that the resulting solution consists of 0·25 M tetramethylammonium chloride, 70 per cent ethanol, 10 per cent acetone and 20 per cent water. A wave recorded in this medium corresponds to the total concentration of the three nitrogen-containing compounds (i.e. nitroglycerine, pentaerythritol trinitrate and 2-nitrodiphenylamine). A second aliquot is allowed to react at room temperature with an ethanolic solution of sodium hydroxide. Nitroglycerine is hydrolysed in this treatment, and the resulting wave corresponds to the concentration of the sum of pentaerythritol trinitrate and 2-nitrodiphenylamine. The concentration of the latter is determined spectrophotometrically in a third aliquot. From the wave-height in the second aliquot, after correction for the 2-nitrodiphenylamine concentration present, the concentration of pentaerythritol trinitrate is determined. By subtraction from the height of the total wave-height in the first aliquot, the nitroglycerin content is calculated.

*Cyclotrimethylenetrinitramine* is reduced at $-0.77$ V in a supporting electrolyte consisting of a sulphite-borate pH 9·98 buffer with 20 per cent acetone.[99] In mixtures of *pentaerythritol tetranitrate and cyclotrimethylenetrinitramine*, a supporting electrolyte was used which was composed of 30 ml. of pyridine, 7 ml. of 1 M potassium nitrate, 35 ml. of ammonium nitrate and 28 ml. of water[100] and in which (using the single-sweep method), the reduction of pentaerythritol tetranitrate occured at $-0.27$ V (vs. Hg-pool), and that of cyclotrimethylenetrinitramine at $-0.85$ V. The presence of nitrocellulose, perchlorates and ethyleneglycol dinitrate has no effect on either of the waves. 2-Nitrodiphenylamine when present gives a reduction current at $-0.6$ V and, consequently, can be determined (when present in advantageous concentration ratios) in a mixture with pentaerythritol tetranitrate and cyclotrimethylenetrinitramine. The reduction potential of *m*-nitrotoluene ($-0.55$ V) permits the detection in comparable concentrations of 2-nitrodiphenylamine by employing a derivative circuit. Pentaerythritol trinitrate is reduced at the same potential as pentaerythritol tetranitrate and interferes in the determination of the latter. Dinitrotoluene is reduced in two steps at $-0.68$ V and $-0.88$ V and has no effect on the determination of pentaerythritol tetranitrate, but it does interfere in the determination of cyclotrimethylenetrinitramine. The presence of trinitrotoluene ($-0.35$ V; $-0.55$ V; $-0.9$ V) influences the determination of both pentaerythritol tetranitrate and cyclotrimethylenetrinitramine. The presence of nitroglycerine increases the wave of pentaerythritol tetranitrate, but the wave of cyclotrimethylenetrinitramine is not affected. The analysis of pentaerythritol tetranitrate in the presence of nitroglycerine is carried out as follows:[100]

*Procedure.* Dissolve 1 g of the sample in 0·5 ml. of pyridine, and dilute to 10 ml. with an aqueous supporting electrolyte containing 0·1 M potassium chloride and 1·0 M ammonium chloride. This medium holds nitroglycerine and cyclotrimethylenetrinitramine in solution while precipitating pentaerythritol tetranitrate. Filter the mixed solution through Whatman No. 40 filter paper; polarograph the filtrate and observe the curves of nitroglycerine and cyclotrimethylenetrinitramine.

*Note.* The reduction current at −0·27 V can be corrected for the dissolved pentaerythritol tetranitrate from a curve obtained with a saturated solution. From a comparison of the currents obtained in nitrate and chloride media, the concentrations of pentaerythritol tetranitrate and nitroglycerine can be computed. The wave in chloride media is better suited to the determination of cyclotrimethylenetrinitramine, than that observed in nitrate-containing supporting electrolyte.

*Amines* can be determined in explosives after nitrosation,[101] as mentioned in Chapter VI. Thus diphenylamine in the presence of centralite (N,N′-diphenyl N,N′-diethylurea) can be determined either after saponification and distillation with successive nitrosation of the distillate, or after dissolving the propellant in ethylacetate–methanol (1:1), followed by the addition of acetic acid and nitrite. After nitrosation (10 min), sulphamic acid is added to destroy the excess of nitrite, and precipitated cotton powder is filtered off. Polarographic electrolysis is carried out in a solution containing about 40 per cent ethanol.

In propellants containing dinitrotoluene, the sample is saponified, diphenylamine is steam distilled and nitrosated in the distillate.

Centralite is hydrolysed with 60 per cent sulphuric acid, and the N-ethylaniline formed can again be determined after nitrosation. The half-wave potentials of nitrosamines derived both from diphenylamine and phenylethylamine are in the neighbourhood of −0·65 V (at pH about 2).

## 8.8. TEXTILE INDUSTRY[102]

Organic substances that can be analysed polarographically in the raw materials, intermediates and products of the textile industry, can be divided[102] into those involved in the production of cellulosic fibres, those encountered in protein-based fibres and finally those in the dyeing process.

### 8.8.1. *Cellulosic Fibres*

In addition to several empirical methods involving the evaluation of the α-cellulose content or the copper number of cellulose, there are methods such as the determination of furfural, mentioned in Chapter VI. Interest was also paid to the determination of sulphur in viscose rayon.

The total *sulphur* (elemental, xanthogenate, thiocarbonate and sulphidic) can be determined[103] by heating the sample at 95–100°C with about 1 N sodium hydroxide for 30 min in the absence of oxygen. By this treatment all the sulphur present is transformed into sulphides, and the anodic wave of sulphide ions is recorded. Elemental sulphur can be determined if the bound sulphur is removed by treating the fibre at 70°C with 10 per cent sulphuric acid for 30 min.

The determination of residual xanthate in cellulosic fibres[104] is carried out as follows:

*Procedure.* Boil the fibre in 30 per cent sulphuric acid and trap the carbon disulphide set free in a U-tube (Fig. 40) filled with a 1 per cent ethanolic solution of diethylamine. Trap the hydrogen sulphide in a tube containing cadmium acetate solution, incorporated between the sulphuric acid and sample and the trapping U-tube. Determine the diethyldithiocarbamate formed polarographically, using the anodic wave of the mercury salt formation, as in the determination of carbon disulphide given in Chapter VI.

### 8.8.2. *Protein-based Fibres*

The *amino acids* in hydrolysates of wool and similar fibres can be determined by the method given in Chapter VI, and the proteins in degradation products or in water extracts by the Brdička reaction.[105]

Among the products of wool hydrolysis, it is possible to determine cystine and tyrosine by special methods. However, other methods given earlier for the determination of histidine and histamine (Chapter VI), or proline and hydroxyproline (this chapter) can also be utilized.

The determination of *cystine* can be carried out by using either the catalytic wave in ammoniacal cobaltous solutions[106], or the reduction wave of cystine at $-0.7$ V in acidic media[107], or at $-1.4$ V in Britton–Robinson pH 11.5 buffers.[108] The results obtained with the catalytic wave are too low,[109] probably due to the effect of other amino acids in the hydrolysate on the height of the catalytic wave.[110] Moreover the method is unable to give directly the amount of both cystine and cysteine.

The procedure for the determination using acidic hydrolysis[107] is:

Add 0.25 g of the wool sample (extracted with ether and dried) in a 25-ml. flask to 5 ml. of a 30 per cent solution of sulphuric acid and allow it to stand for 8 hr at 105°C. Dilute the solution to the mark and filter. Add a 2-ml. aliquot in a Kalousek vessel to 20 ml. of water, and after deoxygenation record the cathodic cystine wave. Later add a 5-ml. aliquot to 20 ml. of deoxygenated water and record the cystein wave.

The content of cystine, cysteine and sulphur dioxide (which gives a reduction wave between the anodic cysteine wave and the cathodic cystine wave) has been determined in wool destroyed in alkaline, acidic, oxidizing and reducing media.[107]

The reduction wave in alkaline media enables the simultaneous determination of cystine, cysteine (care must be taken to prevent oxidation) and sulphide in the alkaline destruction of keratin.

Cystine has also been determined in wool using a polarometric titration[109, 111, 112] based on the principle that sulphite reacts with cystine with the formation of one mole of cysteine per mole of cystine (cf. Chapter VI). The cysteine formed is titrated mercurimetrically. Cysteine and the sum of cysteine and cystine is determined by titration before and after treatment with sulphite.

Finally, it is possible in unhydrolysed wool[109] to determine the free thiol groups by allowing the sample to react with Neohydrin, or with *p*-chloromercuribenzoic acid in a urea containing pH 7–8.5 buffer. In the determination of free S–S bonds the reaction is carried out in a pH 8·5 buffer containing urea and sulphite. The excess of organo-mercurial is determined polarographically.

*Tyrosine* in hydrolysates of wool can be determined using the nitration described in Chapter VI, together with measurement of the 3,5-dinitrotyrosine wave.[113] The amount of tyrosine is related to the destruction caused by treatment with chlorine.

### 8.8.3. *Dyeing Process*

It is surprising how little polarography has been analytically applied to the control of dye production and in the supervision of applications of dyestuffs in the textile industry, considering that most of the dyes used, and the several intermediates and starting materials, are polarographically active. Numerous papers have been devoted to the polarography of dyestuffs, but only the mechanism of the electrode processes and the relations to the structure have been reported.

The determination of nitrobenzene in aniline, and in mixtures of nitrotoluene and *p*-aminobenzaldehyde, have already been reported earlier in this chapter. The determination of phenols, pyrazolones and similar coupling compounds by polarometric titration has also been mentioned in Chapter VI. Thus, only the study of *anthraquinone dyestuffs* in the presence of dithionite[114] will be given. Here the interfering effect of dithionite is eliminated by working at lower temperatures, or by decomposition in an acidic media or by heating. In groups of structurally related dyes, it is possible to estimate the molecular weight from the suppressive effect on polarographic streaming maxima.[115]

### 8.8.4. *Auxiliary Materials*

Among the organic products used in the textile industry it is possible, by using the suppression of streaming maxima,[116, 117] to control the properties of starch after treatment with sodium benzenesulphonamide, hypochlorate or peroxide and during alkaline, acidic oxidizing and enzymatic hydrolysis. The estimation of starch is carried out by boiling it in hydrochloric acid solution, and measuring the resulting wave for 5-hydroxymethylfurfural.[118]

## REFERENCES

(1) Březina, M. and Zuman, P., *Polarography in Medicine, Biochemistry and Pharmacy*, Interscience, New York (1958).

(2) Zuman, P., *Pharmazie* 8, 903 (1953); 11, 449 (1956).

(3) Volke, J., *Leybold polarograph. Ber.* 2, 175 (1954).

(4) Zuman, P. and Březina, M., Polarographic Analysis in Pharmacy, in *Progress in Polarography* (P. Zuman, I. M. Kolthoff, editors), Vol. 2, p. 687, Interscience, New York (1962).

(5) Knobloch, E. and Svátek, E., *Collect. Czechoslov. Chem. Commun.* 20, 1113 (1955).

(6) Page, J. E. and Waller, J. G., *Analyst* 74, 292 (1949).

(7) Blažek, J. and Stejskal, Z., *Československ. farmacie* 5, 344 (1956).

(8) Dušinský, G. and Gruntová, Z., *Československ. farmacie* 5, 340 (1956).

(9) Koryta, J. and Zuman, P., *Collect. Czechoslov. Chem. Commun.* 18, 197 (1953).

(10) Zuman, P., Koryta, J. and Kalvoda, R., *Collect. Czechoslov. Chem. Commun.* 18, 350 (1953).

(11) Kalvoda, R. and Zýka, J., *Československ. farmacie* 2, 154 (1953).

(12) Prokeš, J. and Vorel, F., *Chem. zvesti* 14, 818 (1960).

(13) Manoušek, O. and Zuman, P., *Pharmazie* 11, 530 (1956).

(14) Asahi, Y., *J. Vitaminology (Japan)* 4, 118 (1958).

(15) Dušinský, G., *Československ. farmacie* 10, 181 (1961).

(16) Bitter, B., *Collect. Czechoslov. Chem. Commun.* 15, 677 (1950).

(17) Onrust, H., Jansen, A. P. and Wöstman, B. S. J., *Recueil Trav. Chim. Pays-Bas* 74, 1515 (1955).

(18) Podroužek, V., *Chem. listy* 47, 1869 (1953).

(19) Březina, M., Polarography in Medicine and Biochemistry, in *Progress in Polarography* (P. Zuman, I. M. Kolthoff, editors), Vol. 2, p. 667, Interscience, New York (1962).

(20) Kane, P. O., *Nature* 183, 1674 (1959).

(21) Gisclard, J. B. and Woodward, M. M., *J. Ind. Hyg. Toxicol.* 28, 47 (1946).

(22) Chvapil, M. and Zahradník, R., *Z. physiol. Chem.* 307, 217 (1957).

(23) Heath, J. C., *Nature* 158, 23 (1946).

(24) Filipowicz, B. and Leyko, W., *Bull. Soc. Sci. Lettres Lódź, Cl. III, Sci. Math. Nat.* 4, No. 5, 1 (1953).

(25) Leyko, W., Panusz, H., *Bull. Soc. Sci. Lettres Lódź, Cl. III Sci. Math. Nat.* 5, No. 2, 1 (1954).

(26) Březina, M., Volková, V. and Volke, J., *Collect. Czechoslov. Chem. Commun.* 19, 894 (1954).

(27) Stárka, L., *Naturwiss.* 44, 585 (1957); Stárka, L. and Brabencová, H., *Clin. Chim. Acta* 5, 423 (1960).

(28) Brdička, R., Unpublished results, cf. ref. (1).

(29) Homolka, J. and Krupička, V., *Proc. 1st Internat. Polarograph. Congr., Prague 1951*, Pt. III, p. 662, Prague (1952).

(30) MATHERS, A. P. and SCHOENEMAN, R. L., *J. Assoc. Offic. Agric. Chem.* **35**, 830 (1952).
(31) PRATT, D. E. and POWERS, J. J., *J. Assoc. Offic. Agric. Chem.* **37**, 486 (1954).
(32) CHLOPIN, N. JA., LITVINOVA, N. S. and PRIVALOVA, K. P., *Gigiena i Sanit.* **16**, 48 (1951).
(33) ZUMAN, P., *Collect. Czechoslov. Chem. Commun.* **16**, 510 (1951).
(34) GILLAM, W. S., *Ind. Eng. Chem., Anal. Ed.* **17**, 217 (1945).
(35) LEWIS, W. R., QUACKENBUSH, F. W. and DEVRIES, T., *Anal. Chem.* **21**, 762 (1949).
(36) WILLITS, C. O., RICCIUTI, C., OGG, C. L., MORRIS, S. G., and RIEMENSCHNEIDER, R. W., *J. Amer. Oil Chem. Soc.* **30**, 420 (1953).
(37) KALBAG, S. S., NARAYAN, K. A., CHANG, S. S. and KUMMEROW, F. A., *J. Amer. Oil Chem. Soc.* **32**, 271 (1955).
(38) TACHI, I. and SENDA, M., Polarography in Chemical Industry, in *Progress in Polarography* (P. Zuman, I. M. Kolthoff, editors), Vol. 2, p. 711, Interscience, New York (1962).
(39) FUKAMI, H. and NAKAZIMA, M., *Botyu-Kagaku* **19**, 83 (1954); *Leybold polarograph. Ber.* **2**, 154 (1954).
(40) WATT, J., *Analyst* **79**, 735 (1954).
(41) GIANG, P. A. and CASWELL, R. L., *Agric. Food Chem.* **5**, 753 (1957).
(42) BACHE, C. A. and LISK, D. J., *Agric. Food Chem.* **8**, 459 (1960).
(43) BOWEN, C. V. and EDWARDS, F. I., *Anal. Chem.* **22**, 706 (1950).
(44) ŠINDELÁŘOVÁ, K., BŘEZINA, M. and NEUMAN, V., *Veterinarni medicina* **5**, 875 (1960).
(45) STROMBERG, A. G. and POZDĚJEVA, A. G., *Ž. obšč. chim.* **20**, 54 (1950).
(46) GORNYCH, T. I. and POZDĚJEVA, A. G., *Ž. prikl. chim.* **27**, 118 (1954).
(47) PAŠCIAK, J., *Chem. Analityczna (Warsaw)* **5**, 797 (1960).
(48) KIRILLOVA, A. S. and KORŠUNOV, I. A., *Ž. anal. chim.* **6**, 257 (1951).
(49) GARN, P. D. and BOTT, M. C., *Anal. Chem.* **33**, 84 (1961).
(50) VAJNŠTEJN, JU. I., *Zavod. lab.* **15**, 411 (1949).
(51) NOVÁK, J. V. A., *Collect. Czechoslov. Chem. Commun.* **11**, 573 (1939).
(52) VAJNŠTEJN, JU. I., *Trudy Komissii po analit. chim.* **4** (7), p. 85, Izd. Akad. Nauk SSSR Moscow 1952.
(53) MARKAČEVA, T. M. and STROMBERG, A. G., *Zavod. lab.* **18**, 677 (1952).
(54) SUN, S. CH. and HOLZMANN, R. T., *Anal. Chem.* **29**, 1298 (1957).
(55) ZUMAN, P., Unpublished results.
(56) MANOUŠEK, O. and ZUMAN, P., *Collect. Czechoslov. Chem. Commun.* in the press.
(57) KARCHMER, J. H., *Anal. Chem.* **30**, 80 (1958).

(58) GERBER, M. I., Ž. anal. chim. **2**, 265 (1947).
(59) GRIMES, M. D., PUCKETT, J. E., NEWBY, B. J. and HEINRICH, B. J., Anal. Chem. **27**, 152 (1955).
(60) ZUMAN, P., Collect. Czechoslov.˙Chem. ₌ Commun. **25**, 3225 (1960).
(61) GERBER, M. I. and ŠUŠARINA, A. D., Ž. anal. chim. **5**, 262 (1950).
(62) DRUSHEL, H. V. and MILLER, J. F., Anal. Chim. Acta **15**, 389 (1956); Anal. Chem. **29**, 1456 (1957).
(63) DRUSHEL, H. V. and MILLER, J. F., Anal. Chem. **30**, 1271 (1958).
(64) WHISMAN, M. L. and ECCLESTON, B. H., Anal. Chem. **30**, 1638 (1958).
(65) SANDLER, S. and CHUNG, Y. H., Anal. Chem. **30**, 1252 (1958).
(66) NEIMAN, M. B. and GERBER, M. I., Ž. analit. chim. **2**, 135 (1947).
(67) GAYLORD, V. F., CONRAD, A. L. and LANDERL, J. H., Anal. Chem. **29**, 228 (1957).
(68) BEZUGLYJ, V. D. and OGDANEC, N. D., Ž. prikl. chim. **28**, 1339 (1955).
(69) GIVEN, P. H. and SCHOEN, J. M., J. Chem. Soc. 1958, 2680.
(70) GIVEN, P. H. and PEOVER, M. E., in Advances in Polarography (Proc. 2nd Internat. Congr. Polarography, Cambridge 1959), Vol. 3, p. 955, Pergamon Press, London (1960); Fuel **39**, 463 (1960).
(71) MATYSKA, B. and KLIER, K., Chem. listy **50**, 1089 (1956); Collect. Czechoslov. Chem. Commun. **21**, 1592 (1956).
(72) LACOSTE, R., ROSENTHAL, I. and SCHNITTINGER, C. H., Anal. Chem. **29**, 983 (1956).
(73) BEZUGLYJ, V. D. and DMITRIJEVA, V. N., Zavod. Lab. **24**, 941 (1958).
(74) DMITRIJEVA, V. N. and BEZUGLYJ, V. D., Zavod. Lab. **25**, 555 (1959).
(75) CLAVER, G. C. and MURPHY, M. E., Anal. Chem. **31**, 1682 (1959).
(76) STRAUSE, S. F. and DYER, E., Anal. Chem. **27**, 1906 (1955).
(77) GINZBERG, E. G. and IGONIN, L. A., Chim. Prom. **6**, 355 (1954).
(78) PAŠCIAK, J., Chem. Analityczna (Warsaw) **5**, 477 (1960).
(79) AYRES, W. M. and WHITNACK, G. C., Anal. Chem. **32**, 358 (1960).
(80) USAMI, S., Bunseki Kagaku (Japan Analyst) **5**, 499 (1956).
(81) BARENDRECHT, E., Chem. Weekblad **50**, 785 (1954).
(82) GARN, P. D. and GILROY, H. M., Anal. Chem. **30**, 1663 (1958).
(83) GARN, P. D. and HALLINE, E. W., Anal. Chem. **27**, 1563 (1955).
(84) WHITNACK, G. C. and GANTZ, E. S. C., Anal. Chem. **25**, 553 (1953).
(85) HALL, M. E. and McNUTT, R. C., Anal. Chem. **32**, 1073 (1960).
(85a) KRUPIČKA, J., Private communication.
(86) BOHDANECKÝ, M. and EXNER, J., Collect. Czechoslov. Chem. Commun. **20**, 917 (1955).
(87) EXNER, J. and BOHDANECKÝ, M., Collect. Czechoslov. Chem. Commun. **23**, 239 (1959).
(88) EXNER, J. and BOHDANECKÝ, M., Collect. Czechoslov. Chem. Commun. **20**, 1246 (1955).
(89) HOBART, E. W., Anal. Chem. **26**, 1291 (1954).

(90) VOIGT, J., *Plaste-Kautschuk* **4**, 3 (1957).
(91) UKIDA, J. and KOMINAMI, T., *Review of Polarography (Japan)* **4**, 65 (1956); quoted according to ref. (38).
(92) UKIDA, J., TAKAYAMA, G. and KOMINAMI, T., *J. Chem. High Polymers (Tokyo)* **11**, 176, 212 (1954); quoted according to ref. (38).
(93) BEZUGLYJ, V. D. and DMITRIJEVA, V. N., *Zavod. Lab.* **25**, 1180 (1959).
(94) WHITNACK, G. C., MAYFIELD, M. M. and GANTZ, E. S. C., *Anal. Chem.* **27**, 899 (1955).
(95) WILLIAMS, A. F. and KENYON, D., *Talanta* **3**, 160 (1959).
(96) HETMAN, J. S., *Advances in Polarography* (Proc. 2nd Internat. Congr. Polarography, Cambridge 1959), Vol. 2, p. 640, Pergamon Press, London (1960).
(97) HETMAN, J. S., *Talanta* **5**, 267 (1960).
(98) AYRES, W. M. and LEONARD, G. W., *Anal. Chem.* **31**, 1485 (1959).
(99) LEWIS, D. T., *Analyst* **79**, 644 (1954).
(100) HETMAN, J. S., *Anal. Chem.* **32**, 1699 (1960).
(101) SIFRE, G., *Mem. Poudres* **35**, 373 (1953).
(102) RUSZNÁK, I., PÉTER, F. and MIHALIK, B., *Textil Praxis (Stuttgart)* 1959, 824.
(103) PEČENÝ, R. and NEDVĚDOVÁ, R., *Chem. prům.* **10**, 165 (1960).
(104) PHILIP, B., *Faserforschung u. Textiltechnik* **10**, 493 (1959).
(105) MARRON, T. U. and ROUTH, J. I., *Arch. Biochem.* **4**, 319 (1944).
(106) BRDIČKA, R., *Collect. Czechoslov. Chem. Commun.* **5**, 238 (1933); *Mikrochemie* **15**, 167 (1934).
(107) BENÍŠEK, L., *Z. anal. Chem.* **175**, 244 (1960); *Faserforschung u. Textiltechnik* **12**, 23 (1961).
(108) ČERŇÁK, J., BLAŽEJ, A., ŠTEFANEC, J. and SÍLEŠ, B., *Acta Chim. Acad. Sci. Hungar.* **27**, 87 (1961).
(109) HUMAN, J. P. E., *Textile Research J.* **28**, 647 (1958).
(110) SLÁDEK, J. and LIPSCHÜTZ, M., *Collect. Czechoslov. Chem. Commun.* **6**, 487 (1934).
(111) LEACH, S. J., *Proc. Int. Wool Text. Res. Conf. Australia* 1955, C2, 469.
(112) SCHÖBERL, A., *Textil-Praxis* **14**, 701 (1959).
(113) BENÍŠEK, L., *Faserforschung u. Textiltechnik* **12**, 74 (1961).
(114) PÉTER, F., *Magyar Textiltechnika* **4**, 154 (1958).
(115) RUSZNÁK, I., KRÁLIK, I. and FUKKER, K., *Z. physikal. Chem. N.F. (Frankfurt)* **17**, 56 (1958).
(116) RUSZNÁK, I., KRÁLIK, I. and FUKKER, K., *Collect. Czechoslov. Chem. Commun.* in the press.
(117) RUSZNÁK, I., KRÁLIK, I. and FUKKER, K., *Acta Chem. Acad. Sci. Hungar.* **27**, 295 (1961).
(118) SUN, S. C., LOVE, D. L. and HOLZMANN, R. T., *Anal. Chem.* **30**, 1074 (1958).

CHAPTER IX

# POLAROGRAPHY IN ORGANIC SYNTHESES AND ISOLATION OF NATURAL PRODUCTS

POLAROGRAPHY can improve the situation in electropreparative methods, and can help to ascertain the optimum conditions for organic syntheses, and isolation of natural products from biological materials.

## 9.1. PREPARATIVE ELECTROCHEMISTRY

The study of polarographic curves can offer a great deal of useful information in preparative electrochemistry. The choice of the best conditions for electrolysis, i.e. the most appropriate composition of the supporting electrolyte and the correct potential, can easily be derived from polarographic curves. It is possible, for example, to predict under which conditions a pinacol and an alcohol are formed, by the reduction of a carbonyl compound. It has been shown that sometimes a relatively small change in the molecule of the electroactive compound, completely changes the course of the reduction process, e.g. in 4-bromosydnone the C–Br bond is broken in the resulting parent sydnone, but in 4-chlorosydnone, the reduction of the sydnone ring occurs and a chlorosubstituted hydrazine derivative is formed.[1] This is caused by the fact that in the first instance the C–Br bond is more easily reduced than the sydnone ring, but in the latter instance the C–Cl bond would be reduced at more negative potentials than that of the reduction of the N–O bond in the sydnone ring. Hence in 4-chlorosydnone, the N–O bond in the sydnone ring is reduced first, and the introduction of the chlorine atom only slightly affects the half-wave potential of the reduction of the sydnone ring.

Another example is the comparison of $\alpha$- and $\beta$-aminoketones.[2] Here the presence of one additional methylene group completely changes the course of the reduction. Whereas in $\alpha$-aminoketones

227

the C–N bond is hydrogenolysed and the ketone is formed, in $\beta$-aminoketones the carbonyl group is reduced with the formation of $\beta$-aminoalcohol. In the first instance the C–N bond is so strongly polarized, owing to the neighbouring carbonyl group, that it undergoes reduction at substantially more positive potentials than the keto group. In the latter, the distant CO group is not effective enough to influence sufficiently the C–N bond. Hence the amino group only exerts an effect on a substituent which changes, to a certain degree, the half-wave potential of the reduced carbonyl group.

These two examples are sufficient to demonstrate that the products of preparative electrochemistry can change, even for closely related substances, and even when using controlled potential electrolysis. Polarography can detect and even explain such differences in electrolysis products.

Recently, the possible preparation of different stereoisomers by preparative electroreduction at a controlled potential and pH was derived from polarographic data. Thus for $\alpha, \alpha'$-dibromosuccinic acids, the erythro-form of the free acid and of its anions is reduced to fumaric acid. On the other hand, the threo-epimer is reduced to the fumaric acid only in an undissociated form and as a dibasic anion; the univalent anion is at least partly reduced to maleic acid. Both threo- and erythro-epimers of dialkyl esters of dibromosuccinic acid are reduced only to the dialkyl ester of fumaric acid—similarly to the undissociated free acids.[3, 4]

The one-electron reduction of $\Delta^{1,4}$-3-ketosteroids[5] gives rise to various stereoisomers of pinacols. The yield of the particular stereoisomer is a function of pH: in acidic solutions, where the reduction of the protonized form of the ketosteroid occurs, the formation is assumed of a pinacol bearing the hydroxyl groups in $\alpha$-positions. In alkaline media, the unprotonized ketosteroid is reduced with the formation of the isomer with hydroxyls in the $\beta$-position. The structure of the products, prepared by controlled potential electrolysis, was supported by the rates of dehydration and of oxidations with periodic acid. For $\Delta^4$-3-ketosteroids the difference in the composition of the mixtures of isomeric pinacols in the reduction in acidic and in alkaline media, was not so pronounced as with $\Delta^{1,4}$-3-ketosteroids.

## 9.2. APPLICATIONS IN ORGANIC SYNTHESIS

Polarography can be applied as an analytical tool in the search for the optimum conditions for organic synthesis. The products or the intermediates can be followed, and the influence of the medium on yield can be studied. As an example, the synthesis of allethrolone can be given.[6] Based on the polarographic studies of the optimum conditions for the last step of the synthesis, which is a cyclization process in alkaline solution, it was possible to increase the yield from 20 to 80 per cent.

Another example is the alkaline degradation of the methoiodides of 3-tropinone[10] and its sulphur analogue, the 8-thiabicyclo-(1,2,3)-octane-3-one (II). Both substances undergo two successive elimination reactions detected polarographically. For the methoiodide of 3-tropinone, the first reaction occurs at pH 11 and its rate increases with increasing pH. The second reaction is observed at pH 12 and its rate is also pH-dependent.

$$\text{I} \xrightarrow{\text{pH 11}} \text{III} \xrightarrow{\text{pH 12-13}} \text{Dihydrotropone} + \text{NH(CH}_3)_2$$

It is obvious that the reactions occur simultaneously as a consecutive reaction. The intermediate III is unstable and has not yet been isolated.

On the other hand with the sulphur analogue II, the first elimination occurs at pH 4 and the second at pH 11–12:

$$\text{II} \xrightarrow{\text{pH 4}} \text{IV} \longrightarrow \text{Dihydrotropone} + \text{CH}_3\text{S}^-$$

Thus between pH 5 and 10 intermediate IV is stable. It has been thus possible to isolate it using optimum conditions. These were revealed based on the results of polarographic measurements.

The structure of substance IV has been verified by elemental analysis, molar refraction and i.r.-spectra.

## 9.3. APPLICATIONS IN THE ISOLATION OF NATURAL PRODUCTS

Polarography is also a suitable analytical method for following the progress of isolation, and for the choice of the most effective extraction methods, during the isolation of natural products from biological materials and especially from plants.

Thus the polarographic reduction waves of anthocyanins[7] were used for the study of the optimum conditions for the isolation from flowers. Similarly, the juglone and hydrojuglone contents of different sections of walnut trees and fruits were controlled polarographically during their isolation.[8] Several tropolone derivatives, similar to colchicine, were detected, isolated and characterized by polarographic methods[9] from the seeds of meadow saffron. After separating the fats by a petroleum ether extraction, the sample was extracted with ethanol, treated with moistened lead hydroxide and evaporated. The residue was eluted with water and extracted with chloroform. It was verified that all polarographically reducible substances were concentrated in the chloroform extract and none was left in the aqueous phase.

The substances from the chloroform phase were further separated chromatographically. In addition to colchicine, four other crystalline compounds were isolated. It was detected that two of them showed a polarographic behaviour very similar to that of colchicine. This observation was an important starting point for the further identification of these compounds.

## REFERENCES

(1) ZUMAN, P. *Collect. Czechoslov. Chem. Commun.* **25**, 3252 (1960).
(2) ZUMAN, P. and HORÁK, V., in *Advances in Polarography* (Proc. 2nd Internat. Polarograph. Congr., Cambridge 1959) Vol. 3, p. 804. Pergamon Press, London 1960; *Collect. Czechoslov. Chem. Commun.* **26**, 176 (1961).
(3) ELVING, P. J., MARTIN, A. J. and ROSENTHAL, I., *J. Amer. Chem. Soc.* **77**, 5218 (1955).

(4) ROSENTHAL, I. and ELVING, P. J., *J. Amer. Chem. Soc.* **73**, 1880 (1951).
(5) LUND, M., *Acta Chem. Scand.* **11**, 283 (1957).
(6) KRUPIČKA, J., Private communication.
(7) ZUMAN, P., *Collect. Czechoslov. Chem. Commun.* **18**, 36 (1953).
(8) ZUMAN, P., *Collect. Czechoslov. Chem. Commun.* **19**, 1140 (1954).
(9) ŠANTAVÝ, F. and REICHSTEIN, T., *Helv. Chim. Acta* **33**, 1606 (1950).
(10) HORÁK V. and ZUMAN, P., *Tetrahedron Letters* **21**, 746 (1961).

Q

# CHAPTER X

# POLAROGRAPHIC ANALYSIS IN THE STUDY OF REACTION RATES AND EQUILIBRIA

POLAROGRAPHIC limiting currents allow us to follow some equilibria, rates of reactions occurring in the bulk of the solution and rates of rapid reactions occurring in the neighbourhood of the dropping electrode. From the shift of the half-wave potentials of reversible systems with pH, the approximate values of dissociation constants can be determined. Finally, the shape and slope of polarographic waves are an aid to determining rate constants characterizing the (heterogeneous) electrode process proper.

## 10.1. EQUILIBRIUM CONSTANTS

The shifts of half-wave potentials can be used for the determination of the equilibrium constants, only when the electrode process is reversible in two instances:

(1a) In the presence of the polarographically inactive substance $X$, the equilibrium between this substance and substances $A$ and $B$ is completely mobile.* Either substance $A$ or $B$ is reversibly reduced at a given potential:

$$A + X \underset{\text{mobile}}{\overset{k}{\rightleftharpoons}} B$$

In organic polarography $X$ is practically always hydrogen ion. That means that for reversible systems, the $pK_a$-values can be determined from the shift of half-wave potentials with pH in well-buffered solutions, as intersections of the linear portions on $E_{1/2}$-pH plots.

This method was used for the determination of the approximate values of the dissociation constants of reduced forms of

---

* Mobile is used in the sense "is established very rapidly".

quinoidsy stems, and, for quinones bearing hydroxyl substituents, even of dissociation constants of this group in the oxidized form. The values of $pK_a$ can be determined by this method even in alkaline solutions. The titrimetric methods are excluded, owing to the instability of the quinone, but mainly of the hydroquinone. Approximate $pK_a$-values were determined for several naphthoquinones and related heterocyclic quinones. [1]

(1b) It has been shown recently[2] that even in such instances where substance $X$ is not present in a great excess, and especially in such instances where the reaction rate constant $k$ (see the scheme above) is such that this reaction governs the electrode process (and hence when the kinetic limiting current is observed), it is possible to determine the equilibrium constant from the shift of potentials of the reversibly reducible substance $A$ with concentration of the substance $X$.

No such example of reversible reduction in a poorly buffered media has been observed so far among organic systems.

(2) Measurement of limiting currents enables us to determine the equilibrium constants when the equilibrium is established slowly:

$$D + Y \underset{\text{slow}}{\rightleftharpoons} E$$

Slowly means compared with the drop-time. When using conventional capillaries with a drop-time of $t_1 = 2\text{--}3$ sec, then a slow equilibrium is established during ten or more seconds or after several minutes. For the polarographic determination of the equilibrium constants, it is necessary that substances $D$ and $E$ are reduced at different potentials, in separate waves, and in such a way that at least one ($D$ or $E$) but preferably both, are reduced in the potential range available.

Hence on polarographic curves two waves are observed (Fig. 66) ($i_D$ and $i_E$) the ratio of which changes with the change in concentration of substance $Y$. If the equilibrium is shifted on the left side (i.e. in favour of the reactant $D$, the product $E$ being in concentrations that are only a fraction of the concentration of $D$) and if it is thus necessary that substance $Y$ must be present in excess, then it is favourable, if substance $Y$ is electro-inactive in the

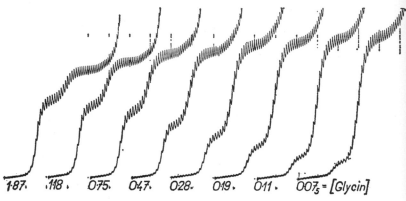

$1·87,$    $·118,$    $0·75,$    $0·47,$    $0·28,$    $0·19,$    $0·11,$    $0·07_5 = [Glycin]$

FIG. 66. Equilibrium between pyruvic acid and glycine.
$5·6 \times 10^{-4}$ M Sodium pyruvate, $0·005$ per cent gelatin, glycine buffer pH $9·2$. Concentration of glycine (species with free amino group) is given in the polarogram. Ionic strength kept constant by addition of sodium chloride. Curves starting at $-0·8$ V, S.C.E., 200 mV/absc., $t_1 = 3·6$ sec, $m = 2·1$ mg/sec, full scale sensitivity $4·2$ μA.

potential range studied. Experimentally the sluggish establishment of the equilibrium between $D$ and $E$ is verified, if the limiting currents $i_D$ and $i_E$ are diffusion controlled (contrary to the case in (1b above). The reversibility of the electrode process plays no important role here.

If the concentration of substance $Y$, necessary for reaching the equilibrium is greater than $10 [D]$, then it is possible to determine the equilibrium constant from the value of $[Y]$ for which $i_D = i_E$. A better way, enabling us simultaneously to verify that our suppositions concerning the stoichiometry of the reaction are correct, is to plot $\log i_D/(\Sigma i - i_D)$ (where $\Sigma i$ is the total limiting current) against $\log [Y]$. The dependence should be linear (Fig. 68) and the value of $-\log [Y]$ at the point, corresponding to zero value of the logarithm of the current, equals numerically the p$K$-value. From the slope of this line the stoichiometry of the reaction can be determined, i.e. the ratio in which $D$ and $Y$ react.

The first attempts to treat the dependence of the polarographic oxime[3] and phthalic acid[4] waves on pH in such a way were incorrect, because the limiting currents were rate and not diffusion controlled (and hence the limiting currents of substance $D$ were not proportional to the concentration of substance $D$ in the bulk of the solution).

The first organic system for which the equilibrium constants were determined (and one of the first systems treated in this way at all) was the reaction between carbonyl compounds and amines.[5] In the reaction

$$\rangle C=O + H_2NR \rightleftharpoons \rangle C\!\!\!<^{NHR}_{OH} \rightleftharpoons \rangle C=NR + H_2O$$

the brutto equilibrium constant between the left and right side was measured. On polarographic curves (Fig. 66) two separate waves occur: The more positive corresponds to the concentration of the imine $\rangle C=N$, and the more negative to the reduction of the carbonyl compound. With increasing concentration of amine, present in a great excess, the height of the more positive wave increases (Fig. 66) in the form of a portion of the dissociation curve (Fig. 67), which can be treated as in Fig. 68 to determine the equilibrium constant.

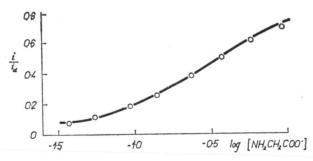

FIG. 67. Equilibrium between pyruvic acid and glycine. Dependence of the wave-height of the more positive (ketimine) wave ($i$) expressed as the ratio $i/id$ on the glycine concentration.

It was early recognized[5] that only the unprotonized form of an amine with a free electron pair reacts with a carbonyl group. In the refined treatment[6, 7] the protonization of the resulting imine is also considered, and from the measured "equilibrium

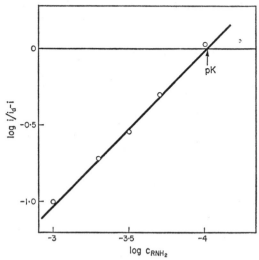

FIG. 68. Reaction of $a$, $\beta$-unsaturated carbonyl derivatives with amines.
Dependence of the value of log $i/(i_d - i)$ on logarithm of amine concentration for reaction of phenyl vinyl ketone and ethylamine. $i$—the first wave of phenyl vinyl ketone, $i_d$—the sum of the first wave of phenyl vinyl ketone and for the Mannich base formed.

constants" at different pH-values* and composition of the reaction mixture, the true value of the equilibrium constant $K_{C=N}$ must be computed considering the equilibria:

$$H_2NR^+ \rightleftharpoons H_2NR + H^+ \qquad K_{NH_2}$$

$$\underset{/}{\overset{\backslash}{>}}C=O + H_2NR \rightleftharpoons \underset{/}{\overset{\backslash}{>}}C=NR + H_2O \qquad K_{C=N}$$

$$\underset{/}{\overset{\backslash}{>}}C=NR + H^+ \rightleftharpoons \underset{/}{\overset{\backslash}{>}}C=\overset{+}{N}HR \qquad K_N$$

For ketones, keto-acids and aliphatic aldehydes the equilibrium constants are reached after 1 min. With benzaldehydes the establishment is slower, the reaction is more complicated and consecutive reactions occur. The reaction was studied for numerous carbonyl compounds and several amines. In solutions

* Near the $pK_{NH_2}$ of the reacting amine, the amine being reactant and buffer simultaneously.

of histidine and histamine in the presence of pyruvic acid, another equilibrium reaction was observed in addition to the formation of a Schiff's base. In this reversible reaction a polarographically inactive product, perhaps of the type I, was formed and the total height of the limiting current was decreased. From this decrease the equilibrium constant of this reaction between pyruvic acid and histamine or histidine was calculated.[8]

$$
\begin{array}{c}
CH_2 \quad NH \\
CH_2 \quad C \quad CH \\
NH \quad C\text{——}N \\
C \\
CH_3 \quad COOH
\end{array}
$$

(I)

In a similar way the equilibrium constants of the cyanhydrine reaction in alkaline media were computed.[9]

In some systems, when the equilibrium is established rapidly, and thus when kinetic currents are observed in classical polarography, it is possible to determine equilibrium constants with impulse polarography. Whereas in classical polarography the rate of potential scanning is about $0 \cdot 006$ V/sec., in impulse polarography triangular voltage sweeps are used with a slope of $0 \cdot 5$–$300$ V/sec. Under such conditions, the electrode is in contact with the solution at a given potential for such a short time-period that the equilibrium remains practically undisturbed. The peaks observed on oscillographic $i$–$E$ curves are thus proportional to the concentration of substance $D$ or $E$. Using the impulse polarography technique, it was possible to determine the equilibrium constants of the reaction between aldehydic and hydrated forms of formaldehyde[10] and of formylpyridine.[11]

To summarize, equilibrium constants can be determined polarographically from the shifts of half-wave potentials for reversible electrode systems, or from the ratio of heights of two separated waves, provided that they are diffusion controlled, but without respect to the reversibility of the electrode process.

## 10.2. HOMOGENEOUS REACTIONS IN SOLUTIONS

The chemical reactions occurring in homogeneous solutions can be followed advantageously by the polarographic method, from the change of limiting currents with time, if at least one of the reactants or products are active polarographically, and provided that the half-time of the reactions is between 30 sec and 3 hr. For faster reactions both the hysteresis (time-constant) of the galvanometer or recorder influences the measurement, and the concentration of the electroactive compound does not remain practically constant during the two or three drop-lives. The latter condition ensures that the mean current recorded with an aperiodically damped galvanometer (or with a recorder of similar properties) corresponds to the mean limiting current. For slower reactions with a half-time of less than 3 hr, many of the advantages of polarographic analysis in reaction kinetics are lost.

The limiting currents used in kinetic studies should be linearly proportional to the concentration of the electroactive substance. Even though the application of other types of limiting currents is principally possible, diffusion controlled limiting currents are the most frequently used.

It is preferable that if two or more components of the reaction mixture are polarographically active, that their waves should be well separated. Sometimes however, it is sufficient that the heights of the waves (with half-wave potentials too near to be separated) are sufficiently different under certain given conditions. The difference in wave-heights can be caused by difference in consumption of the number of electrons transferred[12] in the diffusion coefficients,[13] or in the character of the limiting current.[14] In the latter instance the hydrolysis of pyridoxal-5-phosphate was followed. The resulting pyridoxal gives at pH 2–5 (where the reaction was followed) only a very low kinetic wave (limited by the rate of opening of the hemiacetal ring), but pyridoxal-5-phosphate is reduced in a diffusion controlled two-electron step. The decrease of the current from diffusion current to about 20–30 per cent of the original height (corresponding to the kinetic current) (Fig. 69) was followed and used for the calculation of the rate constant.

The changes in the polarographic waves with time can be recorded in three different ways. For faster reactions the change of the limiting current can be measured continuously. The applied voltage is held constant, at a chosen value corresponding to the potential range of the limiting current of the substance under

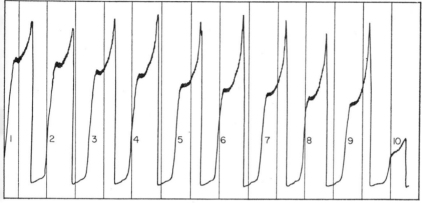

FIG. 69. Polarographic record of the course of hydrolysis of pyridoxal-5-phosphate in 0·01 M perchloric acid.
5 × 10⁻⁴ M Pyridoxal-5-phosphate in 0·01 M perchloric acid, $\mu = 1\cdot0$ at 79°C after: (1) 15; (2) 23; (3) 41; (4) 50·5; (5) 79; (6) 94·5; (7) 110; (8) 125; (9) 152 min; (10) 5 × 10⁻⁴ M pyridoxal. Full scale deflection 10 $\mu$A.

study. As the shift of the paper in the polarographic recording system is usually regular, it is possible to record the current and to register markings after chosen time-intervals (Fig. 70). This type of recording is best suited for reactions with half-times of 30 sec to 5 min.

For reactions with half-times of 3–60 min, it is usually sufficient to record the limiting current only during short time periods, near the time-intervals in which the concentration is to be determined. A constant applied voltage and other arrangements are used, the same as in the previously mentioned modification, and the only difference is that the shift of the paper is not continuous and it is started only a short time before the recording interval (Fig. 71).

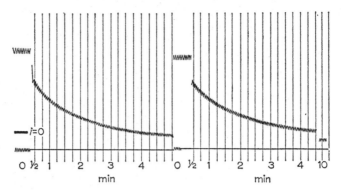

FIG. 70. Oxidation of *threo*-1,2-diphenylethyleneglycol by periodate; decrease in the periodic acid concentration with time.
1 M Acetate buffer pH 4·3, 5 × 10⁻⁵ M potassium periodate, 5 × 10⁻⁵ M diol. Current recorded at − 0·4 V, mercurous sulphate electrode, at 25°C. Time in minutes after mixing. Galvanometer zero and the current before the addition of periodate and after addition at $t = 0$ are marked. Full scale sensitivity 0·7 μA.

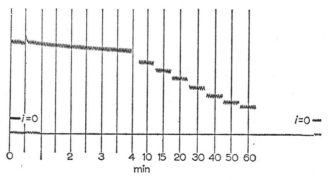

FIG. 71. Oxidation of erythro-butane-2,3-diol by periodate. Decrease of periodic acid limiting current followed continuously up to 4 min, then in the time intervals indicated. 1 M Acetate buffer pH 5·6, 5 × 10⁻⁵ M potassium periodate, 5 × 10⁻⁵ M diol. Current recorded at − 0·6 V, mercurous sulphate electrode, at 25°C. The galvanometer zero and the current before the addition of periodate and after addition at $t = 0$ are marked. Full scale sensitivity 0·7 μA.

When both of these methods are used, it is recommended that a whole polarographic $i$–$E$ curve is recorded after the reaction has finished, to confirm that the potential chosen really corresponded to the limiting current, and that no unexpected side reactions occurred.

Finally, the third type of recording, useful mainly for systems with half-times ranging from 20 min to 3 hr, consists of recording whole polarographic curves (usually at a scanning rate of about 100–200 mV/min) after chosen time intervals. Either the time at the beginning of the recording is registered (also, the time necessary for the shift of paper between this point and the point where the limiting current is measured, is determined once, and always added to the starting time) or the time when the curve reaches the limiting current. With these slower reactions, the precision of time-measurements obtained in this manner is usually sufficient (Figs. 45 and 69).

This latter technique enables us to follow not only the change at a selected point on a polarographic curve, but all changes which occur. Before the first two techniques are used, it is thus necessary to record in the preliminary experiments whole curves, in order to gain any possible information concerning the reaction products and, at the same time, to choose the potential range suitable for the kinetic study.

The advantages of the application of polarography in reaction kinetics can be summarized as follows: In the kinetic run the measurement of the changes of concentration with time can be carried out continuously. The dependence of current (or concentration respectively) on time can be automatically recorded, and the reaction mixture can be often placed directly in the polarographic cell. Also the presence of buffers and neutral salts (contrary to conductimetry), coloured materials, some solvents and even of complicated biological materials do not usually interfere.

The sensitivity of the polarographic method allows the kinetic measurements to be made in $10^{-3}$ M to $10^{-5}$ M solutions. Under these conditions, it is possible to follow the reaction under circumstances in which the reaction is not complicated by side and consecutive reactions of higher orders, that sometimes complicate the course of the reaction. Also the amount of an organic substance needed for an exhaustive kinetic study (often hundreds of concentration–time curves ought to be measured under different conditions) is in polarographic studies substantially smaller than in classical analytical methods.

A striking comparison, demonstrating this type of advantage of polarographic measurement, is the oxidation of diols with periodic acid, followed by both iodimetric titrations and by polarography.[15] With 50 mg of diol it is possible to carry out nine titrations, just enough to construct one concentration–time curve. With the same quantity of sample it is possible to record 100–500 complete concentration–time curves by applying polarography.

Furthermore, it is sometimes possible to measure polarographically simultaneously the concentration change for more than one component of the reaction mixture. When two or more limiting currents at applied potentials are measured, two or more galvanometers are used.[16] The recording of whole curves is often necessary: Thus in the oxidation of hydrobenzoin with periodic acid (Fig. 45) the decrease in the concentration of periodic acid, the increase in the concentration of the benzaldehyde formed and the constant concentration of iodate can be followed. Such measurements enable us to verify the kinetics studied by the use of different equations.

Moreover, polarographic measurements enable us sometimes to detect reaction intermediates (cf. Chapter IX). The result of polarographic kinetic studies can also be sometimes used for the choice of optimum conditions for organic syntheses (cf. Chapter IX).

Special techniques can be used for reactions that are too fast to fall into the limits given for classical polarography. The conditions of mixing become important for these fast reactions, and mixing chambers, similar to those used in flow-methods, are recommended. With such arrangements, it is possible, when measuring the $i$–$t$ curves (on "first drop" or equivalent), to study reactions with half-times between 5 and 15 sec.[17] Even faster reactions, with half-times of the order of 0·01 sec, can be measured using the oscillographic techniques.[18–20]

The scope of polarographic applications in the reaction kinetics of organic compounds is almost as wide as the scope of organic polarography. The reader is referred to the review articles,[21–24] where the particular applications are quoted.

## 10.3. FAST REACTIONS ACCOMPANYING THE ELECTRODE PROCESS AND RATES OF ELECTRODE PROCESS PROPER

From the measurements of polarographic limiting kinetic currents (and sometimes of their half-wave potentials), and their dependence on certain parameters (mainly pH, buffer composition, drop-time etc.), it is possible to compute rate constants for the fast chemical reactions, antecedent, parallel or consecutive to the electrode process proper. Rate constants of the second order reactions of the order $10^5$ to $10^{12}$ l. mol$^{-1}$. sec$^{-1}$ have been determined in this way. The mathematical basis and the method of computation of the rate constants is beyond the scope of this text, and the reader is referred to other texts.[25-33]

From the slope of the polarographic wave much information can be obtained concerning the parameters of the electrode process proper (standard reaction rate $k_0^f$ and the transfer coefficient $\alpha$. The reader is again referred to monographs[25-27] and review articles.[34-36]

### REFERENCES

(1) ZUMAN, P. Unpublished results.
(2) KORYTA, J., *Collect. Czechoslov. Chem. Commun.* **24**, 2903 (1959).
(3) LANGER, A., *Ind. Eng. Chem., Anal. Ed.* **14**, 283 (1942).
(4) FURMAN, N. H. and BRICKER, C. E., *J. Amer. Chem. Soc.* **64**, 660 (1942).
(5) ZUMAN, P., *Collect. Czechoslov. Chem. Commun.* **15**, 839 (1950).
(6) ZUMAN, P. and BŘEZINA, M., *Chem. listy* **46**, 599 (1952).
(7) BŘEZINA, M. and ZUMAN, P., *Chem. listy* **47**, 975 (1953).
(8) ZUMAN, P., *Chem. listy* **45**, 40 (1951).
(9) ZUMAN, P. and ŠANTAVÝ, F., *Collect. Czechoslov. Chem. Commun.* **19**, 174 (1954).
(10) VALENTA, P., *Collect. Czechoslov. Chem. Commun.* **25**, 853 (1960).
(11) VOLKE, J. and VALENTA, P., *Collect. Czechoslov. Chem. Commun.* **25**, 1580 (1960).
(12) HOLLECK, L., and MELKONIAN, G. A., *Naturwiss.* **41**, 304 (1954); *Z. Elektrochem.* **58**, 867 (1954).
(13) BERG, H. and VENNER, H., *Ric. Sci.* **26A**, 646 (1957).
(14) ZUMAN, P. and MANOUŠEK, O., *Collect. Czechoslov. Chem. Commun.* **26**, 2314 (1961).
(15) ZUMAN, P. and KRUPIČKA, J., *Collect. Czechoslov. Chem. Commun.* **23**, 598 (1958).

(16) HOLLECK, L., MELKONIAN, G. A., and KASTENING, B., Z. phys. Chem. (Leipzig) 1958, Sonderheft 197.
(17) BERG, H. and KAPULLA, H., Z. Elektrochem. 64, 44 (1960).
(18) SNOWDEN, F. C. and PAGE, H. T., Anal. Chem. 22, 969 (1950); 24, 1152 (1952).
(19) FAVERO, F., Ric. Sci. 22A, 61 (1952).
(20) DUŠINSKÝ, G., Chem. Zvesti, in the press.
(21) SEMERANO, G., Proc. 1st Internat. Polarograph. Congress, Prague 1951, Pt. I, p. 300, Prague (1951).
(22) BERG, H., Chem. Technik 6, 174 (1954).
(23) SCHWABE, K., Abhandl. sächs. Akad. Wiss., Math. naturwiss. Kl. 44 (1955).
(24) DABARD, R. and TIROUFLET, J., in Advances in Polarography (Proc. 2nd Internat. Congr. Polarography, Cambridge 1959). Vol. 1, p. 288, Pergamon Press, London (1960).
(25) DELAHAY, P., New Instrumental Methods in Electrochemistry, Interscience, New York (1954).
(26) CHARLOT, G., BADOZ-LAMBLING, J., and TRÉMILLON, B., Les Réactions Électrochimiques, Masson, Paris (1959).
(27) VETTER, K. J., Elektrochemische Kinetik, Springer, Berlin (1960).
(28) BRDIČKA, R., Collect. Czechoslov. Chem. Commun. 19S, 41 (1951).
(29) BRDIČKA, R., Z. Elektrochem. 64, 16 (1960).
(30) BRDIČKA, R., in Advances in Polarography (Proc. 2nd Internat. Congress Polarography, Cambridge 1959). Vol. 2, p. 655, Pergamon Press, London (1960).
(31) HANS, W., Z. Elektrochem. 59, 623 (1955).
(32) KORYTA, J., Z. Electrochem. 64, 23 (1960).
(33) NÜRNBERG, H. W. and VON STACKELBERG, M., J. Electroanalyt. Chem. 2, 350 (1961).
(34) GARDNER, H. J. and LYONS, L. E., Revs. Pure Appl. Chem. 3, 134 (1953).
(35) RANDLES, J. E. B., Ric. Sci. 30, Suppl. A, 191 (1960).
(36) RANDLES, J. E. B., Concentration Polarization and the Study of Electrode Kinetics, in Progress in Polarography (P. Zuman, I. M. Kolthoff, editors), Vol. 1, p. 123, Interscience, New York (1962).

# CHAPTER XI

# EFFECTS OF STRUCTURE; POLAROGRAPHY AS A TOOL IN THE ANALYSIS OF STRUCTURES OF ORGANIC SUBSTANCES

CHANGES in the structure of organic substances can be frequently followed by measurements of the shifts in half-wave potentials. Nevertheless other factors, mainly the value of the transfer coefficient $a$ and the number of the electrons transferred during the electrode process, are also of importance in structural problems. Substances on which the effect of the structure can be demonstrated must undergo the electro-reduction or oxidation by the same mechanism. This should be verified with polarographic criteria as well as the auxiliary methods mentioned in Chapters II and III.

## 11.1. EFFECTS OF STRUCTURE ON HALF-WAVE POTENTIALS

Only the half-wave potentials of waves, corresponding to the reductions or oxidations following the same mechanism, should be compared. Moreover, the transfer coefficient $a$ for all waves compared should be practically identical, as should the value of the slope of the dependence of half-wave potentials on pH, $dE_{1/2}/d$ pH. The last condition is best fulfilled when all the half-wave potentials compared are pH-independent. When the pH-region, where the half-wave potentials are no longer pH-dependent, cannot be reached experimentally, the half-wave potentials are compared at a pH-value selected in the pH-region in which the slope of the $E_{1/2}$–pH-dependence is practically identical for all the substances under examination.

The group of substances to be compared can be chosen according to different characteristic properties. Usually the shifts of half-wave potentials are due to (a) an introduction of a substituent (which is polarographically inactive in the given potential range) into the parent compound or (b) an exchange of the polarographically active group.

A selection of structurally related substances $R–A–X$, called reaction series, proved best for the studies of the effects of substituents. In a given reaction series all the substances involved bear, on a given type of skeleton $A$, the same reducible or oxidizable group $R$. The substances in a reaction series differ only in the type of substituent $X$.

For the study of the effect of exchange of the polarographically active grouping, the skeleton (eventually substituted) $A–X$ remains unchanged in the whole group of substances compared. Only the role of the exchange of the reducible or oxidizable group $R$ is followed (e.g. the exchange of Cl for Br or I, of $NO_2$ for NO etc.). The effect of an extension of a conjugated system can also be included here, because a system of conjugated double or triple bonds can be considered as one polarographically active group.

Both these types of effects can be discussed qualitatively, but the recent trend toward quantitative treatments is unambiguous.

The effects of the extension of the conjugated systems (mainly in condensed benzenoid rings, where the reductions of a double bond or a reduction in the side chain are related to the structure of the hydrocarbon), are treated by quantum chemical methods.[1]

The effects of substituents can be treated by the linear free energy relationships, some examples of which will be mentioned here. The most general postulate,[2] on which these treatments are based, is that the shift of the half-wave potentials, ($\Delta E_{1/2}$) relative to that of the parent compound, is due to the more or less independent contributions of the polar $P$, steric $S$ and mesomeric $M$ (resonance) effects of substituents:

$$\Delta E_{1/2} = P + S + M$$

The most generally used special forms of this expression are the modified Hammett equation

$$\Delta E_{1/2} = \rho_{\pi R}\, \sigma_x$$

which is used for benzenoid compounds bearing a reducible group $R$ in the side chain and a substituent $X$ in the $m$- or $p$-position on the benzene ring, and the modified Taft equation

$$\Delta E_{1/2} = \rho_{\pi,R} \ \sigma_X^*$$

which is used for aliphatic and other substances bearing a reducible group $R$ immediately on the "substituent" $X$. In these equations, $\rho_{\pi R}$ and $\rho_{\pi R}^*$ are reaction constants characterizing the reducible group $R$, its susceptibility to the effects of substituents and dependence on reaction conditions, mainly on the supporting electrolyte used; $\sigma_X$ and $\sigma_X^*$ are substituent constants, the values of which, obtained from equilibrium and rate constants, are tabulated. Their value depends on the type and position of substituent, but they are independent of the type of the polarographically active group or the conditions of the polarographic electrolysis.

In practice the measured values of half-wave potentials are plotted against the tabulated values of substituent constants $\sigma$

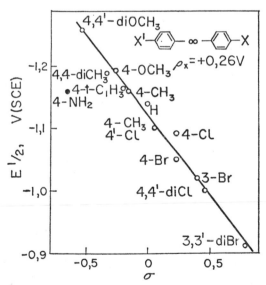

FIG. 72. Dependence of half-wave potentials of the reduction of substituted benzophenones on the Hammett total polar substituent constant $\sigma$. Full point deviates.

R

(Fig. 72) and the value of the reaction constant $\rho$ is determined from the slope. When such a relationship is established in a given reaction series, the values of the half-wave potentials of substances so far unexamined can be predicted. The deviations from the linear relationship enable us to detect deviations from the mechanism of the electrode processes, and to identify, separate and evaluate the steric and mesomeric effects. Applications of these relationships in structural analysis will be mentioned later in this chapter.

## 11.2. STRUCTURAL EFFECTS AND OTHER FACTORS

Polarographic limiting currents also reflect the effects of the structure of organic molecules. The comparison of the height of diffusion currents for different compounds under identical conditions, enable us to discuss the differences in the diffusion coefficients. However, this application has been rarely used because these differences for structurally related compounds are usually small, and thus the comparison depends on the purity of the specimens used.

The possibility mentioned in the last chapter of utilizing limiting currents for the determination of equilibrium and rate constants, can be exploited for the study of structural effects manifested in the values of these constants.

Catalytic currents, maxima and adsorption phenomena also depend on the structure of the organic molecule involved, but no simple and general quantitative relationships for these correlations have been found so far.

## 11.3. POLAROGRAPHY AS A TOOL IN THE ANALYSIS OF THE STRUCTURE OF ORGANIC SUBSTANCES

Polarography can be used for the detection of the type of skeleton, for the identification of a polarographically active group and for the identification of a polarographically inactive substituent.[3] However, with the exception of some special cases, polarography is rarely applied to the detection of the skeleton.

Polarography is more suitable for the verification of the structure of a polarographically active group placed on a skeleton of a given type. For example, the relatively positive waves, corresponding to a four-electron and a two-electron reduction and showing a typical change with pH, can distinguish the nitro-alkanes from practically all other common aliphatic substances which bear other reducible groups. Similarly, the behaviour of substances bearing a thiol group is usually sufficiently characteristic; mainly the pH-dependence of the anodic waves and their dependence on the concentration of the thiol are so typical, that they can be used for the identification of this group.

For benzenoid compounds it is possible, based on the potential-region in which the reduction is observed, to eliminate several reducible groups (Fig. 38). Thus a benzenoid derivative showing a reducible group in the vicinity of $-1.0$ V at pH 5–8 is neither nitro-, nitroso- or an azobenzene derivative. In addition, this compound also cannot be either an iodobenzene derivative or a derivative of a benzoic acid alkylester. Such a method of detection of a reducible group on a benzenoid ring, combined with a study of the polarographic behaviour is thus possible, but surely does not belong to the usual everyday problems of structural analysis.

On the other hand, however, the practical applications of polarography have proved best suited for the detection of some functional groupings in alicyclic, terpenoid and other more complicated substances.

Thus it was possible to determine the presence or absence of an *aldehydic group* in several terpenoid substances. Such a problem was also studied with some antibiotics, alkaloids and pterines. The detection of the *disulphidic group* has also proved useful for some natural compounds.

Even though the possibilities that polarography offers for the identification or verification of the presence of a certain polarographically active group, are substantially more promising than the identification of the skeleton, nevertheless the possibility of this type of polarographic application is still relatively little recognized. One of the reasons is undoubtedly the limited number of polarographically active groups. On the other hand, polarography offers a solution of some problems (e.g. distinguishing an aldehydic or ketonic carbonyl from a lactonic carbonyl) which are rather difficult even by i.r. spectroscopy.

Finally, by using the free energy relationships in the form of the modified Hammett and Taft equations[1] and the tabulated values for the substituent constants $\sigma$, it is possible to distinguish a substituent $X$ in a molecule $X–A–R$ when both the skeleton $A$ and the reducible group $R$ are known. An example of this type is the recently demonstrated possibility of distinguishing the type and position of the substituent on a pteridine ring.[4] Polarography is very well suited for the solution of such problems, but for simpler molecules such questions are rarely important, and for the more complicated substances there is not usually a sufficient number of standard substances available for establishing the $E_{1/2}$–$\sigma$ relationships.

## 11.4. DETECTION OF REACTIVE FORMS AND INTERMEDIATES

Even wider polarographic applications are offered in the identification and detection of reactive forms and intermediates, in chemical and electrochemical reactions.

By this method, it is possible to study in chemical reactions the unstable forms which occur in the bulk of the solution, in the "reaction layer" in the neighbourhood of the dropping electrode, and in electrochemical reactions involving the impact of the organic molecule with an electron or electrode respectively.

### 11.4.1. *Reactions in the Bulk of the Solution*

The formation of reactive forms and intermediates, can be detected polarographically from measurements of the kinetics of homogeneous chemical reactions mentioned in Chapter X. The detection of the reactive forms and intermediates is based on treatments used in chemical kinetics.

In some instances, the reactive forms or the intermediates themselves, show polarographic waves which are separated from those of reactants and products. The formation of the thiol form of thiamine,[5] the bicyclic form of protopine[6] and the enediol forms of some sugars[7] and pyridoine[8] are examples of the formation and detection of reactive forms. A few examples of the detection of intermediates, are the diketone and enediol produced during the alkaline degradation of phenylglyoxal[9] and of $\alpha$, $\beta$-unsaturated ketone as an intermediate in the cleavage[10] of tropane-3-one-methoiodide and its sulphur analogue, mentioned in Chapter IX.

### 11.4.2. *Chemical Reactions Accompanying the Electrode Process*

Among the fast chemical reactions accompanying electrode processes, acid-base, hydration, cyclization and a keto-enol transformation have so far been detected from kinetic current measurements. The existence of several less familiar protonized acid forms can also be detected, e.g. for some carbonyl compounds,[11, 12] oximes[13] and for some nitrogen heterocyclics and azulenes.[14] Predominant existence of the hydrated form was detected for aldehydes[15-23] and keto-acids[23-25], and the importance of cyclic forms for aldoses,[26-29] coumarine,[30, 31] pyridoxal[19] etc. was demonstrated.

### 11.4.3. *Electrochemical Reactions*

The most frequent question that can be answered from an inspection of polarographic curves, is whether or not in a reduction a radical is formed. The formation of a radical intermediate is shown by two separated one-electron waves (Fig. 73) (or by one

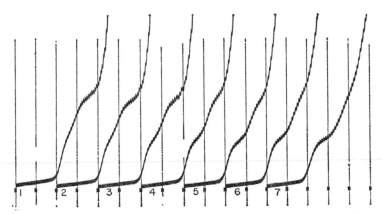

FIG. 73. Effect of ionic strength on reduction of benzaldehyde. $2 \times 10^{-4}$ M Benzaldehyde, acetate buffer pH 3·7. Concentration of acetate: (1) 1·0 M; (2) 0·6 M; (3) 0·3 M; (4) 0·1 M; (5) 0·06 M; (6) 0·03 M; (7) 0·01 M. Curves starting at —0·4, S.C.E., 200 mV/absc., full scale sensitivity 4·2 μA.

single one-electron wave, the other wave being at such negative potentials that it is obscured by the electrolytic current of the particles of the buffer solution). Another example is the detection of the quinoid form, formed as an intermediate in the reduction of *o*- and *p*-nitrophenols and -anilines, as well as of monooximes and dioximes derived from quinones. In substances bearing two different reducible groups, it is possible to distinguish which is reduced at the more positive potentials, and thus which of the two possible partially reduced products is formed (cf. Chapter IX). In substances bearing two identical groups in nonequivalent positions it is sometimes possible to distinguish which undergoes reduction at the more positive potentials, and thus which of the possible intermediates is formed.

Polarography can be also used for the study and interpretation of large-scale electrolysis.[32]

## REFERENCES

(1) ZUMAN, P., Current Trends in the Study of the Influence of Structure on the Polarographic Behaviour of Organic Substances, in *Progress in Polarography* (P. Zuman, I. M. Kolthoff, editors), Vol. 1, p. 319, Interscience, New York (1962), where further references are exhaustively quoted.

(2) ZUMAN, P., *Collection* **25**, 3225 (1960).

(3) ZUMAN, P., *Chem. listy* **55**, 261 (1961); *Z. Chemie* (*Leipzig*) in the press, where further references are given.

(4) KOMENDA, J., *Collect. Czechoslov. Chem. Commun.* **126**, 212 (1961).

(5) BŘEZINA, M. and ZUMAN, P., *Polarography in Medicine, Biochemistry and Pharmacy*, p. 386, Interscience, New York (1958).

(6) SLAVÍK, J., SLAVÍKOVÁ, L., PREININGER, V. and ŠANTAVÝ, F., *Collect. Czechoslov. Chem. Commun.* **21**, 1058 (1956).

(7) PETUELY, F. and KÜNSBERG, V., *Monatsch. Chem.* **83**, 80 (1952).

(8) HOLUBEK, J. and VOLKE, J., *Collect. Czechoslov. Chem. Commun.* **25**, 3292 (1960).

(9) HOLLECK, L., MELKONIAN, G. A. and KASTENING, B., *Z. physikal. Chem.* (*Leipzig*) Sonderheft 1958, 197.

(10) HORÁK, V. and ZUMAN, P., *Tetrahedron Letters* **21**, 746 (1961).

(11) ZUMAN, P., TENYGL, J. and BŘEZINA, M., *Collect. Czechoslov. Chem. Commun.* **19**, 46 (1954).

(12) ZUMAN, P. and HORÁK, V. *Collect. Czechoslov. Chem. Commun.* **26**, 176 (1961).

(13) SOUCHAY, P. and SER, S., *J. Chim. Phys.* **49**, C172 (1952).

(14) ZUMAN, P., *Z. physikal. Chem.* (*Leipzig*) Sonderheft 1958, 246.

(15) VESELÝ, K. and BRDIČKA, R., *Collect. Czechoslov. Chem. Commun.* **12**, 313 (1947).

(16) BIEBER, R. and TRÜMPLER, G., *Helv. Chim. Acta* **30**, 706, 971, 1109, 1286, 1534, 2000 (1947); **31**, 5 (1948).

(17) LANDQVIST, N., *Acta Chem. Scand.* **9**, 867 (1955).

(18) FEDERLIN, P., *Compt. rend.* **232**, 60 (1951); **237**, 254 (1953).

(19) VOLKE, J., *Collect. Czechoslov. Chem. Commun.* **23**, 1486 (1958); *Z. physikal. Chem. (Leipzig)* Sonderheft 1958, 268.

(20) VOLKE, J. and VALENTA, P., *Collect. Czechoslov. Chem. Commun.* **25**, 1580 (1960).

(21) TIROUFLET, J., FOURNARI, P. and CHANÉ, J. P., *Compt. rend.* **242**, 1799 (1956).

(22) TIROUFLET, J. and LAVIRON, E., *Compt. rend.* **247**, 217 (1958); *Ric. Sci.* **29A**, 189 (1959).

(23) ONO, S., TAKAGI, M. and WASA, T., *Bull. Chem. Soc. Japan* **31**, 356 (1958).

(24) KŮTA, J., *Collect. Czechoslov. Chem. Commun.* **24**, 2532 (1959).

(25) ONO, S., TAKAGI, M. and WASA, T., *Collect. Czechoslov. Chem. Commun.* **26**, 141 (1961).

(26) WIESNER, K., *Collect. Czechoslov. Chem. Commun.* **12**, 64 (1947).

(27) LOS, J. M. and WIESNER, K., *J. Amer. Chem. Soc.* **75**, 6346 (1953).

(28) LOS, J. M., SIMPSON, L. B. and WIESNER, K., *J. Amer. Chem. Soc.* **78**, 1564 (1956).

(29) LOS, J. M. and GASPAR, N. J., *Z. Electrochem.* **64**, 41 (1960).

(30) HARLE, A. J. and LYONS, L. E., *J. Chem. Soc.* 1950, 1575.

(31) PATZAK, R. and NEUGEBAUER, K., *Monatsch. Chem.* **82**, 662 (1951); **83**, 776 (1953).

(32) HOLLECK, L. and SCHMIDT, H., *Z. Elektrochem.* **59**, 1039 (1955).

# LITERATURE CONCERNED WITH
# ORGANIC POLAROGRAPHIC ANALYSIS

## TEXTBOOKS

1. BŘEZINA, M. and ZUMAN, P., *Polarografie v lékařství, biochemii a farmacii*, p. 536 (Czech) Zdravotnické nakladatelství, Praha (1952); *Die Polarographie in der Medizin, Biochemie und Pharmazie*, p. 800, Akademische Verlagsgesellschaft, Leipzig (1956); *Polarography in Medicine, Biochemistry and Pharmacy*, p. 883, Interscience, New York (1958).

2. HEYROVSKÝ, J., *Polarographie, theoretische Grundlagen, praktische Ausführung und Anwendungen der Elektrolyse mit der tropfenden Quecksilverelektrode*, p. 514, Springer, Wien (1941). Reprinted Edwards Brothers, Ann. Arbor, Mich. (1944).

3. HEYROVSKÝ, J. and ZUMAN, P., *Úvod do praktickej polarografie* (*Introduction to practical polarography*) p. 206 (Slovak) Práca, Bratislava (1950); (Czech) Nakladatelství Českoslov. Akademie věd, p. 199, Praha (1953); (Hungarian) Akadémiai Kiadó, p. 204, Budapest (1955); (Polish) Panstwowe Wydawnictwo Naukowe, p. 252, Warszawa (1956); (German) Verlag Technik, p. 236, 1959.

4. KOLTHOFF, I. M. and LINGANE, J. J., *Polarography*. Second, completely revised and augmented edition in two volumes. Vol. I, *Theoretical principles, instrumentation and technique*. Vol. II, *Inorganic-organic-biological applications; amperometric titrations*, p. 990, Interscience, New York (1952); (Chinese) Science Publs., p. 285, Peking (1955); pp. i–ix and 287–605 (1957).

5. MEITES, L., *Polarographic techniques*, pp. xiii and 317, Interscience, New York (1955).

6. MILNER, G. W. C., *The principles and applications of polarography and other electroanalytical processes*, p. 729, Longmans, London (1957).

7. MÜLLER, O. H., *The polarographic method of analysis*, Chemical Education Publ. Co., Easton, Pa. 1941; second edition, revised and augmented, *ibid.* p. 209 (1951).

8. SCHWABE, K. (Collab. H. J. Bär, G. Dietz and R. Tümmler), *Polarographie und chemische Konstitution organischer Verbindungen*, p. 447, Akademie Verlag, Berlin (1957).

9. VON STACKELBERG, M., *Polarographische Arbeitsmethoden*, p. 478, Walter de Gruyter, Berlin (1950).

10. TERENT'EV, A. P. and YANOVSKAYA, L. A., Polarograficheskiy method v organicheskoi khimii (Polarographic method in organic chemistry) in *Reakcii i metody issledovaniya organischeskikh soedineni (Reactions and investigation methods of organic compounds)*, vol. 5, p. 388, Gosudarstvennoe nauch.-tekhn. Izdatel'stvo khim. Literatury, Moskva (1957).

11. ZAGÓRSKI, Z., *Metoda polarograficzna v analizie chemicznej (Polarographic method in chemical analysis)*, p. 594, (Polish) Panstwowe Wydawnictwo Naukowe, Warszawa (1956).

12. ZUMAN, P., *Vliv konstituce na polarografické chování organických látek (The influence of structure on polarographic behaviour of organic substances)*, (Czech), Nakladatelství Čs. akademie věd, p. 64, Praha (1954).


BIBLIOGRAPHIES

13. GAGLIARDO, ELENA, *Bibliografia polarografica*, 1922–1951 (*Polarographic bibliography*, (1922–1951), Supplemento N. 4, *Suppl. Ric. Sci.* 21, p. 63 (1951). (Italian, English, French, German).

14. HEYROVSKÝ, J., *Polarographic bibliography*, 1922–1950 (English, French, German, Russian), Part 2 of the Proceedings of the 1st Itnernational Polarographic Congress in Prague 1951, p. 194, Přírodovědecké vydavatelství, Praha (1952).

15. HEYROVSKÝ, J., Bibliography of publications dealing with the polarographic method in 1953 (English, French, German), *Collect. Czechoslov. Chem. Commun.* Suppl. I, **19**, p. 38 (1954) item in 1954, *ibid.* **20**, p. 61 (1955); item in 1955, *ibid.* **21**, p. 76 (1956); item in 1956, *ibid.* **22**, p. 79 (1957); item in 1957, *ibid.* **23**, p. 79 (1958); item in 1958, *ibid.* **24**, p. 96 (1959).

16. HEYROVSKÝ, J. and HAN, J. E. S., *Subject index to polarographic literature*, vol. 2, 1951–1955 (English, Chinese), p. 519, Academia Sinica, Peking (1958).

17. HEYROVSKÝ, J. and MÜLLER, O. H., Bibliography of publications dealing with the polarographic method in 1951 (English, French, German), *Collect. Czechoslov. Chem. Commun.* Suppl. I, **16/17**, p. 31 (1951–52); item in 1952, *ibid.* **18**, p. 46 (1953).

18. ISHIBASHI, M. and FUJINAGA, T., *Bibliography of polarographic publications* (issued quarterly) (*A*) *Metallic elements*, No. 1, p. 8 (1956); No. II, p. 12 (1957); No. III, p. 8; No. IV, p. 6. Supplement to the former bibliographies: No. V, p. 10, No. VI, p. 6. Publ. Shimadzu, Kyoto, Japan.

19. LEEDS NORTHRUP CO., Philadelphia, *Bibliography of the polarized dropping mercury electrode* (1941); (1943); *Bibliography of polarographic literature* (E-90/1), p. 102 (1955).

20. MENEGUS-SCARPA, MARIA, Bibliografia polarografica (1922–1954), Supplemento N. 6, Supp. *Ric. Sci.* **24**, p. 56 (1954).

21. MENEGUS-SCARPA, MARIA and GAGLIARDO, ELENA, Bibliografia polarografica (1922–1953), Supplemento N. 5, Suppl. *Ric. Sci.* **23**, p. 94 (1953).
22. MENEGUS-SCARPA, MARIA and TOSINI, BIANCA, Bibliografia polarografica (1922–1954), Supplemento N. 7, Suppl. *Ric. Sci.* **25**, p. 49 (1955).
23. SARGENT, E. H., AND CO., *Bibliography of polarographic literature*, 1922–1941, Chicago, Ill., p. 29 (1941); item, 1922–1945, *ibid.*, p. 169 (1946).
24. SCHMITZ, C. L. and EVEN, E. F., *Bibliography of polarographic literature* 1922–1955 (with Subject Index), E. H. Sargent & Co., 4647, West Foster Avenue, Chicago, 30, Ill., p. 192 (1956).
25. SEMERANO, G., Bibliografia polarographica (1922–1949). Parte I. Elenco dei lavori e indica degli autori. (Polarographic bibliography 1922–1949). Part I. List of papers and authors index (Suppl. *Ric. Sci.* **19**, p. 140 (1949).
26. TOSINI, BIANCA, Bibliografia polarografica (1922–1955), Supplemento N. 9, *Suppl. Ric. Sci.* **26**, p. 58 (1956); item (1922–1956), Supplemento N. 9, *ibid.* **27**, p. 63 (1957); item (1922–1957), Supplemento N. 10, *ibid.* **28**, p. 79 (1958); item (1957). Parte II. Indice per soggetti. (Part II, Subject Index), Supplemento N. 10A, *ibid.* **28**, p. 96 (1958) (in English).

## PROCEEDINGS OF CONGRESSES AND SPECIAL ISSUES OF JOURNALS

27. *Acta Chim. Acad. Sci. Hungar.* **9**, No. 1–4 (1956) (Hungarian–Czechoslovak Polarographic Conference, Veszprém 1955); **18**, No. 1–4 (1959) (Conference of the Society of Hungarian Chemists, Budapest, 1958).
28. *Advances in Polarography* (Proc. 2nd Internat. Congr. Polarography, Cambridge, 1959) edited by I. S. Longmuir, vol. 1–3, p. 1204, Pergamon Press, Oxford (1960).
29. *Chem. listy* **54**, No. 12 (1960) (70th Birthday of Professor Heyrovský).
30. *Chem. Zvesti* **8**, No. 10 and 10A (1954) (Discussion Polarographic Meeting, Smolenice, 1954).
31. *Collect. Czech. Chem. Communs.* **15**, No. 12 (1950) (60th Birthday of Professor Heyrovský); **25**, No. 12 (1960) and **26**, No. 1 (1961) (70th Birthday of Professor Heyrovský).
32. Contributi teorici e sperimentali di polarografia (Theoretical and experimental contributions to polarography) A supplement to *Ric. Sci.* Vol. 1 (1952), Vol. II (1956), Vol. III (1957), Vol. IV (1959), Vol. V (1960) (Proceedings of the Conferences at Bressanone).
33. *Prace konferencji polarograficznej w Warszawie 1956* (*Proceedings of the Polarographic Conference in Warsaw*) p. 548, Państwowe wydawnictwo naukowe, Warszawa (1957).

34. *Proc. Internat. Symposium on Microchemistry, Birmingham 1958,* p. 248–304, Pergamon Press, Oxford (1960).
35. *Proc. 1st Internat. Congr. of Polarography, Prague 1951. Přírodovédecké vydavatelství,* Praha, Part I, p. 865 (1951); Part III, p. 774 (1952).
36. *Z. anal. Chem.* **173,** No. 1 (1960) (Internat. Polarograph. Symposium, Bonn 1958).
37. *Z. Elektrochem.* **64,** No. 1 (1960) (Internat. Symposium on Fast Reactions, Hahnenklee 1959).
38. *Z. physikal. Chem. (Leipzig),* Sonderheft (1958) (Internat. Polarograph. Symposium, Dresden 1957).

REVIEWS

39. BERG, H., Polarographie und Reaktionskinetik (Polarography and reaction kinetics), *Chem. Technik* **8,** 5 (1956).
40. BERG, H., Polarographischen Reaktionsgeschwindigkeitsmessungen in Mikrobiologie und Biochemie, *Ric. Sci.* **27,** Suppl. 184 (1957).
41. BOBROVA, M. I. and SOKOLOV, N. P., Tablica potencijalov vosstanovlenija organičeskich veščestev na rtutnom kapelnom elektrode (Tables of Reduction Potentials of Organic Compounds at the Dropping Mercury Electrode), *Zavodskaja Lab.* **15,** 36 (1949).
42. BRDIČKA, R., Vlastnosti organických sloučenin ve světle polarografické elektrolysy (The Properties of Organic Compounds in the Light of Polarographic Electrolysis). *Časopis českého Lékárnictva* **4,** 53 (1948).
43. DABARD, R. and TIROUFLET, J., Quelques applications de la polarographie en cinétique organique (Some applications of polarography in organic kinetics), *Advances in Polarography.* Vol. 1, p. 288, Pergamon Press, Oxford (1960).
44. DELMARCO, A., Recenti applicazioni del metodo polarografico in cinetica chimica. (Recent applications of polarographic method in chemical kinetics), *Ric. Sci.* **27,** Suppl. 134 (1957).
45. ELVING, P. J., Application of Polarography to Organic Analysis in in J. MITCHELL Jr., *Organic Analysis* Vol. II, p. 195, Interscience, New York (1954).
46. ELVING, P. J., Mechanism of reduction of organic substances, *Ric. Sci.* **30,** Suppl. 205 (1960).
47. ELVING, P. J., Polarography in Organic Analysis, in *Progress in Polarography,* vol. 2, p. 625, Interscience, New York (1962).
48. FREESE, F., Polarografie van organische verbindingen (Polarography of Organic Compounds), *Chem. Weekbl.* **50,** 781 (1954).
49. GARDNER, H. J. and LYONS, L. E., The Polarographic Reduction of Organic Compounds, *Rev. pure appl. Chem.* **3,** 134 (1953).
50. GIVEN, P. H. and PEOVER, M. E., Some Aspects of the Polarography of Organic Substances in Organic Solvents, in *Advances in Polarography,* Vol. 3, p. 948. Pergamon Press, Oxford (1960).

51. GRIGGIO, L., Indagini polarografiche su sistemi organici (Polarographic Investigations on Organic systems), *Ric. Sci.* **27**, Suppl. 79 (1957).
52. HANUŠ, V., The Polarographic Behaviour of Organic Compounds, in *Proc. 1st Internat. Polarograph. Congr. Prague* 1951, Vol. 3, p. 103, Prague (1952).
53. KAPCAN, O. L. and NEIMAN, M. B., Uspechi polarografii organičeskich sojedineniji (Success of the Polarography of Organic Substances), *Zh. Anal. Chim.* **5**, 178 (1950).
54. KOIDE, S., Recent Application of Organic Polarography. *Rev. modern. Polarography (Japan)* Nr. 11, p. 40 (1950).
55. KORŠUNOV, I. A., Primenenie poljarografii v organičeskom analize. (Application of Polarography in Organic Analysis), *Zavodskaja Lab.* **24**, 543 (1958).
56. MÜLLER, O. H., Polarography, in S. WEISSBERGER, *Physical Methods of Organic Chemistry*, p. 1785, Interscience, New York (1949).
57. MÜLLER, O. H., Oxidation and Reduction of Organic Compounds at the Dropping Mercury Electrode, *Chem. Rev.* **24**, 95 (1939).
58. NAGATA, J., Recent Polarographic Studies on the Carbonyl Compounds, *Review of Polarography (Japan)* **6**, 124 (1958); **7**, 12 (1959).
59. NÜRNBERG, H. W., Die Anwendung der Polarographie in der organischen Chemie (Applications of Polarography in Organic Chemistry), *Angew. Chem.* **72**, 433 (1960).
60. PAGE, J. E., Polarography of Organic Compounds, *Quart. Rev. Chem. Soc. Lond.* **6**, 262 (1952).
61. PAGE, J. E., Application of Polarography in Pharmaceutical Analysis. *J. Pharm. Lond.*, **4**, 1 (1952).
62. SCHWABE, K., Neuere polarographische Untersuchungen (New Polarographic Studies), *Chem. Techn.* **9**, 129 (1957).
63. SCHWABE, K., Polarographie in nichtwässrigen Lösungen (Polarography in Nonaqueous solutions), in *Progress in Polarography*, Vol. 1, p. 333, Interscience, New York (1962).
64. SEMERANO, G., L'indagine polarografica in cinetica chimica (Polarographic Investigations in Chemical Kinetics), *Ric. Sci.* **22**, Suppl. 197 (1952).
65. SOUCHAY, P., Applications of polarography to analytical chemistry, *Proc. 7th Meeting Internat. Commit. of Electrochem. Thermodyn. and Kinetics, Poitiers 1954*, p. 425, Butterworths, London 1955.
66. VON STACKELBERG, M., Elektrochemische Potentiale organischer Stoffe. (Electrochemical Potentials of Organic Substances) in HOUBEN-WEYL, *Methoden der organischen Chemie*, edited by E. Müller, Vol. III/2, p. 257, 4th edition, G. Thieme, Stuttgart (1954).
67. VON STACKELBERG, M., Polarographie organischer Stoffe. (Polarography of Organic Substances) in HOUBEN-WEYL, *Methoden der organischen Chemie*, edited by E. Müller. Vol. III/2, p. 297, 4th edition, G. Thieme, Stuttgart (1954).

68. TACHI, I., Polarographic Analysis of Organic Compounds. *Recent Advances Analyt. Chem. (Japan)* **4**, 107 (1952).
69. TACHI, I. and KOIDE, S., Applications of Polarography in Organic Chemistry, *J. Org. Synthesis (Japan)* **11**, 244 (1953).
70. TIROUFLET, J., Le méchanisme de réactions en chimie organique. Les apparts de la polarographie (Mechanism of Reactions in Organic Chemistry. Applications of Polarography), Communic. 84e Congres des Sociétés savantes, p. 215, Dijon 1959.
71. TIROUFLET, J., Structure chimique et comportement polarographique en chimie hétérocyclique (Chemical Structure and Polarographic Behaviour in Heterocyclic Chemistry), in *Advances in Polarography*, vol. 2, p. 740, Pergamon Press, Oxford (1960).
72. TIROUFLET, J. and DABARD, R., L'analyse polarographique en série aromatique. (Polarographic Analysis in Aromatic Series). *Ric. Sci.* **29**, Suppl. 211 (1959).
73. TIROUFLET, J. and LAVIRON, E., L'analyse polarographique en séries hétérocycliques (Polarographic Analysis in Heterocyclic Series), *Ric. Sci.* **29**, Suppl. 189 (1959).
74. TIROUFLET, J. and PERSON, M., Le méchanisme de la réduction polarographique en chimie organique (Mechanism of Polarographic Reduction in Organic Chemistry), Communic. 84e Congres des Sociétés savantes, p. 209, Dijon 1959.
75. VELDSTRA, H., On the Use of the Polarographic Method in Organic Chemistry and in Biochemistry. *Chem. Weekbl.* **44**, 245, 261 (1948).
76. VOLKE, J., Die Anwendung der Polarographie in der Pharmazie, *Leybold polarograph. Ber.* **2**, 175 (1954).
77. WAEL, J. DE, Polarografie in de biochemie (Polarography in Biochemistry), *Chem. Weekbl.* **50**, 778 (1954).
78. WAWZONEK, S., Organic Polarography, *Analyt. Chem.* **21**, 61 (1949); **22**, 30 (1950); **24**, 65 (1954); **28**, 638 (1956); **30**, 661 (1958); **32**, 1445 (1960).
79. ZUMAN, P., A List of Half-Wave Potentials. *Collect. Czechoslov. Chem. Commun.* **15**, 1107 (1950).
80. ZUMAN, P., Polarographie in der organischen Analyse. (Polarography in Organic Analysis), *Proc. 1st Internat. Polarograph. Congr., Prague 1951*, Vol. 3, p. 167 Prague (1952).
81. ZUMAN, P., Polarographie in der Pharmazie (Polarography in Pharmacy), *Pharmazie* **8**, 903 (1953); *Československ. Farmac.* **2**, 413 (1953).
82. ZUMAN, P., Vliv konstituce na polarografické chování organických látek (The Influence of Structure on Polarographic Behaviour of Organic Substances), *Chem. listy.* **48**, 94 (1954).
83. ZUMAN, P. Pokroky polarografie ve farmacii (Advances of Polarography in Pharmacy), *Československ. Farmac.* **5**, 44 (1956); *Pharmazie* **11**, 449 (1956).
84. ZUMAN, P., A General Equation for the Effect of Substituents on Half-Wave Potentials, *Ric. Sci.* **30**, Suppl. 229 (1960).

85. ZUMAN, P., Sterische Einflüsse in der organischen Polarographie (Steric Effects in Organic Polarography), *Acta chim. Acad. Sci. Hungar.* **18**, 141 (1959).
86. ZUMAN, P., Influence of Substituents in Aliphatic and Heterocyclic Series, in *Advances in Polarography*. Vol. 3, p. 812, Pergamon Press, Oxford (1960).
87. ZUMAN, P., Studium vlivu konstituce na polarografické chování organických látek v Polarografickém ústavu ČSAV (Study of the Influence of Structure on Polarographic Behaviour of Organic Substances in Polarographic Institute ČSAV), *Chem. listy* **54**, 1244 (1960), *J. Polarograph. Soc.* **7**, 66 (1961).
88. ZUMAN, P., Použití polarografie k studiu konstituce organických látek a meziproduktů (Applications of Polarography for the Study of Structure of Organic Substances and Intermediates), *Chem. listy* **55**, 261 (1961), 2. f. Chemie (Leipzig) in the press.
89. ZUMAN, P., Current Trends in the Study of the Influence of Structure on the Polarographic Behaviour of Organic Substances, in *Progress in Polarography*, Vol. 1, p. 319, Interscience, New York (1962).
90. ZUMAN, P. and BŘEZINA, M., Polarographic Analysis in Pharmacy, in *Progress in Polarography*, Vol. 2, p. 687, Interscience, New York (1961).
91. ZUMAN, P. and WAWZONEK, S., Trends in Organic Polarography, in *Progress in Polarography*, Vol. 1, p. 303, Interscience, New York 1962.

# AUTHOR INDEX

*(Page numbers in italic indicate that the name is in a reference list)*

ADAMS R. N.   34, *58*
ANTWEILER H. J.   2, *29*
ASAHI Y.   190, *223*
AYRES W. M.   211, 217, *225, 226*

BACHE C. A.   203, *224*
BADOZ-LAMBLING J.   243, *244*
BÄR H. J.   *254*
BAGGESGAARD-RASMUSSEN H.   118, *166*
BALTES J.   163, *171*
DAMBACH K.   133, *167*
BARENDRECHT E.   211, *225*
BARKER G. C.   44, *59*
BARTEL E. T.   16, 17, *30*
BECKER M.   16, *30*
BENESCH R.   156, *169*, 176, *184*
BENESCH R. E.   156, *169*, 176, *184*
BENÍŠEK L.   221, 222, *226*
BERG H.   18, *30*, 238, 242, *243, 244, 257*
BERGEROVA'-FIŠEROVA' V.   116, *165*
BERGMEYER H. V.   133, *168*
BESSO Z.   117, *165*
BEZUGLYJ V. D.   115, *165*, 209 210, 213, 214, *225, 226*
BIEBER R.   12, *29*, 251, *253*
BISTER F.   134, *168*
BITTER B.   176, *184*, 191, *223*
BLAEDEL W. J.   139, 140, *168*
BLAŽEJ A.   158, 163, *170, 171*, 221 *226*
BLAŽEK J.   159, *170*, 187, *223*
BOBROVA M. I.   *257*

BOGDANOV S. G.   160, *170*
BOHDANECKÝ M.   212, 213, *225*
BORROWS E. T.   174, *184*
BOTT M. C.   205, *224*
BOVEY F. A.   163, *171*
BOWEN C. V.   203, *224*
BOYD M. J.   133, *167*
BOZSAI I.   156, *169*
BRABENCOVA' H.   195, *223*
BRDIČKA R.   1, 12, 13, 15, 20, *29*, 195, 196, 197, 198, 199, 220, 221, *223, 226*, 243, *244*, 251, *253, 257*
BREIIMER CII.   100, *106*
BREYER B.   44, 52, *59*
BŘEZINA M.   20, 29, *30*, 63, 65, *82*, 100, *106*, 120, 121, 125, 155, *166, 167, 169*, 185, 192, 194, 203, *223 224*, 235, *243*, 250, 251, *252, 254, 260*
BRICKER C. E.   234, *243*
BÜCHNER M.   100, *106*
BURKHARDT R.   140, *168*

CANNON W. A.   133, *167*
CASWELL R. L.   203, *224*
ČERŇA'K J.   221, *226*
CERVONE E.   159, *170*
ČIHA'KOVA' M.   157, 159, *169*
ČIHALÍK J.   156, *169*
CHANÉ J. P.   251, *253*
CHANG S. S.   201, *224*
CHARLOT G.   243, *244*
CHLOPIN N. JA.   200, *224*
CHODKOWSKI J.   17, 26, *30*
CHUNG Y. H.   209, *225*

CHVAPIL M. 193, *223*
CLAVER G. C. 210, *225*
CONN J. B. 159, *170*
CONRAD A. L. 209, *225*
COULSON D. M. 124, 160, *166*, *170*
CROWELL W. R. 160, *170*
CZARNECKI K. 161, *170*, *171*

DABARD R. 242, *244*, *257*, *259*
DANIEL R. L. 136, *168*
DAVÍDEK J. 119, 120, *166*
DELAHAY P. 2, 243, *244*
DELMARCO A. *257*
DESHPANDE S. M. 160, *170*
DeVRIES T. 201, 209, *224*
DIETZ G. *254*
DIRSCHERL W. 133, *168*
DLEZEK J. 145, *169*
DMITRIJEVA V. N. 210, 213, 214, *225*, *226*
DOBRINSKAJA A. A. 176, *184*
DOLEŽAL J. 156, 158, 160, *169*, *170*
DOMANSKÝ R. 141, *168*
DREWES S. E. 164, *171*
DRUSHEL H. V. 208, *225*
DUŠINSKÝ G. 188, 190, *223*, 242, *244*
DUYCKAERTS G. 163, *171*
DYER E. 211, *225*

ECCLESTON B. H. 209, *225*
EDWARDS F. I. 203, *224*
ELOFSON R. M. 162, *171*
ELVING P. J. 65, *82*, 130, 133, 143, *167*, *168*, 228, *230*, *231*, *257*
ENGLISH F. L. 119, *166*
ENOKI T. 162, *171*
ERBEN J. 178, *184*
EVEN E. F. *256*
EXNER J. 212, 213, *225*
EXNER O. 15, *30*

FARAGGI S. 132, *167*
FARSANG GY. 20, *31*
FASSBENDER H. 20, *31*
FAVERO F. 242, *244*
FEDERLIN P. 251, *253*
FERNANDO Q. 163, *171*
FIESER L. F. 125, 126, *166*, *167*
FILIPOWICZ B. 194, *223*
FILOV V. A. 132, *167*
FISHER D. J. 78, *82*
FODIMAN Z. I. 58, *60*
FOREJT J. 44, 50, *59*
FOURNARI P. 251, *253*
FRANCIS C. V. 145, *168*
FREEDBERG A. S. 134, *168*
FREESE F. *257*
FRUMKIN A. N. 16, 26, *30*, 68, *82*
FUJINAGA T. 44, *59*, 165, *171*, *255*
FUKAMI H. 202, *224*
FUKKER K. 101, *106*, 222, *226*
FURMAN N. H. 142, *168*, 234, *243*

GAGLIARDO E. *255*, *256*
GANTZ E. S. C. 127, *167*, 212, 215, 217, *225*, *226*
GARDER H. J. 243, *244*, *257*
GARN P. D. 205, 212, *224*, *225*
GASPAR N. J. 13, *30*, 251, *253*
GAYLORD V. F. 209, *224*
GERBER M. I. 172, *184*, 207, 208, 209, *225*
GIANG P. A. 203, *224*
GILBERT E. 140, *168*
GILLAM W. S. 200, *224*
GILROY H. M. 212, *225*
GINZBERG E. G. 211, *225*
GISCLARD J. B. 193, *223*
GIVEN P. H. 209, *225*, *257*
GNJUBKIN V. I. 176, *184*
GORDON B. E. 175, *184*
GORNYCH T. I. 204, *224*
GOSMAN B. A. 173, *184*
GRABOWSKI Z. R. 16, 17, *30*
GRAIZON M. 124, *166*
GREENBERG L. A. 134, *168*

GRIGGIO L. *258*
GRIMES M. D. 156, *169*, 207, *225*
GROHMANN H. 140, *168*
GRUNTOVA' Z. 188, *223*
GRUSS L. S. 156, *169*
GRY O. 119, *166*
GUDBJARNASON S. 100, *106*
GUERNE R. 117, *166*
GYÓRBÍRÖ K. 103, *106*

HAAS J. W. 127, *167*
HÄFLIGER O. 125, 126, *167*
HAHN C. 118, *166*
HALL M. E. 122, 135, *166*, *168*, 212, *225*
HALLINE E. W. 212, *225*
HAN J. E. S. *255*
HANS W. 16, 20, *30*, *31*, 50, *60*, 243, *244*
HANUŠ V. 2, 16, 20, 26, *29*, *30*, *31*, *258*
HARLE A. J. 251, *253*
HARRIS W. E. 155, *169*
HASLAM J. 163, *171*
HASSELBACH H. 131, *167*, 174, *184*
HATA T. 156, 157, *169*
HEATH J. C. 194, *223*
HEINRICH B. J. 156, *169*, 207, *225*
HEMS B. A. 174, *184*
HENDERSON J. 134, *168*
HENKE K. H. 16, *30*
HENNE W. 50, *60*
HENNING K. 140, *168*
HERSHBERG E. B. 125, 126, *166*, *167*
HETMAN J. S. 215, 217, 218, 219, *226*
HEYNDRICKX A. 157, *169*
HEYROVSKÝ J. 1, *29*, 38, 41, 44, 46, 50, *58*, *59*, *106*, 131, 140, *167*, *168*, 178, *184*, *254*, *255*
HILLER A. 163, *171*
HINSWARK O. N. 160, *170*
HOBART E. W. 213, *225*
HOLLECK L. 238, 242, *243*, *244*, 250, 252, *252*, *253*

HOLUBEK J. 250, *252*
HOLZMANN R. T. 206, 222, *224*, *226*
HOMOLKA J. 198, *223*
HORA'K V. 57, *60*, 179, 184, 227, 229, *230*, 250, 251, *252*
HORTON A. D. 135, *168*
HOYLE W. 137, 138, *168*
HUBICKA K. 160, *170*
HUMAN J. P. E. 221, *226*
HURTON J. T. 160, *170*

IGNACZAK M. 161, *171*
IGONIN L. A. 211, *225*
ILKOVIČ D. 1, 6, *29*
ILVER K. 118, *166*
ISHIBASHI M. 165, *171*, *255*
IVANOV C. 102, *106*
IWAKI G. 157, *169*

JAMIESON D. R. 121, 166
JANSEN A. P. 191, *223*
JASELSKIS B. 164, *171*
JENESS R. 160, *170*
JENSCH W. 20, *31*
JENŠOVSKÝ L. 127, *167*
JINDRA A. 120, 162, *166*, *171*
JONES H. C. 78, *82*
JONES L. C. 175, *184*
JONES T. S. G. 138, 139, *168*
JUNGR V. 120, 162, *166*, *171*

KALBAG S. S. 201, *224*
KALOVSEK M. 36, 38, 39, 48, 52, 56, *58*, *59*
KALVODA R. 26, *31*, 44, 50, *60*, 118, 120, 141, 156, 157, 158, 162, *166*, *168*, *169*, *170*, *171*, 188, *223*
KANE P. O. 192, *223*
KAPCAN O. L. *258*
KAPULLA H. 18, *30*
KARCHMER J. H. 207, *224*
KASTENING B. 242, *244*, 250, *252*

S

KATZLMEIER H. 100, *106*
KELLEY M. T. 78, *82*, 135, *168*
KEMULA W. 16, *30*, 48, *59*, 78, *82*, 127, *167*, 179, 180, 181, 182, *184*
KENYON D. 215, 217, *226*
KERN D. M. H. 26, *31*
KEVEI I. 162, *171*
KIRILLOVA A. S. 205, *224*
KISZEL J. 162, *171*
KLIER K. 210, *225*
KNIGHT W. S. 164, *171*
KNOBLOCH E. 64, *82*, 186, 187, *223*
KOIDE S. *258, 259*
KOIZUMI K. 143, 144, *168*
KOLTHOFF I. M. 34, 52, *58*, 155, 156, 157, 160, 161, 163, *169*, 170, *171*, *254*
KOMENDA J. 250, *252*
KOMINAMI T. 214, *226*
KOPECKÝ M. 64, *82*
KORŠUNOV I. A. 205, *224, 258*
KORYTA J. 26, *31*, 188, *223*, 233, 243, *243, 244*
KOŠTÍŘ J. 179, *184*
KOUTECKÝ J. 2, 6f., 20, 26, *29*, *31*, 52, *60*
KOVA'Č J. 141, *168*
KRA'ČMAR J. 159, *170*
KRA'LIK I. 101, *106*, 222, *226*
KRA'TKÝ L. 63, *82*
KRESTÝNOVA' O. 118, *166*
KRJUKOVA T. A. 28, *31*
KRUPIČKA J. 133, 143, 144, *167*, *168*, 212, *225*, 229, *231*, 242, *243*
KRUPIČKA V. 198, *223*
KUBÍČEK R. 15, *30*
KUBIS J. 132, *167*
KUIK M. 20, *31*, 100, *106*
KUMMEROW F. A. 201, *224*
KÜNSBERG V. 250, *252*
KŮTA J. 50, *60*, 251, *253*

LACOSTE R. 210, *225*
LADIK J. 143, *168*

LAITINEN H. A. 156, *169*
LAMPRECHT W. 100, *106*
LANDERL J. H. 209, *225*
LANDQUIST N. 251, *253*
LANDRY A. S. 115, *165*
LANGER A. 183, *184*, 234, *243*
LARSON B. L. 160, *170*
LAUČÍKOVA' O. 154, 157, *169*
LAVIRON E. 251, *253, 259*
LEACH S. J. 221, *226*
LEBLANC R. B. 136, *168*
LECLERCQ M. 119, 124, *166*
LEONARD G. W. 217, *226*
LÉVÈQUE M. P. 46, *59*
LEVIN E. S. 58, *60*
LEWIS D. T. 218, *226*
LEWIS W. R. 201, 209, *224*
LEYKO W. 194, *223*
LIBERTI A. 159, 160, *170*
LICKINT F. 100, *106*
LINGANE J. J. *254*
LIPSCHÜTZ M. 221, *226*
LIŠČETA L. I. 17, *30*
LISK D. J. 203, *224*
LITVINOVA N. S. 200, *224*
LJALIKOV J. S. 165, *171*
LOS J. M. 13, 16, *29*, *30*, 251, *253*
LOVE D. L. 222, *226*
LUND H. 104, *106*, 118, 119, *166*, **228, 231**
LUPTON J. M. 127, *167*
LYNCH C. C. 127, *167*
LYONS L. E. 243, *244*, 251, *253*, *257*

McCOMB E. A. 174, *184*
MACKELA A. A. 102, *106*
McNUTT R. C. 212, *225*
MAJOR E. 103, *106*
MAJRANOVSKIJ S. G. 17, 20, *30*, *31*
MANDEL J. 143, *168*
MANN C. K. 142, *168*
MANOU EK O. 13, 15, *30*, 49, *59*, 65, *82*, 119, 120, *166*, 189, 206, *223*, *224*, 238, *243*

MANSFELD V. 127, 128, *167*
MANZ R. 132, *167*
MARGOLIT J. 133, *167*
MARKAČEVA T. M. 205, *224*
MARRON T. U. 220, *226*
MARTIN A. J. P. 65, *82*, 138, *168*, 228, *230*
MARUYAMA M. 159, *170*
MATHERS A. P. 199, *224*
MATOUŠEK L. 154, 157, *169*
MATSUMOTO K. 116, *165*
MATSUO M. 157, *169*
MATUŠŮ Z. 121, *166*
MATYSKA B. 210, *225*
MAY D. R. 156, *169*
MAYFIELD M. M. 215, 217, *226*
MECHERLY P. 162, *171*
MEDALIA A. I. 156, 160, *169*, *170*
MEDONOS V. 121, 129, *166*, *167*
MEITES L. 41, 53, *59*
MELKONIAN A. G. 238, 242, *243*, *244*, 250, *252*
MENEGUS-SCARPA M. *255*, *256*
MENŠÍKOVA' J. 116, *165*
MEURER E. 50, *60*
MICHALSKI E. 161, *170*, *171*
MICHEL G. 164, *171*
MICHL J. 179, *184*
MIHALIK B. 220, *226*
MILLER H. H. 78, *82*
MILLER I. K. 156, *169*
MILLER J. F. 208, *225*
MILNER G. W. C. *254*
MIRKIN L. S. 16, *30*
MITTELMANN R. 138, *168*
MONNIER D. 117, 132, 145, *165*, *166*, *167*, *168*
MORGAN P. 156, *169*
MORISAKA K. 162, *171*
MORREN L. 157, *169*
MORRIS S. G. 201, *224*
MÜLLER O. H. *254*, *255*, *258*
MURPHY M. E. 210, *225*

NAGAI T. 165, *171*

NAGATA J. *258*
NAKAZIMA M. 202, *224*
NARAYAN K. A. 201, *224*
NATARJAH R. 160, *170*
NEDVĚDOVA' R. 220, *226*
NEIMAN M. B. 172, 176, *184*, 209, *225*, *258*
NEISH W. J. P. 126, *167*
NEUGEBAUER K. 251, *253*
NEUMAN V. 203, *224*
NEWBY B. J. 156, *169*, 207, *225*
NEWLANDS G. 163, *171*
NIKOLAJEVA-FEDOROVIČ N. 68, *82*
NORMAN S. L. 159, *170*
NORTON D. R. 142, *168*
NOSEK J. 118, *166*
NOVA'K J. V. A. 36, 37, 40, *58*, *59*, 103, *106*, 142, *168*, 205, *224*
NOVA'K L. 48, 52, *59*
NOVOTNÝ B. 117, 118, 120, *165*, *166*
NÜRNBERG H. W. 20, *31*, 243, *244*, *258*

O'BRIEN A. S. 156, *169*
OGAWA T. 159, *170*
OGDANEC N. D. 115, *165*, 209, *225*
OGG C. L. 201, *224*
OKINAKA Y. 34, 52, *58*
ONO S. 15, 16, *30*, 122, 124, *166*, 251, *253*
ONRUST H. 173, *184*, 191, *223*
OSTERYOUNG R. A. 164, *171*

PAGE H. T. 242, *244*
PAGE J. E. 174, *184*, 187, *223*, *258*
PALEČEK E. 179, *184*
PANOVA G. D. 129, *167*
PANUSZ H. 194, *223*
PARRA'K V. 145, *169*
PAŚCIAK J. 204, 211, *224*, *225*
PASTERNAK R. 63, *82*, 173, *184*

PATTON S. 160, *170*
PATZAK R. 251, *253*
PAVLOV D. 102, *106*
PEČENÝ R. 220, *226*
PEOVER M. E. 209, *225*, *257*
PERSON M. *259*
PÉTER F. 220, 222, *226*
PETUELY F. 250, *252*
PHILIP B. 220, *226*
PIETZSCH A. 100, *106*
PIHAR O. 157, *169*
PLETICHA R. 158, *170*
PODROUŽEK V. 192, *223*
POTTER E. F. 174, *184*
POWERS J. J. 199, *224*
POZDĚJEVA A. G. 203, 204, *224*
PRATT D. E. 199, *224*
PREININGER V. 250, *252*
PRELOG V. 125, 126, *167*
PRIVALOVA K. P. 200, *224*
PROCHA'ZKA Ž. 161, *171*
PROKEŠ J. 188, *223*
PROSKE G. 175, *184*
PUCKETT J. E. 156, *169*, 207, *225*
PUNGOR E. 20, *31*

QUACKENBUSH F. W. 201, 209, *224*

RA'BEK V. 179, *184*
RA'LEK M. 48, 52, *59*
RANDLES J. E. B. 50, *60*, 243, *244*
REICHSTEIN T. 230, *231*
REILLEY C. N. 22, *31*
RENTSCHLER R. H. 141, *168*
RICCIUTI C. 201, *224*
RICCOBONI L. 47, *59*
RICE M. W. 131, *167*
RIEMENSCHNEIDER R. W. 201, *224*
ŘÍHA J. 46, 48, *59*, 67, 187
RJABOV A. V. 129, *167*
ROSENTHAL I. 65, *82*, 210, *225*, 228, *230*, *231*

ROTH F. 46, *59*
ROUBAL J. 116, *165*
ROUBALOVA' D. 160, *170*
ROUTH J. I. 220, *226*
RUBEŠ T. 118, *166*
RUEDI W. F. 145, *168*
RULFS C. L. 102, *106*
RUSCONI Y. 117, *165*
RUSZNA'K I. 101, *106*, 220, 222, *226*
RŮŽIČKA V. 121, *166*

SANDLER S. 209, *225*
ŠANTAVÝ F. 15, 17, 26, *30*, 122, *166*, 174, *184*, 230, *231*, 235, 237, *243*, 250, *252*
SAPARA V. 102, *106*, 176, *184*
SCHANTZ E. L. 102, *106*
SCHILLEROVA' V. 157, *169*
SCHMIDT H. 252, *253*
SCHMIDT O. 132, *167*
SCHMITZ C. L. *256*
SCHNITTINGER C. H. 210, *225*
SCHÖBERL A. 221, *226*
SCHOEN J. M. 209, *225*
SCHOENMAN R. L. 199, *224*
SCHWABE K. 242, *244*, *254*, *258*
ŠEDIVEC V. 115, 129, *165*, *167*
SEMERANO G. 47, *59*, 242, *244*, *256*, *258*
SENDA M. 202, 209, *224*
SER S. 15, *30*, 251, *252*
ŠERA'K L. 41, *59*
ŠEVČÍK A. 50, *60*
SHIKATA M. 41
SHOEMAKER E. 133, *167*
SICHER J. 144, *168*
SIFRE G. 219, *226*
SÍLEŠ B. 221, *226*
SIMON V. 156, *169*
SIMPSON L. B. 13, *30*, 251, *253*
ŠINDELA'ROVA' K. 203, *224*
SISLER H. M. 127, *167*
ŠKRAMOVSKÝ S. 113, 116, *165*
SLA'DEK J. 221, *226*

SLAVÍK J. 250, *252*
SLAVÍKOVA' L. 250, *252*
SMALES A. A. 119, *166*
SMITH L. I. 161, *171*
SMOLEŘ I. 32, 33, 47, 50, *58, 60,* 140, *168,* 175, *184*
SNOWDEN F. C. 242, *244*
SPANYAR P. 162, *171*
SPILLANE L. J. 161, *171*
SOKOLOV N. P. *257*
SOUČEK B. 127, 128, *167*
SOUCHAY P. 15, *30,* 124, *166,* 251, *252, 258*
SOUČKOVA' M. 159, *170*
SRBOVA' J. 114, *165*
STACKELBERG M. von 6, 20, 28, *29, 31,* 52, *60,* 243, *244, 254,* 258
STA'RKA L. 195, *223*
ŠŤASTNÝ J. 132, 140, *167, 168*
ŠTEFANEC J. 221, *226*
STEJSKAL Z. 118, 159, *166, 170,* 187, *223*
STONE K. G. 160, *170*
STRAUSE S. F. 211, *225*
STREHLOW H. 16, *30*
STRICKS W. 156, 157, 161, *169, 171*
STRNAD F. 142, *168*
STROMBERG A. G. 203, 205, *224*
STUMM W. 22, *31*
SUCHOBOKOVA N. S. 160, *170*
SULLIVAN B. 156, *169*
SUN S. C. 222, *226*
SUN S. CH. 206, *224*
SVA'TEK E. 186, 187, *223*
SVOBODA M. 144, *168*
SZÉKA'CS I. 143, *168*

TACHI I. 141, *168,* 202, 209, *224, 259*
TAKAGI M. 15, 16, *30,* 122, 124, *166,* 251, *253*
TAKAYAMA G. 214, *226*
TAKIURA K. 143, 144, *168*
TANAKA N. 41, *59*

TANNER H. 141, *168*
TEISINGER J. 113, *165*
TENYGL J. 63, 65, *82,* 251, *252*
TERENT'EV A. P. *255*
THOMASON P. F. 135, *168*
TIROUFLET J. 242, *244,* 251, *253,* 257, *259*
TODD J. W. 139, 140, *168*
TOSINI B. *256*
TRÉMILLON B. 243, *244*
TRIFONOV A. 102, *106*
TRÜMPLER F. 12, *29*
TRÜMPLER G. 251, *253*
TÜMMLER R. *254*

UKIDA J. 214, *226*
USAMI S. 211, *225*

VAJNŠTEJN JU. I. 205, *224*
VALENTA P. 237, *243,* 251, *253*
VAN ATTA R. E. 121, 130, *166, 167*
VAŠA'K V. 129, *167*
VELDSTRA H. *259*
VESELÝ K. 12, *29,* 251, *253*
VETTER K. J. 243, *244*
VLČEK A. K. 63, *82*
VOGEL J. (Czech) 44, 46, 49, 51, *59, 60,* 67, 187
VOGEL J. (Swiss) 117, *166*
VOIGT J. 214, *226*
VOLKE J. 13, 15, *30,* 118, 125, *166, 167,* 185, 194, *223,* 237, *243,* 250, 251, *252, 253, 259*
VOLKOVA' V. 15, 17, *30,* 125, *167,* 194, *223*
VOREL F. 188, *223*
VOROBJEV V. 163, *171*

WAEL J. DE *259*
WALLER J. G. 187, *223*

WARSHOWSKY B. 102, *106*, 131, 133, 143, *167*, *168*
WASA T. 15, 16, *30*, 122, 124, *166*, 251, *253*
WATT J. 202, *224*
WAWZONEK S. 104, *106*, *259*, *260*
WEISSBERGER S. *258*
WENGER P. E. 117, 132, *165*, *166*, *167*
WENIG K. 64, *82*
WEST T. S. 137, 138, *168*
WHEATLEY M. 16, *30*
WHETTON S. M. A. 163, *171*
WHISMAN M. L. 209, *225*
WHITNACK G. C. 127, 143, *167*, *168*, 211, 212, 215, 217, *225*, *226*
WIESNERK 1, 13, 15, 16, 17, *29*, *30*, 251, *253*
WILLIAMS A. F. 215, 217, *226*
WILLIAMS K. T. 174, *184*
WILLITS C. O. 201, *224*
WILSON H. N. 119, *166*
WOLFE J. K. 125, 126, *166*, *167*
WOLFF J. H. 134, *168*
WOODWARD M. M. 193, *223*
WÖSTMANN B. S. J. 173, *184*, 191, *223*

YANOVSKAYA L. A. *255*
YOSHINO T. 159, *170*
YOUNG J. E. 127, *167*

ZAGÓRSKI Z. 40, *59*, *255*
ZAHRADNÍK R. 127, 128, *167*, 193, *223*
ZAPLETA'LEK A. 132, *167*
ŽDANOV S. I. 16, 17, 26, *30*
ZDRAŽIL J. 116, *165*
ZINNER H. 12, *29*, 173, *184*
ZOBOV E. V. 165, *171*
ZUMAN P. 12, 13, 15, 16, 17, 20, 26, 29, *29*, *30*, *31*, 39, 49, 55, 57, *59*, *60*, 63, 65, *82*, 100, 101, 104, 106, *106*, 120, 121, 122, 124, 127, 128, 133, 143, 144, 155, 161, *166*, *167*, *168*, *169*, 173, 178, 179, *184*, 185, 192, 200, 206, 207, *223*, *224*, *225*, 227, 229, 230, *230*, *231*, 233, 235, 237, 238, 242, *243*, 246, 248, 250, 251, *252*, *254*, *255*, *259*, *260*
ZUMANOVA' R. 127, 128, *167*
ZÝKA J. 120, 141, 156, 157, 158, 159, 162, *166*, *168*, *169*, *170*, *171*, 188, *223*

# SUBJECT INDEX

ABSINTHINDIOL 124
ABSOLUTE METHODS 77
ACCUMULATOR 150, 180
ACCURACY 77–79
ACETALDEHYDE 8, 9, 62, 132
  besides propionaldehyde and bu-
    tyraldehyde 175
  crotonaldehyde in 204
  formation of 132, 133, 195
  in alcohol 175
  in oxidation products 209
  in spirit 175, 199
  vinyl acetate, in presence of 211
ACETALDEHYDE SEMICARBAZONE
  89
ACETALDEHYDOGENIC STEROIDS
  195
ACETATE
  ammonium 163, 213
  cadmium 220
  ethyl 213, 214, 219
  lead 172, 199
  mercuric 117, 118, 211
  sodium 75, 129, 134, 163, 188,
    207
ACETATE BUFFER 19, 47, 62, 63,
  74, 75, 108, 109, 115, 119,
  134, 143, 144, 157, 162, 192,
  200, 201, 203, 214, 240, 241,
  251
ACETIC ACID 75, 115, 125, 134,
  160, 178, 203, 205, 219
  effect of 211
  glacial 61, 80, 116, 129, 131,
    138, 160, 163, 188, 193, 195,
    207, 208
    polarography in 80
  vinyl ester of 132

ACETOIN 192, 198
  in blood 134
  in butter cultures 134
  oxidation of 134
ACETONE 87, 141, 160, 182, 207,
  212, 217, 218
  as solvent 128
  besides butyraldehyde 124, 125
  besides ethanol 145
  deproteination with 173, 178
  determination of 121, 142
  reaction of
    butylamine with 121
    hydrazine with 127
ACETONIMINE 89
ACETOPHENONE 57, 58, 87, 105
  besides butyraldehyde 124
  formation of 176
2-ACETOXYACETOPHENONE 87
ACETYLENE 129, 130
ACETYLPYRIDINES 87
ACETYLPYRROLES, 87
ACID,
  acetic 75, 115, 125, 134, 160,
    178, 203, 205, 211, 219
  aconitic 85
  p-aminosalicylic 141, 186
  5-aminosalicylic 141,
  ascorbic 26, 62, 73, 74, 75, 83,
    122, 123, 153, 161, 162, 186,
    189, 190, 200, 201
  aspartic 131
  barbituric 99
  boric 66, 173
  brønsted 99
  o-carboxyphenyliminodiacetic
    138

ACID,
  *p*-chloromercuribenzoic   97, 221
  citric   130, 132, 161
  crotonic   84
  *trans*-cycloheptane-1,2-diamine-
    N,N,N′,N′-tetracetic   138
  *trans*-cyclohexane-1,2-diamine-
    N,N,N′,N′-tetracetic
    138
  cytidylic   194
  dehydroascorbic   26, 123
  dehydroreductic   123
  dialuric   83
  o-diamisidine-N,N,N′,N′-tetra-
    acetic   138
  diazotized sulfanilic   90
  dibromoacetic   130
  a-a′-dibromosuccinic   228
  diethyl barbituric (*see* Barbital)
  diethylenetriamine-N,N,N′,N″,
    N″-pentaacetic   138
  2,3-diketogulonic   123
  dithiocarbaminoacetic   99
  dithiocarbaminocarbonic   128
  esters of benzoic   105
  ethylenediamine tetracetic (*see*
    EDTA)
  5-ethyl-5(1-methylbutyl)-thio-
    barbituric   156
  flavianic,   159
  folic (*see* Pteroylglutamic acid)
  fumaric   65, 131, 140, 228
  glacial acetic   61, 80, 116, 129,
    131, 138, 160, 163, 188, 193,
    195, 207, 208
  glycyrrhetic   191
  glycyrrhizic   191
  glyoxylic   88
  guanylic   194
  hexuronic   191
  hydrochloric   8, 9, 118, 126,
    127, 133, 137, 138, 140, 141,
    160, 163, 178, 187, 188, 190,
    193, 195, 200, 204, 205, 212,
    213, 222

ACID,
  imine of phenylglyoxylic   90
  imino diacetic   138
  indolsulphonic   99
  a-ketoglutaric   126, 127
  lactic   133, 140, 192
  lewis   17
  lipoic   93
  maleic   7, 8, 65, 85, 131, 140,
    212, 228
  malic   140, 178, 198, 199
  mandelic   134, 192
  meconic   95
  metaphosphoric   200, 201
  methacrylic   213
  methyliminodiacetic   138
  muconic   85
  naphtholsulphonic   99
  1-naphthol-4-sulphonic   159
  napthylaminesulphonic   99
  nicotinic   64
  nitric   102, 112, 114, 116, 117,
    111, 136, 153, 164, 191, 215
  nitrilotriacetic   136, 137, 138,
    203
  nitronaphthalene sulphonic   91
  nitrous   193
  organic   200
  oxalacetic   126, 127
  oxalic   88, 160
  oxidation with chromic   115,
    116, 145, 158
  pencillic   95
  perchloric   160, 161, 173, 193,
    239
  periodic   39, 195, 214, 228, 240,
    242
  4-phenylester of 2-benzoylthio-
    benzoic   93
  phenyl ethyl barbituric (*see*
    Phenobarbital)
  phenylglyoxylic   16a, 88
  phenylpropiolic   84
  phosphomolybdic   173
  phosphoric   14, 133, 134
  phthalic   46, 85, 212, 234

ACID,
  picric 91, 159, 193
  polarography in
    glacial acid 80
    sulphuric 80
  pteroylglutamic 96, 189, 190
  pyridazine-4-carboxylic 95
  pyrrolsulphonic 99
  pyruvic 47, 88, 126, 127, 178,
    179, 234, 237
  quinoline carboxylic 97
  reduction of
    anion of pyruvic 11
    pyruvic 11
  silicotungstic 158, 159
  stearic 163
  sulphamic 219
  sulphosalicylic 173, 197
  sulphuric 9, 35, 38, 108, 113,
    115, 117, 119, 126, 131, 134,
    140, 141, 160, 165, 191, 205,
    207, 212, 215, 219, 220, 221
  sulphurous 142
  tannic 141, 178
  tartaric 160, 161, 165
  terephthalic 85, 212
  trichloroacetic 86, 173, 194
  two waves of pyruvic 11
  uramil-N,N-diacetic 138
  uric 100
  xanthen-9-carboxylic 159
ACID-BASE CATALYSIS 13, 127f.
  of dehydration, 12
ACID-BASE EQUILIBRIA 15, 16, 17,
    65, 100, 108
ACID-BASE REACTIONS 152, 251
ACIDITY SCALE 63
ACIDS, 61
  amino 112, 117, 118, 120, 127,
    128, 129, 131, 138, 139, 140,
    142, 164, 178, 183, 192, 193,
    194, 220, 221
  amino-polycarboxylic 136
  determination of carboxylic 106
  heteropoly- 152, 158, 159
  hydroxyamino 133

ACIDS,
  keto- 15, 16
  reduction of weak 11, 15, 16
  strong 62
  weak 20
ACONITIC ACID 85
A.C. polarography 44, 52
ACRIDINE 97, 158
ACRIDONE 96
ACROLEIN 87, 104
  in technical glycerol 205
ACRYLONITRILE 85, 213
  in copolymers 210, 211
  in polymers 210
ACTINOMYCINE 96
ACTIVE GROUP,
  exchange of 246
  identification of 248, 249
ACTIVE SUBSTANCES 83–101
ADDITIVITY,
  of diffusion currents 7
  of limiting currents 7, 12
ADDITIONS, APPLICATION OF 112,
    129–132, 142–143, 152, 163
ADENINE 95
  in hydrolysates 193, 194
  in pancreas 194
  in tissues 194
  separation of 194
ADENINE-N-OXIDE 91
ADMINISTRATION OF DRUGS 192
ADRENALINE 62, 192
  oxidation of 134, 135
ADSORBABILITY 100, 101
ADSORPTION
  of buffers 20
  of catalyst 20
  of depolarizer 71
  effect of 76, 176
  of electroactive substances 20,
    22
  of fatty alcohols 22
  of mercury salts 20
  of products 22
  of proteins 155
  of pyridine 22

ADSORPTION
of reduced form 20
of thiols 20
ADSORPTION CURRENTS 1, 20, 22,
23, 24, 25, 27, 28, 50, 51, 52,
99, 101, 128, 248
equation of 20
of methylene blue 20
of quinine 22
ADSORPTION ISOTHERM 183
ADVANTAGES IN REACTION KINE-
TICS 241
AGAR BRIDGE 39, 40
AGENTS, OXIDIZING 18
AGRICULTURAL CHEMISTRY, AP-
PLICATION IN 198–203
AIR, (see also Atmosphere)
atmospheric 37
carbon disulphide in 192
toluene in 114
ALANINE, DETERMINATION OF 142
ALBUMIN 197
tyrosine in serum 118
ALCOHOL,
Acetaldehyde in 175
formation of 227
ALCOHOLS 61
adsorption of 22
ALDEHYDES,
ALIPHATIC 12
2,4-dinitrophenylhydrazones
of 127, 183
mixture of 175, 167
reaction of amines with 236
fatty 104
formation of 145
hydrated 251
in beverages 199
in ether 173, 174
in mixture with ketones 122,
124
reaction of
ammonia with 120
hexamethylenediamine with
122
primary amines with 120

ALDEHYDES,
reaction of
semicarbazide with 124
unsaturated 104
ALDEHYDIC GROUP(S) 104, 124,
249
detection of 249
ALDEHYDIC TERPENES 191
ALDIMINES, FORMATION OF 120–
124
ALDOL, FORMATION OF 134, 175
ALDOPENTOSE HYDRAZONES 127
ALDOSES,
aldehydic form of 13
cyclic forms of 13, 251
reduction of 12
ALICYCLIC SUBSTANCES 249
ALIPHATIC ALDEHYDES 12
ALIPHATIC COMPOUNDS 105, 247
ALIZARIN SULPHONATE, AS TIT-
RANT 159
ALKALI METALS, ELECTROLYSIS OF
177
ALKALOIDS 100, 186, 249
salts of 156
titration of 159, 162
ALKOXIDES 62
ALKOXYKETONE 104
ALKYL ARYL KETONES 142
ALKYL RESINS, PHTHALIC ANHY-
DRIDE IN 212
ALKYLMETHACRYLATES 210
ALKYLPHTHALATE ESTERS
in explosives 212
in plastics 212
in resins 212
N-ALKYLPYRIDINIUM IONS 96
N-ALKYLQUINOLINIUM IONS 97
ALLERGENS, POLLEN 192
ALLETHROLONE, SYNTHESIS OF
229
ALLOXAN 83, 123
ALLYL ALCOHOL, REACTION OF
MERCURIC ACETATE WITH
211
ALLYLBROMIDE 85

ALUMINA COLUMN 178
ALUMINIUM-*tert*BUTOXIDE 126
AMALGAM, FORMATION OF 4, 50
AMALGAM REFERENCE CATHODES
80
AMIDE, NICOTINIC ACID 64
AMIDINES 89
AMIDOXIMES 89
AMINES 62
aliphatic 104
determination of primary 124
electrolytic separation of 177
formation of 9
heterocyclic 104
in explosives 219
mixtures of 203
nitrosation of secondary 119
primary 63, 119, 142
quaternary 62
reaction of
aldehyde with primary 120
aliphatic aldehydes with 236
benzaldehydes with 236
carbon disulphide with 120,
127–129
carbonyl compounds with
235, 236, 237
keto-acids with 236
ketones with 236
ketones with primary 120
phenyl vinyl ketone with 236
piperonal with primary 124
tertiary 63, 119
AMINO ACIDS 100, 112, 131, 153,
192, 193, 194
complexes of 138, 139, 140
determination of 138, 139, 140
effect of 164, 221
in casein 118
in pepton 118
in wool 220
mixtures of 128
phenyl bearing 117
reaction of
carbon disulphide with 120,
127–129

AMINO ACIDS,
reaction of
phthalaldehydewith 120, 142
separation of 178, 183
α-AMINO ALCOHOLS,
determination of 143
oxidation of 133
β-AMINO ALCOHOLS, FORMATION
OF 228
AMINO DERIVATIVES 215
AMINO GROUP 153
effect of 228
AMINOACETONITRILE 89
*p*-AMINOBENZALDEHYDE BESIDES *p*-
NITROTOLUENE 205, 222
α-AMINOKETONES 57, 104, 227,
228
β-AMINOKETONES 227, 228
AMINOMETHYLCYCLOPENTYL-
AMINE 136
AMINOMETHYLPYRIDINE 89
*m*-AMINOPHENOL,
DIAZOTISATION OF 141
in *p*-aminosalicylic acid 141,
186
titration of 160
*p*-AMINOPHENOL 83
AMINOPLAST 216
AMINO-POLYCARBOXYLIC ACIDS
136
identification of 137, 138
*p*-AMINOSALICYLIC ACID 160
*m*-aminophenol in 186
5-aminosalicylic acids in 141
in *m*-aminophenol 141
5-AMINOSALICYLIC ACID BESIDES
*p*-AMINOSALICYLIC ACID
141
AMMONIA 14, 21, 34, 63, 70, 99,
109, 119, 121, 123, 129, 130,
141, 153, 155, 157, 161, 173,
177, 190, 196, 197, 199, 206,
214
buffers 79
determination of 142
effect of 157

AMMONIA
  reaction of
    aldehydes with   120
    ascorbic acid with   122, 123
    diketogulonic acid with   122, 123
    ketones with   120
AMMONIACAL COBALTIC SOLUTIONS   20, 21, 192, 196, 197, 199
AMMONIACAL COBALTOUS SOLUTION   20, 21, 221
AMMONIUM ACETATE   163, 213
AMMONIUM CHLORIDE   14, 21, 63, 109, 121, 123, 130, 155, 173, 190, 196, 197, 199, 206, 217, 219
AMMONIUM IONS   103
  role of   65
AMMONIUM NITRATE   68, 115, 131, 157, 177, 213, 218
AMMONIUM SULPHATE   182, 121
AMPEROMETRIC TITRATIONS   102, 112, 142, 145–165, 177, 206, 221, 222
ANALYSERS, CONTINUOUS   41
ANALYSES, SERIAL   76, 79
ANGELICA LACTONE   95
ANILINE,
  derivatives   116, 209
  nitrobenzene in   205, 222
ANILINES   112
  coupling of   162
  titration of   160
ANION-EXCHANGE COLUMN   174, 178, 182
ANIONS, EFFECT OF   110
ANODIC CURRENTS   4, 5
ANODIC PEAK   49
ANODIC STRIPPING   78
ANODIC WAVES   4, 5, 10, 22, 26, 38, 45, 55, 56, 62, 71, 74, 83, 99, 102, 103, 109, 122, 128, 129, 131, 146, 148, 160, 164, 188, 189, 190, 200, 201, 206, 207, 208, 209, 213, 220, 221, 249

ANODIC WAVES
  measurement of   46
ANTECEDENT REACTIONS (see PRECEDING REACTIONS)
ANTHOCYANINS   95, 230
ANTHRACENE   85
  in coal tars   204
9-ANTHRACENEALDEHYDE   87
ANTHRAQUINONE   83, 88
  effect on benzanthrone   205
  in capacitor dielectrics   205
ANTHRAQUINONE DYESTUFFS   222
ANTHRONE   88
ANTIBIOTICS   249
  in preparations   198, 202, 203
ANTIHISTAMINICS, TITRATION OF   159
ANTIMONY, COMPLEXES OF   157
ANTIOXIDANTS IN GASOLINE   209
ANTIPYRINE   186
  nitrosation of   120
  titration of   157
ANTI-TUBERCULAR DRUGS   192
  in blood serum   192
  in cerebrospinal fluid   192
  in urine   193
APPLIED CURRENT   50
APPLIED VOLTAGE   50
ARGENTOMETRIC TITRATIONS   153, 155–156, 206, 207
AROMATIC COMPOUNDS   101, 112
ARSENITE   133
ARTABSIN   144
ARTEMAZULENE   124
ARYL-ALKYL SULPHONES   208
ASCARIDOL   93
  in *Oleum Boldo*   191
  in *Oleum Chenopodii*   191
ASCORBIC ACID   26, 62, 73, 74, 75, 83, 186, 189, 190
  in excess of
    chlorides   122
    thiols   122
  in fruit   200
  in juice   200

ASCORBIC ACID,
  in mixture with dehydro ascorbic
    acid 123
  interference of 153
  in tomato 201
  in vegetables 200
  reaction of ammonia with oxi-
    dized 122, 123
  titration of 160, 161, 162
ASCORBIGENE 144
ASPARAGINE 131
ASPARTIC ACID,
  determination of 131
  in proteins 131
ATMOSPHERE, (see also Air)
  aromatics in 192
  benzene in 113
  carbon disulphide in 129
  naphthalene in 115
ATTACLAY, ADSORPTION ON 203
AUTOCATALYTIC REACTION 51
AUXILIARY METHODS 22, 48–58,
  107, 110, 245
AZAURACIL 96
AZOBENZENE 83, 90, 105, 249
AZOCOMPOUNDS, FORMATION OF
  162
AZULENES 84, 100
  protonation of 16, 251
AZULENIUM ION 16


BACK-PRESSURE, CORRECTION FOR
  23
BARBITAL 26, 34, 188
  besides phenobarbital 118
BARBITURATES 62, 186, 188
  titration of 157
BARBITURIC ACID 99
BARIUM CHLORIDE 140
BARIUM SALT 102
BASE ELECTROLYTE (see SUPPORT-
  ING ELECTROLYTE)
BASES 61
  nitrogen containing 158, 159

BASES
  strong 62
  weak 20
BAYER L 13/59 202
BAYTINAL 189
BEAKERS FOR ELECTROLYSIS 35, 36
BENZALACETONE 141
BENZALANILINE 90
BENZALAZINE 127
BENZALDEHYDE 87, 104, 105, 251
  formation of 134, 143, 242
  in unbuffered media 10
  in wines 199
  reaction of
    amines with 236
    bisulphite with 142
  two waves of 10
BENZALDEHYDE DIMETHYLHYDRA-
    ZONE 127
BENZANTHRONE BESIDES ANTHRA-
    QUINONE 205
BENZENE 61, 131, 143, 175, 178,
    180, 182, 201, 207, 210, 211,
    212, 213
  in atmosphere 113, 192
  in blood 113, 114, 192
  in breath 113, 192
  in the presence of its homo-
    logues 115, 116
  in urine 113, 114, 192
  nitration and oxidation of 116
  styrene in 203
  thiophene free 208
  volatility of 176
BENZENEDIAZONIUM CHLORIDE 90
BENZENE SULPHOCHLORIDE 92
BENZENOID COMPOUNDS,
  identification of 249
  m- and p-substituted 247
  monosubstituted 104
BENZENOID RINGS, CONDENSED
  246
BENZHYDRAZIDINE 90
BENZIL 63, 87, 88, 173
BENZIL MONOXIME 89
BENZOCINNOLINE 90

BENZOCINNOLINE MONOXIDE 90
BENZOIC ACID ALKYLESTERS 249
BENZOIC ACID ESTERS 105
α-BENZOINOXIME 158
BENZOPHENONE HYDRAZONE 90
BENZOPHENONES 87, 105
  substituted 247
p-BENZOQUINONE DIOXIME 90
o-BENZOQUINONES 83
p-BENZOQUINONES 83, 88
  reduction of 10
BENZOYL PEROXIDE 93, 210
  in polymethylmethacrylate 213
2-BENZOYLTHIOBENZOIC ACID, Ψ-
  PHENYLESTER OF 93
BENZYL CHLORIDE 68, 85
BENZYL IODIDE 86
3-BENZYL SYDNONE 55
BERBERINE 97
BERNTROP EXTRACTION APPARATUS
  173
BETAINYL HYDRAZONES 125, 126
  of 3-ketosteroids 104
BEVERAGES,
  aldehydes in 199
  carbonyl compounds in 199
  ketones in 199
  malic acid in alcoholic 198, 199
BHC 202
BIACETYL 88
BIANTHRONYL 88
BICARBONATE, SODIUM 174
BIFUNCTIONAL COMPOUNDS 53, 57
BIHISTIDINATOCOBALTOUS ION, FOR-
  MATION OF 164
BILE, MANDELIC ACID IN 134, 192
BIOCHEMISTRY, APPLICATIONS IN
  185, 192–198
BIOLOGICAL FLUIDS,
  analysis of 71, 75, 76, 79
  drugs in 192, 193
BIOLOGICAL MATERIAL, (see also
  Biological fluids)
  analysis of 104, 173
  barbiturates in 188
  cysteine in 156

BIOLOGICAL MATERIAL,
  deproteination of 173
  drugs in 192, 193
  glutathione in 156
  keto-acids in 126
  ketosteroids in 194, 195
  lactic acid in 134
  natural products in 227, 230
  thiols in 154, 192
BISMUTH, COMPLEXES OF 157,
  158
BISMUTH HYDROXIDE, TITRATION
  OF 165
BISULPHITE, LITHIUM 195
BLASTING EXPLOSIVES 217
BLOOD,
  acetoin in 134
  benzene in 113, 114
  carbon disulphide in 192
  deproteination of 194
  disulphides in 156
  ethanol in 145
  hemolysed 197
  morphine in 118, 178, 192
  nitrosamines in 193
  pyruvic acid in 178, 179
  toluene in 114
BLOOD PROTEINS, ANALYSIS OF
  179
BLOOD SERUM 196
  anti-tubercular drug in 192
BLOOD SUGAR, DETERMINATION OF
  144
BORATE BUFFERS 3, 4, 13, 22, 55,
  56, 62, 63, 109, 139, 140,
  157, 190
BORATE IONS,
  catalysis by 13
  reaction with mercury of 4
BORATES, COMPLEXES OF 63
BORAX 188
BORIC ACID 66
  as titrant 165
  complexes with 173
BRDIČKA CATALYTIC WAVE 195–
  198, 199

BRDIČKA FILTRATE TEST 196, 197, 198, 199
BRDIČKA REACTION 220
BREATH,
  aromatics in 192
  benzene in 113
BRIDGE, AGAR 39, 40
BRITTON-ROBINSON BUFFERS 51, 63, 126, 164, 221
BROMATE
  as titrant 160
  potassium 160, 163
BROMIDE,
  phenacyl 85, 105
  potassium 160
  sodium 129, 163
  tetramethylammonium 174, 210, 212
  tropylium 51
BROMIDES
  besides cysteine 154
  besides mercaptans 152
  effect of 215
  titration of 156
BROMINATION 214, 216
BROMINE 214
  reaction of
    olefins with 129, 142, 163
    unsaturated compounds with 129, 142, 163
BROMOBENZENES 86
BROMO-DERIVATIVES 104
BROMOFORM 130
BROMONAPHTHALENE 58
BROMOPYRIDINES 86
4-BROMOSYDNONE 57, 58, 227
BRUCINE
  in mixture with strychnine 183
  separation of 191
BUFFER COMPONENTS, EFFECT OF 16
BUFFER COMPOSITION 110
  effect of 243
BUFFER CONCENTRATION 110
BUFFERS 61, 62, 66, 79,

BUFFERS,
  acetate 19, 47, 62, 63, 74, 75, 108, 109, 115, 119, 134, 143, 144, 157, 162, 192, 200, 201, 203, 214, 240, 241, 251
  adsorption of 20
  ammonia 79
  borate 3, 4, 13, 22, 55, 56, 62, 63, 109, 139, 140, 157, 190
  Britton-Robinson 51, 63, 126 164, 221
  Clark lubs 162
  effect of 100, 101, 152
    composition of 24, 25
    concentration of 20, 22, 24, 110
  glycine 63, 79, 121, 234
  interaction with 63
  McIlvaine 16a, 63, 117, 118
  mixed 63
  phosphate 14, 63, 65, 109, 134, 143, 159, 164, 176, 187, 190, 199
  phosphate-borate 213
  sulphite-borate 218
  trimthylamine-citrate 159
  triethylamine 68
  urea containing 221, 222
  veronal 62, 63, 67, 79, 109
BURETTE 149, 150
BUTADIENE 84, 209
  in gaseous mixtures 143
BUTANE-2,3-DIOL, OXIDATION BY PERIODATE 241
BUTANOL 174, 178
BUTTER, DIACETYL IN 175, 198
BUTTER CULTURES, ACETOIN IN 134
BUTYLAMINE, REACTION OF ACETONE WITH 121
BUTYL METHACRYLATE 210
  in polymer 210
  oxidation of 212
BUTYRALDEHYDE 127
  besides acetaldehyde and propionaldehyde 175

BUTYRALDEHYDE,
in excess of acetone  124, 125
in excess of acetophenone  124
BUTYRALDOXIME  89

CABBAGE  200
CADMIUM
besides cysteine  153
complexes of  157
interference of  153
CADMIUM ACETATE  220
CADMIUM ION, COMPLEXES OF
136, 137
CADMIUM NITRATE,  137, 207
CALCIUM CHLORIDE  174
CALCIUM IONS, EFFECT OF  212
CALCIUM PANTOTHENATE  189
CALCIUM SALT, REACTION OF  214
CALCIUM STEARATE  113
CALIBRATION CURVE METHOD  40,
46, 73–77
CALOMEL ELECTRODE  2, 33, 34,
35, 38, 40, 79, 80, 149, 150,
155, 161, 163
normal  79
saturated  79
CAMPHORQUINONE  88
CANCER,
detection of  197, 198
success of treatment of  198
CAPACITY CURRENTS
(see CHARGING CURRENTS)
CAPILLARY  2, 3, 32, 35, 37, 38, 39,
40, 44, 47, 75, 76, 150, 180,
197, 233
characteristics of  6, 7
drawn-out  32
for microanalysis  32
position of  7
Smoler  32, 33
CAPSAICINE  199
in plants  163
titration of  162
CARBAZOLENINE  93
C–BR BONDS  85, 86, 227
reduction of  58

C–C BONDS  84, 85
C–CL BONDS  85, 86, 227
CARBON DIOXIDE  35, 69, 200, 201
formation of  160
CARBON DISULPHIDE  220
determination of  128, 129
in air  192
in blood  192
in excess of hydrogen sulphide
129
in fibre industry  129
reactions of
amines with  120, 127–129
amino acids with  120, 127–
129
diethylamine with  128, 129
volatility of  176
C–F BONDS  85
C–I BONDS  53, 58, 86
C–N BONDS  57, 89, 90, 104, 228
C–O BONDS  87, 88, 104
C–OH BOND  121
CARBON OXYSULPHIDE  129
C–S BONDS  92, 104
CARBON TETRABROMIDE  85
CARBONATE  114, 115
lithium  134
sodium  126, 133, 174, 200
CARBONYL COMPOUNDS  27, 52,
100, 120, 121, 122, 125
in beverages  199
in coal extracts  209
in technical products  204
protonation of  251
reaction of
amines with 63, 235, 236, 237
bisulphite with  142
reduction of  227, 228
titration of  165
CARBONYL GROUP  104, 228, 249
determination of  105
in polyvinylalcohol  214
CARBOXY GROUP(S)  153
in polyvinyl alcohol  214
CARBOXYLIC ACIDS, DETERMINA-
TION OF  106

o-CARBOXYPHENYL IMINODIACETIC ACID 138
CARCINOM PORTIONIS VAGINALIS 199
CARCINOM VENTRICULI 199
CARDIAC GLYCOSIDES 186
 aldimine formation of 122
CARDIAZOLE 145, 186
CAROTENE 186
 determination of 131
 separation of chlorophyll from 178
CAROTENOIDS 178
CARROTS 200
CASEIN 100
 amino acids in 118
 thyroxine in oidinated 173, 174
CATALYSIS,
 ACID-BASE 12, 13
 by borate ions 13
 by OH⁻ ions 13
 of hydrogen evolution 24
CATALYSTS 17, 18, 19, 209, 210, 212
 adsorption of 20
CATALYTIC CURRENTS 1, 17, 18, 19, 20, 21, 23, 24, 25, 51, 73, 78, 83, 99–101, 110, 183, 190, 192, 195, 196, 197, 198, 221, 248
 effects of
  buffer concentration on 20
  concentration on 19
  ionic strength on 20
  pH on 19
 height of 19
 mechanism of 20
 of indigo sulphonates 18
 types of 17, 100
CATALYTIC HYDROGEN EVOLUTION 63, 83, 99–101
CATALYTIC MAXIMUM OF CYSTINE 20, 21
CATALYTIC WAVES
 in buffers 99, 100
 in presence of Co ORNi 99, 100

CATECHOL,
 nitrosation of 120
 titration of 162
CATIONS,
 effect of 110
 polyvalent 66
 role of 66, 68
CATHODIC CURRENTS 4, 5
CATHODIC PEAK 49
CATHODIC STRIPPING 78
CATHODIC WAVES 4, 5, 10, 34, 38, 45, 71, 83, 109, 122, 146, 148, 190, 221
CAULIFLOWER 200
CELLOPHANE MEMBRANE 35, 39, 40, 81
CELLOSOLVE 61
CELLS (see also Vessels)
 special-purpose 40
CELLULOSE 141, 220
 acetate, as filler 182
 pentosans in 203
 pentose in 203
CELLULOSIC FIBRES 220
CENTRALITE 219
 in propellants 219
CEPHAELINE 186
 in injections 120
 in tinctura ipecacuanhae 120
 nitrosation of 120
 titration of 162
CEREBROSPINAL FLUID, ANTI-TUBERCULAR DRUG IN 192
CERIUM SALTS, AS TITRANT 160
CHALKONES 87
CHANGE OF SENSITIVITY 44
CHARACTER OF POLAROGRAPHIC PROCESS 50–52
CHARGING CURRENT, AUTOMATIC SUBTRACTION OF 78
CHARGING CURRENTS 2, 3, 5, 23, 27, 44, 71, 77, 78, 162
 compensation of 44
 correction for 71
CHEMICALS, PURITY OF 206
CHEMISORPTION 101

CHICKEN FEEDS, NITROFURAZONE IN 203
CHLORAL 87
CHLORAMPHENICOL 91
  purity of 186, 187
CHLORANIL REFERENCE ELECTRODE 163
CHLORATES 18
CHLORIDE,
  ammonium 14, 21, 63, 109, 121, 123, 130, 155, 173, 190, 196, 197, 199, 206, 217, 219
  barium 140
  benzenediazonium 90
  benzyl 85
  besides ascorbic acid 122
  besides cysteine 154
  besides mercaptans 152
  calcium 174
  cobaltous 21, 190
  cupric 139
  diphenylarsine 98
  effect of 157, 188, 200
  gold 161
  lithium 9, 129, 133, 175, 201, 204, 208, 212, 215, 216
  magnesium 205
  mercuric 157
  β-methoxyethylmercuric 97
  phenacyl 86, 105
  potassium 28, 32, 34, 79, 127, 157, 182, 183, 192, 200, 202, 206, 217, 219
  sodium 14, 234
  tetrabutylammonium 211
  tetramethylammonium 62, 215, 216, 217
  tetraphenylarsonium 98
  tetraphenylphosphonium 97
  tetraphenylstibonium 98
  titration of 156
  triphenylselenonium 98
  triphenyltelluronium 98
  waves of 102, 103
1-CHLORO-1,2-DIBROMOETHANE 129

CHLOROFORM 85, 191, 205, 230
  extraction with 174
p-CHLOROMERCURIBENZOATE AS TITRANT 152, 153, 154, 157
p-CHLOROMERCURIBENZOIC ACID 97, 221
CHLOROPHYLL, SEPARATION OF CAROTEN FROM 178
4-CHLOROSYDNONE 227
CHOCOLATES, PHENOLPHTHALE IN 188
CHOLESTEROL 126
CHROMATE, CONSUMPTION OF 145
CHROMATES, AS TITRANT 158
CHROMATOGRAPHIC COLUMN 140, 179, 180, 181, 182
CHROMATOGRAPHY,
  adsorption 177, 178
  application of 172, 177–183, 188, 191, 203, 230
  paper 54, 118, 135, 138, 178, 179, 183, 188, 191
  partition 175, 177
  on ion-exchanges 141, 174, 177, 178, 179, 182, 183
CHROMATO-POLAROGRAM 179, 180, 181, 182
CHROMATO-POLAROGRAPHY 127, 140, 179–183
  arrangement for 179, 180
  columns for 182
  effect of oxygen in 181
  solvents for 182
CHROMIC ACID, OXIDATION WITH 115, 116, 145, 158
CHROMOUS SALT 69
CINAMALDEHYDE 87
CINNABARINE 96
CIRCUIT,
  derivative 46
  resistance in the 2
CITRACONIC ACID ANHYDRIDE 94
CITRAL 87
CITRATE BUFFER 159
CITRIC ACID 132
  determination of 130

CITRIC ACID,
titration of 161
CITRONELLAL 87
CITRUS FRUITS 200
CLARK LUBS BUFFER 162
CLATHRATES, AS FILLERS 182
CLINICAL ANALYSIS 196
CLINICAL CHEMISTRY, APPLICATIONS IN 192
COAL EXTRACTS,
carbonyl compounds in 209
quinones in 209
COAL-TARS 163
anthracene in 204
isoquinoline in 205, 206
phenanthrene in 204
quinoline in 205, 206
COBALAMIN 19, 78, 100, 189
COBALT
interference of 153
solutions ammoniacal 20, 21, 190, 221
COBALTIC SOLUTIONS, AMMONIACAL 192, 196, 197, 199
COBALTOUS CHLORIDE 21, 190
COBALTOUS ION, COMPLEXES OF 164
CODEINE 118, 186
COINCIDENT WAVES 64
COKE GAS, NAPHTHALENE IN 209
COLCHICINE 87
in meadow saffron 230
COMMUTATOR METHOD 48, 52, 55, 56
COMPENSATION METHOD 78
COMPENSATION, OF CHARGING CURRENT 44
COMPLEX FORMATION, APPLICATION OF 62, 112, 135–140, 145, 149, 152, 163–165, 172, 173
COMPLEX-FORMING REAGENT 149
determination of 135–138
COMPLEX STABILITY CONSTANT, EFFECT OF 149
CONCENTRATION, EFFECT OF 22, 23, 24, 25, 107, 109

CONCENTRATION POLARIZATION 50
CONCENTRATION RANGE 77, 78, 81
CONDENSATION REACTIONS 152, 165
CONDENSATIONS, APPLICATION OF 112, 120–129, 142, 152, 165
CONDENSER CURRENTS (see CHARGING CURRENTS)
CONDUCTIVITY 61
CONJUGATION,
effect of 246
extension of 103
CONSTANT CURRENT POLAROGRAPHY 44
CONSTANT POTENTIAL ELECTROLYSIS 53, 54, 55
CONSTANTS, DISSOCIATION 26, 54, 57
CONTINUOUS ANALYSIS 41, 179
vessels for 40, 41
CONTROLLED POTENTIAL ELECTROLYSIS 228
COPOLYMERS 216
acrylonitrile in 210
methylmethacrylate in 210
COPPER, INTERFERENCE OF 153
COPPER AMINOPOLY CARBOXYLATES, SEPARATION OF 178
COPPER COMPLEXES 183
COPPER ION, COMPLEXES OF 135, 137, 138, 145, 164
COPPER NUMBER 220
COPPER PHOSPHATE 139, 140
as filler 183
COPPER SULPHATE 138
CORONENE 85
COULOMETRY 53
COUMARINE 96
cyclic form of 251
COUPLING REACTIONS 152, 162–163
CRACKING GASES 209
p-CRESOL
in urine 116

p-CRESOL
  nitration of 119
CRESOL FRACTIONS, ANALYSIS OF
  163
CROTONALDEHYDE
  in acetaldehyde 204
  vinyl acetate in pressure of
  211
CROTONIC ACID 84
CRUDE OIL 208
CUMENEHYDROPEROXIDE 93
CUMINALDEHYDE 186
  in Semen Cumini Cymini 176
CUPRIC CHLORIDE 139
CUPRIC IONS, AS TITRANTS 152,
  153, 154, 161, 164
CUPROUS OXIDE 145
CURRANTS 200
CURRENT,
  additivity of diffusion 7
  additivity of limiting 7
  adsorption 1, 20, 22, 23, 24, 25,
    27, 28, 50, 51, 52, 99, 101,
    128, 248
  anodic 4, 5
  applied 50
  capacity (see current, charging)
  catalytic 1, 17, 18, 19, 20, 21,
    23, 24, 25, 51, 73, 78, 83, 99–
    101, 110, 183, 190, 192, 195,
    196, 197, 198, 221, 248
  cathodic 4, 5
  charging 2, 3, 5, 23, 27, 44, 71,
    77, 78, 162
  condenser (see charging currents)
  constants of diffusion 77
  dependence of diffusion, on con-
    centration 7
  derivative 47
  diffusion 6, 7, 19, 23, 24, 25, 26,
    27, 28, 50, 51, 78, 183, 197,
    234, 238, 248
  effect of temperature on diffusion
    7
  electrolytic 3
  instantaneous 50, 51

CURRENT,
  kinetic 1, 12, 13, 14, 15, 16, 17,
    23, 24, 25 ,40, 50, 51, 52, 78,
    127, 132, 133, 237, 238, 239,
    243, 251
  limiting 5, 6, 7, 12, 18, 22, 25,
    26, 27, 28, 32, 33, 34, 40, 43,
    46, 52, 53, 54, 70–73, 78, 79,
    107, 108, 127, 146, 151, 175,
    238, 240, 248
  mean 43
  measurements of limiting 70–
    73
  migration 27
  peak 73
  reaction (see Kinetic currents)
  regeneration 18
CURRENT OSCILLATIONS 43, 44, 73
CURRENT-VOLTAGE CURVES 1, 5,
    33, 41, 42, 44, 48, 58
  recording of 37, 39, 41, 42, 43,
    75, 80, 81, 102
CYANHYDRINE REACTION 237
CYANIDE 211
  interference of 152
CYCLANONES 142
CYCLIZATION 251
  of electrode process 54
TRANS-CYCLOHEPTANE-1,2-DIA-
    MINE-N,N,N',N'-TETR-
    ACETIC ACID 138
TRANS-CYCLOHEXANE-1,2-DIA-
    MINE-N,N,N'N'-TETR-
    ACETIC ACID 138
CYCLOHEXANOL 202
CYCLOHEXANONE,
  autoxidation of 121
  reaction of hexamethylenedia-
    mine with 122
  reaction of methylamine with
    121
CYCLOHEXAN-1-ONE-2-OL AUTOXI-
    DATION OF 121
CYCLOHEXANONE SEMICARBAZONE
    125
CYCLOHEXYLHYDROXYLAMINE 91

CYCLOHEXYLNITRATE 91
CYCLONITE 217
CYCLO-OCTA DIONE 88
CYCLO-OCTATETRAENE 68, 84
CYCLOPENTANONE,
   reaction of hexamethylene di-
      amine with 122
   reaction of methylamine with
      121
CYCLOTRIMETHYLENETRINITRAMINE
   217, 218, 219
CYSTEINE 99, 100, 153, 154, 156,
   157, 161, 221
   in biological material 156
   titration of 153, 154, 156, 157,
      161
CYSTINE, 20, 21, 93
   amalgam reduction of 156, 161
   catalytic maximum of 20, 21
   in proteins 156
   in wool 220, 221
   mixtures of cysteine and 161
   reaction of
      bisulphate with 161
      sulphite with 156, 221
   titration of 157
CYTIDINE 194
CYTIDYLIC ACID 194


DAMPING OF OSCILLATIONS 44
p,p'-DDT 68, 85
DEAERATION 61, 69–70, 75, 109,
   114, 117, 118, 128, 138, 140,
   141, 150, 152, 155, 157, 159,
   161, 162, 164, 187, 190, 191,
   192, 195, 200, 201, 204, 205,
   207, 221
   vessels for 35
dE/dt — E CURVES 50, 54, 56, 179
DEFORMATIONS OF POLAROGRAPHIC
   CURVES 69
DEHYDRATION,
   acid-base catalyzed 12
   of erythrose 12
   of formaldehyde 12

DEHYDROASCORBIC ACID,
   hydration of 26
   reaction of o-phenylenediamine
      with 123
DEHYDROISOANDROSTERONE DI-
   METHYL GLYCYLHYDRA-
   ZONE 195
DEHYDROREDUCTIC ACID 123
DENATURATION OF PROTEINS 196
DEOXYCORTICOSTERONE 65
DEOXYGENATION (see DEAERATION)
DEOXYRIBONUCLEIC ACID, HYDRO-
   LYSATE OF 194
DEPOLARIZERS,
   adsorption of 20, 71
   mixture of 45
DEPROTEINATION
   of biological material 173
   with organic solvents 173
   with trichloroacetic acid 194
DERIVATIVE CIRCUIT 46, 65, 187
DERIVATIVE CURVES 46, 47, 138,
   217
DERIVATIVE METHODS 45–48, 107,
   111
DETERGENTS 61, 202
DEVELOPER, PHOTOGRAPHIC 114
DIACETYL,
   formation of 134
   in butter 175, 198
   in fats 175
DIACETYLDIOXIME 90
DIACETYLENE 84
DIACETYLMORPHINE 118
5,5-DIALKYLBARBITURATES 188
DIALKYLDISULPHIDES 208
DIALKYL ESTERS
   of dibromosuccinic acid 228
   of fumaric acid 228
DIALKYLKETONES 142
DIALKYL PEROXIDES, TITRATION OF
   160
DIALKYLPHENACYL SULPHONIUM
   IONS 68
DIALKYL SULPHIDES 208
   determination of 106

DIALKYL SULPHONES  208
DIALURIC ACID  83
DIALYSIS  172, 176, 177
DIAMIDINES  186
  titration of  159
1,2-DIAMINOCYCLOHEXANE IN HEX-
  AMETHYLENEDIAMINE  135,
  136, 209
o-DIANISIDINE-N,N,N′,N′-TETR-
  ACETIC ACID  138
DIARYLIODONIUM SALTS  105
DIARYLSELENOXIDES  98
DIARYLSULPHONES  208
p-DIAZOBENZENE SULPHONIC ACID
  AS TITRANT  162
DIAZONIUM SALT AS TITRANT  162
DIAZOTIZATION OF m-AMINOPHE-
  NOL  141
DIAZOTIZED SULFANILIC ACID  90
α,β-DIBROMIDES, ELIMINATION OF
  129, 130
DIBROMOACETIC ACID  130
DIBROMODERIVATIVES  104
DIBROMOETHYLENE  85
α,α′-DIBROMOSUCCINIC ACID  228
DIBUTYLPHTHALATE  210, 217
1,2-DICHLORO-1,2-DIBROMOETHANE
  129
DICHLOROACETALDEHYDE  86
2,6-DICHLOROCYCLOHEXANONE  86
DICHLORODIETHYL TIN  98
1,2-DICHLOROETHYLENE  129, 130
2,6-DICHLOROPHENOLINDOPHENOL
  AS TITRANT  161
DICHROMATE, AS TITRANT  160
DIELECTRICS, ANTHRAQUINONE IN
  CAPACITOR  205
DIETHYLAMINE, REACTION OF CAR-
  BON DISULPHIDE WITH
  128, 129, 220
DIETHYL BARBITURIC ACID (see
  Barbital)
DIETHYLDISULPHIDE  93
DIETHYLDITHIOCARBAMATE  99,
  129
  formation of  220

DIETHYLENETRIAMINE-N,N,N′,N′′,
  N′′-PENTACETIC ACID  138
O,O-DIETHYL-O,p-NITROPHENYL-
  THIOPHOSPHATE  203
DIETHYLPHTHALATE BESIDES STY-
  RENE  211
BIS-(DIETHYLTHIOCARBAMYL) DI-
  SULPHIDE  93
DIFFERENTIAL POLAROGRAPHY  47
DIFFUSION, RATE OF  6, 7
DIFFUSION COEFFICIENTS  7, 52,
  53, 139, 238, 248
DIFFUSION CURRENTS  6, 7, 19,
  23, 24, 25, 26, 27, 28, 50,
  51, 78, 183, 197, 234, 238,
  248
  additivity of  7
  constants of  77, 175
  dependence of, on concentration
  7
  effect of temperature on  7
DIGITOXINE  95
DIGLYCOLS, DETERMINATION OF
  144, 145
DIHYDROXYACETONE  100
α-DIHYDROXY COMPOUNDS  63
DI-(2-HYDROXYETHYL) GLYCINE
  138
5,8-DIHYDROXYNAPHTHOQUINONE
  206
3,5-DIIODOTYROSINE  86
  effect of  173, 174
3,5-DIKETO-1,2-DIPHENYL-4-BU-
  TYLPYRAZOLIDINE  157
2,3-DIKETOGULONIC ACID  123
  reaction of ammonia with  122,
  123
DIKETONES  173
  formation of 250
DIMEDONE  209
  reaction with  172
2,3-DIMERCAPTOPROPANOL  99
DIMERIZATION OF RADICALS  26
DIMETHYLAMINE, METHYLAMINE IN
  124

DIMETHYLAMINOETHYL ESTER OF *p*-
  BUTYLAMINOBENZOIC ACID
  HYDROCHLORIDE 120
5-DIMETHYLAMINO-3-PHENYL-1,2,
  4-THIADIAZOLE 94
DIMETHYLDISULPHIDE 207f.
N,N-DIMETHYLFORMAMIDE 27,
  61, 127, 182, 183, 210,
  211
DIMETHYLGLYCYLHYDRAZIDE 125,
  195
1,1-DIMETHYLHYDRAZINE 127
DIMETHYLPEROXIDE 93
DIMETHYLSULPHATE 131
O,O-DIMETHYL-2,2,2-TRICHLORO-
  -1-HYDROXYETHYL PHOS-
  PHONATE IN FLY BAIT FOR-
  MULATIONS 202
2,2-DINAPHTHYL 84
*m*-DINITROBENZENE 64, 113, 114,
  115
  substituted 132
DINITROFLUORENONE 91
DINITROGLYCOL 215, 217, 218
2,4-DINITROPHENOL IN URINE
  193
2,4-DINITROPHENYL HYDRAZINE
  124
  as titrant 165
2,4-DINITROPHENYLHYDRAZONES
  of aliphatic aldehydes 127
  of keto-acids 126, 127
  separation of 178, 183
2,2-DINITROSOBIPHENYL 92
2,4-DINITROSORESORCINOL 119
2,4-DINITROSTRYCHNINE 190
DINITROTOLUENE 114, 115f, 217,
  218, 219
3,5-DINITROTYROSINE, FORMATION
  OF 222
DINITROXYLENES 115f.
1,2-DIOLS,
  determination of 143
  epimers of 144
  oxidation with periodic acid
  242

DIOXANE 27, 61, 142, 182, 191,
  204, 210
DIOXINDOLE 94
DIPHENYL 84
DIPHENYLACETYLENE 84
DIPHENYLAMINE 219
DIPHENYLARSINE CHLORIDE 98
N,N'-DIPHENYL-N,N'-DIETHYL-
  UREA 219
DIPHENYLDIPIAZSELENOLE 94
DIPHENYLDISULPHIDE 93, 207f.,
  208
DIPHENYL DISULPHONE 92
1,1-DIPHENYLETHYLENE 84
1,2-DIPHENYLETHYLENEGLYCOL,
  OXIDATION BY PERIODATE
  240
DIPHENYLS, CHLORINATED 205
DIPTEREX 202
DIPYRIDYLETHYLENE 84
DIRECT METHODS 102, 102–111
DISEASES 197, 198
DISSOCIATION
  OF ELECTRO ACTIVE FORM 26
  rate of 100
DISSOCIATION CONSTANTS 26, 54,
  57, 232, 233
DISSOCIATION CURVE,
  polarographic 15, 16
  titration 16
DISTILLATIONS, APPLICATION OF
  172, 175–176, 195, 203
DISTORTION OF WAVES 28, 29
DISULPHIDE BOND 207, 249
DISULPHIDES 206, 207, 208
  formation of 155
  in blood 156
  in petroleum 156
  in polymers 156
  in the presence of mercaptans
  156
  reaction of hydroxyl ions with
  156, 157
DITHIOCARBAMATES, FORMATION OF
  127–129

DITHIOCARBAMINO CARBONIC ACID
99, 128
DITHIOHYDANTOIN 99, 100
DITHIONITE 222
DITHIOPYRIMIDINE 100
DIVINYLACETYLENE 84
DIVINYLBENZENE 213
DODECYL MERCAPTAN 207
DOUBLE-BASE POWDER 217
DOUBLE BONDS, CONJUGATED 246
DOUBLE LAYER 71, 217
effect of 68
DOWEX 50 182
DROP-TIME 7, 32, 43, 48, 50, 51,
52, 70, 77, 79, 81, 151, 233,
243
effect of 25
regulated 33, 51
DROPPING MERCURY ELECTRODES
1, 2, 3, 4, 12, 20, 27, 32, 33,
34, 35, 37, 40, 44, 46, 50, 54,
55, 149, 150, 156, 180, 188,
207, 213, 215, 232
advantages of 33
synchronized 46
DRUGS,
administration of 192
anti-tubercular 192
in biological fluids 192, 193
terpenes in 191
DULCIN 116, 186
DYE PRODUCTION 222
DYEING PROCESS 220, 222
DYESTUFFS 83, 101, 222
Leuco forms of 83
titration of 159


EDTA 80, 99, 138, 140
copper chelate of 139
determination of 140
N,N-ethylenediglycine in 137
nitrilotriacetic acid in 136, 137,
203
titration of 163, 164
zinc complex of 214

ELECTRIC FIELD,
EFFECT OF, ON EQUILIBRIUM
CONSTANTS 17
ELECTROACTIVE FORM,
adsorption of 22
dissociation of 26
ELECTROCAPILLARY CURVES 52
ELECTRODE,
amalgam reference 80
calomel 2, 33, 34, 35, 38, 40, 79,
80, 149, 150, 155, 161, 163
chloranil reference 163
dropping mercury 1, 2, 3, 4,
12, 20, 27, 32, 33, 34, 35, 37,
40, 44, 46, 50, 54, 55, 149,
150, 156, 180, 188, 207, 213,
215, 232
graphite 80, 209
hanging mercury drop 48, 49,
50, 51, 54
indicator 2, 32, 40, 41, 146,
149, 163, 183
mercuric iodide reference 150
mercuric sulphide reference
150
mercurous sulphate 34, 35, 36,
38, 67, 74, 79, 80, 144, 189,
240, 241
mercury 33
mercury pool 34, 35, 36, 38, 54,
79, 149, 150, 197
reference 2, 3, 32, 33, 34, 35,
36, 38, 39, 40, 41, 48, 50, 70,
79, 80, 81, 146, 149, 150,
163, 180, 183
rotating platinum 149, 153,
154, 156, 157, 160, 161,
163
separated reference 2, 34, 35,
36, 38, 149
silver chloride 34, 39, 40, 79,
81
smoler-type 47
sodium acetate 80
solid 34
stationary platinum 208

ELECTRODE,
  streaming mercury 52, 188f.
  synchronized dropping mercury
    46
  three, system 40
  with regulated drop-time 47
  zinc amalgam reference 150
ELECTRODE PROCESS PROPER 243
ELECTRODE PROCESSES,
  characterization of 22
  effect of 109
  irreversible (see Irreversible sys-
    tems)
  reaction of a product of 8
  reversible (see Reversible sys-
    tems)
ELECTRODE REACTIONS 243
  intermediate in 250, 251, 252
  mobile 24
ELECTRODE SURFACE 20, 27, 50
ELECTRO-INACTIVE COMPOUNDS,
  ADSORPTION OF 22
ELECTROLYZED SOLUTION, VOLUME
  OF 1
ELECTROLYSIS
  AS SEPARATION TECHNIQUE 172,
    177
  controlled potential 53, 54, 55,
    228
  interpretation of large scale 252
  preparative 227, 228
  product of 48, 49, 50, 53–58
  vessels 2, 3, 32, 35–41, 43, 44,
    69, 70, 75, 78, 149, 150, 176,
    179, 180, 197, 214
ELECTROLYTE,
  motion of 2
  streaming of 69
  supporting 4, 6, 12, 24, 27, 28,
    34, 41, 46, 47, 52, 54, 57, 61–
    69, 71, 73, 75, 76, 77, 79, 81,
    102, 107, 108, 109, 110, 121,
    128, 129, 143, 151, 173, 177,
    182, 185, 206, 208, 209, 213,
    217, 218, 219, 227, 247
ELECTROLYTIC CURRENTS 3

ELECTRONS, NUMBER OF 7, 25, 26,
    52, 53, 107, 109, 238, 245
ELECTROPHEROGRAM, EVALUATION
    OF 198
ELECTROPHORESIS 177
  application of 198
  paper 126, 128, 137, 178, 198
ELEMENTAL ANALYSIS 102, 103
ELIMINATIONS 104, 229
ELUTION METHOD 179, 180, 181,
    183
EMETINE
  besides cephaeline 120
  titration of 162
EMULSIONS, PHENOLPHTHALEIN IN
    187, 188
ENEDIOLS 83, 122, 123
  in sugars 250
  oxidation products of 122
ENZYMATIC SYSTEMS 70
EOSIN 206
$E_{1/2}$—pH PLOTS 232, 245
EPIMERS 228
EQUATION,
  corrected Ilkovič 6
  for the limiting current 1, 6, 52
  of adsorption current 20
EQUILIBRIA 232–243
  acid-base 15, 16, 17, 65, 100,
    108
  heterogenous 17
  mobile 232
  slowly established 233
EQUILIBRIUM CONSTANTS 232–
    238, 247, 248
  effect of electric field on 17
EQUIVALENCE POINT 146, 149,
    151, 162, 165
ERYTHROSE 87, 173
  dehydration of 12
  pH-dependence of waves of 14
  purity of 206
ESTRONE 186
  nitration of 119
ETHANE, OXIDATION PRODUCTS OF
    209

ETHANOL  4,  63, 102, 108, 115,
    128, 141, 142, 165, 174, 177,
    187, 191, 192, 195, 200, 208,
    209, 210, 211, 213, 215, 217,
    218, 219, 230
  besides glycols  133
  deproteination with  173, 178
  effect of  143, 155
  extraction with  203
  in blood  145
  oxidation of  132
  reaction of periodic acid with
    144
ETHER  193, 195, 200, 215, 221
  aldehydes in  173, 174
  autoxidation of  173
  extraction with  206
  for narcosis  174
  peroxides in  173, 174, 186
  purity of  173, 174
ETHEREAL OILS, TERPENES IN
    191
ETHYL ACETATE  213, 214, 219
ETHYLAMINE, REACTION OF PHENYL
    VINYL KETONE WITH  236
N-ETHYLANILINE, NITROSATION OF
    219
ETHYLCELLULOSE  216
ETHYLCENTRALITE  217
ETHYLENE CHLOROHYDRINE  133
ETHYLENEDIAMINE  99
ETHYLENEDIAMINE TETRACETIC
    ACID (see EDTA)
N,N-ETHYLENEDIGLYCINE,
  cyclic imide from  137
  in EDTA  137
ETHYLENE GLYCOL,
  determination of  143
  oxidation of  132, 133, 145
ETHYLENEGLYCOL DINITRATE  217,
    218
ETHYLENES, HALOGENATED  209
ETHYLHYDROPEROXIDE  93
ETHYLMERCURIHALIDES  97
ETHYLMERCURITHIOSALICYLATE
    187

5-ETHYL-5-(1-METHYLBUTYL)-
    THIOBARBITURIC ACID SO-
    DIUM SALT  156
ETHYLNITRATE  91
2-ETHYL-4-THIOCARBAMIDOPYRI-
    DINE  192
EXHALATIONS, CARBON DISUL-
    PHIDE IN  129
EXPLOSIVES  215–219
  alkylphthalate esters in  212
  amines in  219
  blasting  217
EXTRACTIONS, APPLICATION OF
    115, 172, 173–175, 188, 191,
    193, 195, 200, 203, 206, 208,
    211, 215, 230


FALSE WAVE  28
FAST REACTIONS  242, 243
FATS,
  diacetyl in  175
  oxidation of  201
  peroxides in  201, 209
  separation of  230
  tocopherol in  161
  unsaturation in  163
FEHLING'S SOLUTION  145
FENAZINE-N-OXIDE  91
FERMENTATION PRODUCTS,
    GLYCEROL IN  133
FERRIC CHLORIDE, OXIDATION WITH
    134
FERRIC IONS, COMPLEXING OF  210
FERRICYANIDE AS TITRANT  160
FERROUS IONS REDUCTION OF PER-
    OXIDES WITH  160
FERROUS SULPHATE AS CATALYST
    210
FEVER DISEASES  197, 198
FIBRE INDUSTRY, CARBON DISUL-
    PHIDE IN  129
FIBRES, IN XANTHATE  220
FILTER PAPER, ADSORPTION ON  197

FILTRATE PROTEIN REACTION 196, 197, 198
FIRST DROP 50
FLAVANOLES 95
FLAVANONES 95
FLAVIANIC ACID AS TITRANT 159
FLAVONES 95
FLORES CINAE, SANTONINE IN 174
FLORISIL, CHROMATOGRAPHY ON 203
FLOTATION LIQUIDS, XANTHATES IN 206
FLOUR, THIOLS IN 156
FLOW-METHODS 242
FLUORENONE 88
FLUORESCENCE 138
FLUORIDE, PHENACYL 85
1-FLUORO-2,4-DINITROBENZENE 132
FLY BAIT 202
FOLIC ACID (see PTEROYLGLUTAMIC ACID)
FOOD, SACCHARIN IN 199, 200
FOOD CHEMISTRY, APPLICATION IN 198–203
FORAGE, PENTACHLORONITROBENZENE 203
FORMALDEHYDE 8, 9, 87
    besides acrylonitrile 211
    dehydration of 12
    effect of pH on 13
    formation of 132, 133, 195
    hydration of 237
    in oxidation products 209
    reaction of amines with 120
    removal of 172, 209
FORMALDEHYDOGENIC STEROIDS 195
FORMAZANE 90
FORMYLPYRIDINES 88
    hydration of 237
FRONTAL METHOD 179, 180, 181, 183
FRUCTOSE 87
    complex of boric acid with 165

FRUCTOSE
    in fruit 174, 178, 199
    titration of 161
FRUIT,
    fructose in 174, 178, 199
    glutathione in 200, 201
    thiols in 200, 201
FUCHSINE 188
FUEL OIL 208
FUELS 206–209
FUMARATE ESTER, BESIDES STYRENE 211
FUMARIC ACID 65, 131
    formation of 140, 228
FUNCTIONAL ANALYSIS 103–106
    modified methods of 104
FUNGICIDES, ANALYSIS OF 198, 202, 203
FUNGUS GENUS SINISTRI 199
FURFURAL 88, 104, 220
    formation of 141

GALACTOSE 210
GALLOCYANINE 96
GALVANOMETER 2, 3, 149, 150, 180, 197
    critically damped 43, 73, 238
    hysteresis of 81, 238
    mirror 41
    overdamping of 81
    sensitivity of 81
    solution of 70
    string 50
    undamped 73
    zero line of 4, 5, 45, 146, 162, 240, 241
GAMMEXANE 202
GAS,
    butadiene in 143
    indifferent 35, 38, 69, 75
GASOLINE,
    antioxidants in 209
    hydroperoxides in 209
    mercaptans in 207

GELATIN   8, 28, 68, 69, 100, 110, 116, 118, 138, 140, 162, 187, 199, 202, 204, 206, 234
  reaction of phthalaldehyde with 142
GIRARD'S REAGENTS   125, 126, 195
GLOBULINS   197
GLUCOSE   87
  as standard   145
  titration of   161
GLUTATHIONE   99, 153, 156, 157
  in biological material   156
  in fruits   200, 201
  oxidized   156
  titration of   153, 156, 157
GLYCERINALDEHYDE   100
GLYCEROL,
  acrolein in technical 205
  determination of   143
  in fermentation products   133
  oxidation of   133
GLYCEROL-PHOSPHATES   186
  titration of   158
GLYCINE   63, 121, 122
  determination of   142
  effect of   164
  reaction of pyruvic acid with 234, 235
GLYCINE BUFFERS   63, 79, 121, 234
GLYCOLALDEHYDE   87
1,2-GLYCOL GROUPS IN POLYVINYL ALCOHOL   214
GLYCOLONITRILE BESIDES ACRYLONITRILE   211
GLYCOSIDES, ALDIMINE FORMATION OF CARDIAC   122
GLYCYRRHETIC ACID   191
GLYCYRRHIZIC ACID IN *SUCCUS LIQUIRITAE*   191
GLYOXAL   88
GLYOXYLIC ACID   88
GOLD CHLORIDE AS TITRANT   161
GOOSEBERRIES   200
GRAPHITE ELECTRODE   80, 209
GUAIACOL TITRATION OF   162
GUAJAZULENE   84

GUAJTRIOL C   124
GUANINE   194
GUANOSINE   194
GUANYLIC ACID   194

$H_0$-FUNCTION   63
HALF-TIMES   238, 239, 240, 242
HALF-WAVE POTENTIALS   1, 6, 7, 8, 10, 22, 24, 25, 26, 27, 34, 38, 42, 46, 48, 57, 63, 64, 65, 68, 72, 79–82, 104, 105, 107, 108, 109, 110, 128, 135, 136, 137, 138, 175, 183, 202, 207, 215, 219, 227, 228, 232, 233, 237, 238, 245–248
  effect of concentration on   25, 26
  effect of drop-time on   25, 26
  effect of pH on   26, 27, 245
  measurement of   34, 79–82
  prediction of   248
  shifts of   248
  structual effects on   245-248
HALOGEN DERIVATIVES   27, 62, 68
HALOGENIDE COMPLEXES
  of antimony as titrant   157
  of bismuth as titrant   157, 158
  of cadmium as titrant   157
  of mercury as titrant   157
HALOGENIDES   62
HALOGENS, DETERMINATION OF 102
HAMMETT EQUATION   105, 246, 250
HANGING MERCURY DROP ELECTRODE   48, 49, 50, 51, 54
HCH   202
HEMIACETAL RING OPENING   13, 15, 66, 238
HEPATITIS   198
HEPTACHLOROCYCLOHEXANES   202
HEPTANE   181, 182
HEROIN   118, 186
HETEROCYCLICS   20
  five-membered   93, 94, 95

HETEROCYCLICS
nitrogen-containing 100
oxygen-containing 100
protonation of nitrogen 251
six-membered 95, 96, 97
titration of nitrogen containing 157
HETEROGENEOUS EQUILIBRIUM 17
HETEROGENEOUS REACTION 17, 18
HETEROPOLYACIDS, AS TITRANTS 152, 158, 159
HEXACHLORANE 202
HEXACHLOROCYCLOHEXANE 85, 202
isomers of 202
HEXAMETHYLENEDIAMINE
BESIDES 1,2-DIAMINOCYCLOHEX-ANE 135, 136
1,2-diaminocyclohexane in 209
reaction of aldehydes with 122
reaction of cycloanones with 122
HEXAMOCOBALTICHLORIDE 196, 197, 199
HEXURONIC ACID 191
HIGH-MOLECULAR COMPONENTS, SEPARATION OF 176
HINDRANCE OF REDUCTION 22
HISTAMINE 192, 221
besides histidine 128
effect of 164
reaction of pyruvic acid with 237
separation of 178
HISTIDINE 192, 221
besides histamine 128
determination of 142
in proteins 164
reaction of 1-fluoro-2,4-dinitro-benzene 132
reaction of pyruvic acid with 237
separation of 178
titration of 164
HOMOGENOUS REACTIONS 40, 238–242

HOMOLOGOUS SERIES, FRACTIONA-TION OF 175
HOMOLOGUES, ANALYSIS OF 183
HORMONES, STEROID 194
HUMBLE SCHEME 207
HYDANTOIN 100
HYDRASTININE 97
HYDRATION 251
HYDRAZINE 99
chlorosubstituted 227
derivatives of 56, 57
mixture of 127
reaction of acetone with 127
reaction of pentoses with 127
1-HYDRAZINOPHTHALAZINE 95
HYDRAZOBENZENE 83
HYDRAZONES 89, 90
formation of 120, 125–127, 214
hydrolysis of 125
protonation of 125
HYDROBENZOIN, OXIDATION WITH PERIODIC ACID 242
HYDROCARBONS 100, 112, 246
mercaptans in 207
mixture of aromatic 115
oxidation of 209
sum of aromatic 116
unsaturated 62, 203
HYDROCHLORIC ACID 8, 9, 118, 126, 127, 133, 137, 138, 140, 141, 160, 163, 178, 187, 188, 190, 193, 195, 200, 204, 205, 212, 213, 222
HYDROGEN 35, 69
catalytic evolution of 24, 63, 83, 99–101
evolution of 33, 196
HYDROGEN IONS,
consumption of 8, 9, 10, 11, 12
effect of 232
reduction of 19
rate of supply of 10
HYDROGENOLYSIS 104
of C–N bond 228
HYDROGEN OVERVOLTAGE 33
lowering of 19

HYDROGEN PEROXIDE 69, 118, 145
  as catalyst 210
  elimination of 209
  in oxidation products 209
  reaction with thiophene 208
  wave of 122
HYDROGEN SULPHIDE 206, 207, 220
  besides carbon disulphide 129
  formation of 49
HYDROJUGLONE IN WALNUT 230
HYDROPEROXIDES 18, 27
  in gasoline 209
HYDROPHOBITY 101
HYDROQUINONE 83, 233
  anodic wave of 10, 18
  formation of 19
  in polymers 213
  instability of 233
  in vinylic monomers 213
  nitrosation of 120
  oxidation of 10
  reaction of 211
HYDROSULPHITE 69
HYDROXIDE,
  lead 230
  lithium 9, 13, 14, 63, 65, 132, 133, 134, 173, 174, 175, 212
  nickel 136
  potassium 117, 118, 136, 137, 141, 191, 196, 212, 215
  sodium 14, 66, 68, 109, 113, 114, 115, 119, 121, 122, 124, 131, 140, 157, 174, 189, 190, 193, 195, 206, 218, 220
  tetra-alkylammonium 103
  tetrabutylammonium 62
  tetraethylammonium 62, 117
HYDROXYACIDS, FORMATION OF 193
HYDROXYAMINO ACIDS, OXIDATION OF 133
α-HYDROXYCARBONYL COMPOUNDS 63, 109
5-HYDROXYCHROMANE 83
5-HYDROXYCOUMARANE 83

α-HYDROXYKETONES 104, 173
16-HYDROXY-17-KETOSTEROIDS 87
HYDROXYLAMINE 18, 67, 105, 125
  as intermediate 113
HYDROXYLAMINO DERIVATIVES 215
  formation of 9
HYDROXYL IONS,
  catalysis by 13
  formation of 69
HYDROXYLS, NUMBER OF VICINAL 144
5-HYDROXYMETHYLFURFURAL 222
HYDROXYPROLINE 221
  in proteins 193, 194
8-HYDROXYQUINOLINE 97
3-HYDROXY-$\Delta^5$-STEROIDS 126
21-HYDROXYSTEROIDS IN URINE 195
HYPOIODITE 141

IGELIT 216
ILKOVIČ EQUATION 1, 6, 52
  extended form of 6, 52
IMINES 89, 90
IMINODIACETIC ACID 138
IMPREGNANTS 205
IMPULSE POLAROGRAPHY 237
INACTIN 189
INACTIVATION REACTION 26
INCISIONS ON d$E$/d$t$—$E$ CURVES 50
INDANDIONE 94
INDICATOR ELECTRODE 2, 32, 40, 41, 146, 149, 163, 183
INDIFFERENT GAS 35, 38, 69
INDIGOSULPHONATES 18, 83
INDIRECT METHODS 102, 112–165, 183
  for polymers 214
INDOLENINE 93
INDOLSULPHONIC ACIDS 99
INDOPHENOLS 83
INDUSTRIAL HYGIENE, APPLICATIONS IN 192
INERT GAS 35, 38, 69

INFLAMATORY DISEASES 197, 198
INHIBITORS 209
INITIATORS 209, 211
INJECTIONS, CEPHAELINE IN 120
INSECTICIDES,
  analysis of 198, 202, 203
  in preparations 198
  in residues 198
INSOLUBLE PRODUCTS 26
INSTANTANEOUS CURRENT 50, 51
INTERCAIN 186
  nitrosation of 120
INTERFERENCES, SEPARATIONS OF
  172–183
INTERFERING SUBSTANCES 45, 46
  47, 48, 107
INTERMEDIATES 49, 250–252
  electroactive 250
  of electrode processes 54, 57
  quinoid 104
  reaction 229, 242
IODATE 143
  as titrant 160
  formation of 242
  oxidation with 134
  reaction of 144
IODIC ACID 143
IODIDE,
  benzyl 86
  besides cysteine 153
  interference of 152, 154
  in thiamine-Bi-complex 158
  potassium 62, 134 180, 181,
    182, 214
  tetrabutylammonium 204, 208,
    209, 210, 211
  tetramethylammonium 208,
    213, 214
IODINE 131, 141
  as titrant 152, 155, 159, 160
IODOADRENOCHROME 134
IODOBENZENES 105, 249
  reduction of 53
IODOFORM 141
IODOMETRIC TITRATIONS 155, 159
  160, 242

$p$-IODONITROBENZENE 53
IODONIUM SALTS 57, 58
IODONORADRENOCHROME 134
IODOPHENOL 86
IODOPYRIDINES 86
IODOPYRROLE 86
$o$-IODOSOBENZOATE AS TITRANT
  160
ION-EXCHANGE RESINS, APPLICA-
  TION OF 141
IONIC STRENGTH, EFFECT OF 20
  24, 100, 101, 110, 128,
  251
$iR$ DROP 81, 82
IRGAPYRIN 186
  titration of 157
IRREVERSIBLE SYSTEMS 10, 26, 27,
  50, 83, 84–98
IRREVERSIBLE WAVES, SLOPE OF 26
I.R. SPECTROSCOPY 249
ISATINE 94
ISOALLOXAZINES 96
ISOBENZPYRYLIUM SALTS 95
ISOBUTYRALDEHYDE HYDRAZONE
  89
ISOMERS,
  analysis of 183
  $cis$-$trans$ 65
  distinguishing of 64
ISOOCTANE 127, 183
ISOPROPYL ALCOHOL 19, 173, 174
ISOQUINOLINE IN COAL TAR 205,
  206
ISOTHUJONE 87
$i$–$t$ CURVES 50, 51, 242

JUGLONE IN WALNUT 230

KALOUSEK CELL 36, 38, 39, 200,
  201, 221
  advantages of 39
KERATIN, SULPHUR DERIVATIVES IN
  221
KEROSENE 202, 208

KETIMINES, FORMATION OF 120–124

α-KETO-ACID OXIMES 89

KETO-ACIDS 15, 16, 192
  dinitrophenylhydrazones of 126, 127
  hydrated 251
  reaction of amines with 236

6-KETOCAMPHOR 87

KETO-ENOL TAUTOMERISM 16

KETO-ENOL TRANSFORMATION 251

α-KETOGLUTARIC ACID IN BIOLOGICAL MATERIAL 126, 127

KETONES 104
  formation of 228
  in beverages 199
  in mixture with aldehydes 122, 124
  reaction of
    amines with 236
    ammonia with 120
    bisulphite with 142
    Girard reagent with saturated 126
    primary amines with 120
    semicarbazide with 124

KETONIC GROUP 249

KETONIC TERPENES 191

KETOSTEROIDS 186, 192
  in biological material 194, 195

3-KETOSTEROIDS 126
  betainylhydrazones of 104

17-KETOSTEROIDS 126
  betainylhydrazones of 89
  in urine 194, 195

20-KETOSTEROIDS 126

Δ⁴-3-KETOSTEROIDS 63, 87, 104, 228
  betainylhydrazones of 89

Δ¹,⁴-3-KETOSTEROIDS 228

KINETIC CURRENTS 1, 12, 13, 14, 15, 16, 17, 23, 24, 25, 40, 50, 51, 52, 78, 127, 132, 233, 237, 238, 239, 243, 251
  effect of pH on 12
  effect of temperature on 12

KINETICS, HOMOGENEOUS 40

KJELDAHL MINERALIZATION 103

KOHLRABI 200


LACTARVIOLINE 124

LACTIC ACID 140, 192
  in biological material 134
  oxidation of 133

LACTONIC CARBONYL 249

LASERPITIN 144

LEAD, MONOCHLOROTRIETHYL 98

LEAD ACETATE 172, 199

LEAD HYDROXIDE 230

LEAD NITRATE 159
  as titrant 156, 158

LEAD PERCHLORATE 159

LEAD SALT 102

LEAD TANNATE, TITRATION OF 164

LEVCO FORMS OF DYESTUFFS 83

LEWIS ACID 17

LIMITING CURRENTS 5, 6, 7, 12, 18, 22, 25, 26, 27, 28, 32, 33, 34, 40, 43, 46, 52, 53, 54, 70–73, 78, 79, 107, 108, 127, 146, 151, 175, 238, 240, 243, 248,
  additivity of 7, 12, 110
  change with time 238
  effects on 22, 23, 24, 25
  increase of 28
  measurement of 34, 70–73

LINDANE 202

LINEAR FREE ENERGY RELATIONSHIPS 246, 250

LIPOIC ACID 93

LIQUID BOUNDARY 35, 38

LIQUID JUNCTION, SEPARATION BY 81

LIQUID JUNCTION POTENTIAL 79, 80

LITHIUM BISULPHITE 195

LITHIUM CARBONATE 134

LITHIUM CHLORIDE 9, 129, 133, 175, 201, 204, 208, 212, 215, 216

LITHIUM HYDROXIDE 9, 13, 14, 63, 65, 132, 133, 134, 173, 174, 175, 212
LITHIUM SALTS 62
LITHIUM SULPHATE 14, 174, 191, 215
LIVER DISEASES 198
LOGARITHMIC ANALYSIS 24, 25, 26
LOGARITHMIC PLOT (see LOGARITHMIC ANALYSIS)
LUCIGENINE 97
LYSINE, DETERMINATION OF 142

McILVAIN BUFFERS 16a, 63, 117, 118
MACROMOLECULAR SUBSTANCES 101
MAGNESIUM CHLORIDE 205
MALAPRADE REACTIONS 143, 144, 145
 mechanism of 144
MALEATE ESTER BESIDES STYRENE 211
MALEATE UNSATURATION IN POLYESTERS 213, 214
MALEIC ACID 7, 8, 65, 85, 131, 212
 esters of 213
 formation of 140, 228
 polymerized 214
MALEIC ANHYDRIDE 94
 besides styrene 211
 in phthalic anhydride 211, 212
 reaction of unsaturated bonds with 129f., 142, 143
 saponification of 212
MALEIC HYDRAZIDE 95
MALIC ACID
 besides tannic acid 178
 determination of 140
 in alcoholic beverages 198, 199
MALIGNANCY 198
MALTOSE 87
MANDELIC ACID
 in bile 134, 192
 in urine 134, 192

MANGANESE, EFFECT OF 131
MANGANOUS SULPHATE 133, 134
MANNICH BASE, FORMATION OF 236
MANUAL POLAROGRAPHS 41, 42, 43, 47
MAXIMA 27, 28, 68, 73, 101, 151, 183, 207, 222, 248
 of the first kind 28
 of second kind 28
 rounded 28
 sharp 28
 suppression of 28, 29, 83, 101
MEADOW SAFFRON, COLCHICINE IN 230
MEAN CURRENT 43
MECHANISMS
 of catalytic currents 20
 of electrode process 245
 deviations from 248
 of reactions 192
MECONIC ACID 95
MEDICINE, APPLICATIONS IN 185, 192–198
MELONS 200
MEMBRANES 35
 cellophane 39, 40
 sintered glass 39
MENADIONE 173
MERCAPTANS 99, 106, 206, 207, 209
(see also Thiols)
 dodecyl 207
 in gasoline 207
 in hydrocarbons 207
 primary 155
 tertiary 155
 titration of 152, 155, 156, 159
MERCAPTOBENZIMIDAZOLE 99
MERCAPTOBENZTHIAZOLE 99, 158
MERCAPTO KETONES 104
4-MERCAPTOPYRIDOXOL 49
MERCURIC ACETATE 117, 118
 reaction of
  allyl alcohol with 211
  styrene with 211

MERCURIC ACETATE
vinyl acetate with 211
vinyl butyrate with 211
MERCURIC CHLORIDE 157
MERCURIC IODIDE REFERENCE ELEC-
TRODE 150
MERCURIC PERCHLORATE AS TIT-
RANT 157
MERCURIC SULPHIDE REFERENCE
ELECTRODE 150
MERCURIMETRIC TITRATIONS 154,
156–157
MERCUROUS IONS, FORMATION OF
4
MERCUROUS SULPHATE 38
MERCUROUS SULPHATE ELECTRODE
34, 35, 36, 38, 67, 74, 79, 80,
144, 189, 240, 241
MERCURY,
complexes of 157
dissolution of 4, 62, 71
rate of outflow of 7
MERCURY COLUMN (see MERCURY
RESERVOIR)
MERCURY COMPOUNDS AS TITRANTS
152, 153, 154, 156–157
MERCURY DROP ELECTRODE, HANG-
ING 48, 49, 50, 51, 54
MERCURY DROP GROWTH 43
MERCURY ELECTRODES 33
MERCURY HEAD (see MERCURY
RESERVOIR)
MERCURY POOL ELECTRODE 35,
35, 36, 38, 54, 79, 149, 150,
197
MERCURY PRESSURE (see MERCURY
RESERVOIR)
MERCURY RESERVOIR (h) 2, 3, 7,
22, 23, 25, 27, 28, 32, 70, 75,
107, 109, 150, 197
MERCURY SALTS,
adsorption of 20, 101
formation of 22, 26, 56, 83, 99,
128, 188, 189, 206, 207, 220
MESITYLOXIDE 87
MESOMERIC EFFECTS 246, 248

MESOXAL ALDEHYDE 123
MESOXALIC ACID HYDRAZONE 89
METABOLISM, STUDIES OF 192
METAPHOSPHORIC ACID 200, 201
METHACRYLATES 213
oxidation of 212
METHACRYLIC ACID 213
METHANE 69
METHANOL 61, 115, 119, 125, 126,
129, 131, 141, 163, 180, 181,
182, 201, 205, 207, 208, 210,
212, 213, 214, 215, 219
besides glycols 133
effect of 143
oxidation of 132
reaction of periodic acid with
144
METHODS,
auxiliary 22
derivative 45-48
subtractive 45–48
β-METHOXYETHYLMERCURIC CHLO-
RIDE 97
METHYLAMINE,
in dimethylamine 124
reaction of cyclanones with
121
O-METHYLBENZALDOXIME 92
3-METHYLBENZOTHIAZOLONIMIDE
94
METHYLBROMIDE 85
METHYL BUTYL PHENACYL SUL-
PHONIUM ION 92
METHYLCELLULOSE 118
3-METHYLCHLOANTHRENE 85
METHYLCYCLOHEXANONE, REACTION
OF METHYLAMINE WITH 121
METHYLENE BLUE 96
adsorption current of 20
METHYLGLYOXAL 88
METHYLIMINODIACETIC ACID 138
5-METHYLIMINO-3-PHENYL-4-
METHYL-1,2,4-THIADIAZO-
LINE 94
METHYLMETHACRYLATE 216
in copolymers 210

2-Methyl-1,4-Naphthohydro-
    quinone Diacetate 190
2-Methyl-1,4-Naphthoquinone
    28
  in poultry feed 173
N-Methyl-5,5-Phenylethylbar-
    bituric Acid 188
Methyl Red 213
Methyltestosterone 65
4-Methylthiouracil 99
Microammeter 149, 150
Microcoulometry 53
Migration, Effect of 61
Migration Current 27
Millicoulometry 53
Mineralization Kjeldahl 103
Minima on $i$–$E$ Curves 68
Mixing Chambers 242
Mixtures,
  analysis of 111, 172
  of depolarizers 45
Molecular Weight, Effect of
    101
Monochlorotriethyl Lead 98
Monomers 209, 210–212
  in polymerization reactions 143
  peroxides in 122
  pyruvate in 212
Morphine 186
  determination of 158
  in blood 118, 178, 192
  in poppy seed 118
  in tinctura opii 158
  nitration of 118, 119
  titration of 162
Motion of the Solution 20,
    27
Muconic Acid 85
Mucoproteins 198
Multi-Sweep Polarography 44
Multivitamin Preparations 189
Myrtenal 87

Naphtha, Sulphur Compounds
    in Petroleum 207

Naphthalene 85
  chlorinated 205
  in atmosphere 115, 192
  in blood 192
  in coke gas 209
Naphthols, Titration of 162
Naphtholsulphonic Acids 99,
    159
$\beta$-Naphthoquinoi ine 97
Naphthoquinone Imine 90
Naphthoquinones 83, 88, 212,
    233
  for potential measurements 80
  photo-decomposition of 173
  phthalic acid in presence of 46
Naphthylaminesulphonic Acids
    99
Natural Products 101, 227, 230,
    249
  distinguishing of 29
Neoeserine 116, 186
Neohydrin Reaction of Thiols
    with 221
Neostigmine 116
Nesdonal 189
Neutral Red 95, 214
Neutral Salts, Effect of 110
Niacinamide (see Nicotinamide)
Nickel Hydroxide 136
Nickel Ion, Complexes of 135,
    136
Nicotinamide 64, 96, 186, 189,
    190
Nicotinic Acid 64
Nicotinic Acid Amide (see Nico-
    tinamide)
Nigrosine Black 207
Ninhydrin 63, 94, 138
Nitranilines 104, 180, 252
Nitrate,
  ammonium 68, 115, 131, 157,
    177, 213, 218
  cadmium 137, 207
  lead 158, 159
  potassium 10, 103, 113, 117,
    137, 188, 218

*U

NITRATE,
  silver 118, 177, 207
  sodium 157
NITRATES 62
  formation of 215
  organic 215
NITRATION 214, 215, 216, 222
  applications of 112–119, 190
  conditions of 113
NITRATION MIXTURE 112, 113, 114, 115, 116, 118, 215
NITRIC ACID 102, 112, 114, 116, 117, 118, 136, 153, 164, 191, 215
NITRILOTRIACETIC ACID 138
  in EDTA 136, 137, 203
NITRITE 219
  potassium 118, 119
  sodium 117, 118
NITROACETANILIDES 91
NITRO-ALKANES 104, 249
  homologues of 181
  separation of 182
NITROBENZENE 64, 83, 91, 104, 105, 205, 249
  in aniline 205, 222
  in presence of phenylhydroxyl-amine 46
1-NITRO-2-BUTANOL 91
2-NITRO-1-BUTENE 91
NITROCELLULOSE 217, 218
  pentaerythritol trinitrate in 217, 218
NITRO-COMPOUNDS 9, 49, 52, 112–119, 193
  aromatic 64
NITROCYCLOHEXANE 91
NITRO DERIVATIVES AS TITRANTS 159
2-NITRODIPHENYLAMINE 217, 218
4-NITRO-ESTRONE 119
5-NITRO-2-FURANALDEHYDE SEMI-CARBAZONE 203
NITROFURANES 91
NITROFURAZONE IN CHICKEN FEEDS 203

NITROGEN 35, 69
  determination of 103
NITROGEN CONTAINING BASES, TITRATION OF 158, 159
NITROGEN CONTAINING HETERO-CYCLICS 20, 100, 157
N—N BONDS 90
N—O BONDS 91, 92, 215, 227
NITROGLYCERINE 91, 217, 218, 219
  in propellants 215
NITRO-GROUP 214, 215
  reduction of 53
  wave of 203
NITROMETHANE 91
2-NITROMORPHINE 118
α-NITRONAPHTHALENE 115
NITRONAPHTHALENE SULPHONIC ACIDS 91
NITRONES 15, 91
NITROPHENOLS 64, 104, 116, 252
p-NITROPHENYLHYDRAZINE 214
NITROPYRIDINES 91
NITROSAMINES 104, 119, 219
  formation of 193
  in blood 193
  in urine 193
NITROSATION,
  application of 112, 119–120
  of amines 219
NITROSOBENZENE 92, 105
NITROSO-COMPOUNDS 119, 120
N-NITROSODIMETHYLAMINE 91
N-NITROSOHYDROXYPROLINE 193, 194
1-NITROSO-2-NAPHTHOL 92, 158
N-NITROSOPHENYLHYDROXYLAMINE 91
N-NITROSOPROLINE 91, 193, 194
NITROTETRALINE 91
NITROTHIOPHENES 91
m-NITROTOLUENE 218
p-NITROTOLUENE BESIDES p-AMINO BENZALDEHYDE 205, 222
NITROUS ACID 193
NON-ADDITIVITY OF WAVES 8

NONAQUEOUS SOLUTIONS 33, 61, 63, 107, 108
iR drop in 81
potential standards in 80
reference electrodes for 79, 80
NORADRENALINE, OXIDATION OF 134, 135
NOVA'K CELL 36, 37
NUCLEOSIDES 179
NUCLEOTIDES 179
NYLON 66, INTERMEDIATES OF 136

OCTACHLOROCYCLOHEXANES 202
OLEFINS, ADDITION OF BROMINE TO 129, 142, 163
OLEUM BOLDO, ASCARIDOL IN 191
OLEUM CHENOPODII, ASCARIDOL IN 191
OPPENAUER OXIDATION 126
ORGANIC SOLVENTS 27
deproteination with 173
ORGANOMETALLIC COMPOUNDS 97, 98
ORCINOL, TITRATION OF, 162
OSCILLATIONS 32, 43, 44, 46, 47, 48, 73
damping of 44
effect of 77
OSCILLOGRAPHIC METHODS 49
OSCILLOGRAPHIC POLAROGRAPHY 44, 50, 54, 188
OSCILLOGRAPHIC REVERSIBILITY 50
OSCILLOGRAPHIC TECHNIQUES 242
OSCILLOSCOPE 49, 50
OUT-FLOW VELOCITY 32, 48, 51, 52, 70, 76, 77, 79, 151
OVER-OXIDATION 143
OVERGLYCINE 178
OVERVOLTAGE, HYDROGEN 19
OXALACETIC ACID, IN BIOLOGICAL MATERIAL 126, 127
OXALATE, SODIUM 161
OXALATES, REMOVAL OF 199

OXALIC ACID 88
titrations of 160
OXAZINES 96
OXIDATION
of fats 201
of hydrocarbons 209
of hydroquinone 10
of methacrylates 212
permanganate 195
with chromic acid 115, 116, 145, 158
with periodic acid 195, 228
OXIDATION-REDUCTION POTENTIAL 10, 25
OXIDATION-REDUCTION REACTIONS 152, 159–162
OXIDATION-REDUCTION WAVE 190
OXIDATIONS, APPLICATION OF 112, 132–135, 143–145, 152, 159 –162
OXIDE,
cuprous 145
silver 124, 194
zinc 134
N-OXIDES 104
OXIDIZABLE COMPOUNDS 83
OXIDIZED FORM 48
OXIDIZING AGENTS 18, 34
OXIMES 15, 65, 89, 90, 158, 234
formation of 120, 125
protonation of 251
total amount of 105
OXINE, TITRATION OF 162, 163
8-OXOCAMPHOR 87
$\psi$-OXOTRIAZOLES 95
OXYGEN,
concentration of 69
effect of 69, 150, 151
effect on chromatopolarography 181
in subtractive method 48
reduction of 69
removal of (see Deaeration)
waves of 205
OXYGEN-CONTAINING HETEROCY-CLICS 100

OXYGEN DERIVATIVES 208
O—O BONDS 93
OXYTOCINE 196

PALLADIUM SOL 18
PANCREAS, ADENINE IN 194
PANTOTHENATE, CALCIUM 189
PAPER CHROMATOGRAPHY 54
PARATHIONE 91
  in preparations 203
PARTIALLY MOBILE SYSTEMS 27
PARTITION COEFFICIENTS 175, 181
PARTITION POLAROGRAPHY 175
PEAK,
  anodic 49
  cathodic 49
PEN-RECORDING POLAROGRAPHS
  41, 43, 81
PENICILLAMINE, NITROSATION OF
  120
PENICILLIC ACID 95
PENILLO-ALDEHYDE, NITROSATION
  OF 120
PENTABROMOACETONE 130
PENTACHLORONITROBENZENE IN
  FORAGE 203
PENTAERYTHRITOL TETRANITRATE
  217, 218, 219
PENTAERYTHRITOL TRINITRATE IN
  NITROCELLUSE 217, 218
PENTAMETHYLENETETRAZOLE 145
PENTOSANS,
  determination of 141
  in cellulose 203
PENTOSES
  determination of 141
  in cellulose 203
  reaction of hydrazine with 127
PENTOTHAL 156, 189
PEPTIDES 196
  tyrosine in 118
PEPTON, AMINO ACIDS IN 118
PERCHLORATE, 62, 218
  lead 159
  potassium 193

PERCHLORIC ACID 160, 161, 193,
  239
  determination with 173
PERIODATE,
  Oxidation with 144, 145, 240,
  241
  removal of excess of 133
PERIODIC ACID 39, 240
  oxidations with 132, 133, 143,
  144, 145, 195, 228, 242
  reaction of 214
PERMANGANATE
  as titrant 160
  oxidation with 133, 195
  potassium 118, 134
PEROXIDES
  in ether 173, 174, 186
  in fats 201, 209
  in monomers 212
  in petroleum products 209
  in polymethacrylates 212
  titration of dialkyl 160
PERSULPHATE AS INITIATOR 211
PESTICIDES, ANALYSIS OF 202
PETROLEUM, 206, 209
  disulphides in 156
PETROLEUM ETHER 115, 131, 178,
  188, 230
PETROLEUM NAPHTHA, SULPHUR
  COMPOUNDS IN 207
PETROLEUM PRODUCTS, PEROXIDES
  IN 209
pH,
  effect of 12, 13, 14, 15, 16a, 22,
  25, 26, 27, 107, 109, 127,
  128, 136, 152, 243, 249
  effect on
    catalytic currents 19
    half-wave potentials 245
pH-CONTROL 62, 63, 127
PHARMACEUTICALS 73, 100, 185–
  192
  determination of 157
  titration of 159
PHARMACY, APPLICATIONS IN 185–
  192

PHENACETIN 116, 186
PHENACYLAMINE 89
PHENACYL BROMIDE 85, 105
PHENYACL CHLORIDE 86, 105
PHENACYL FLUORIDE 85
PHENACYLPYRIDINIUM ION 89
PHENANTHRENE IN COAL TARS 204
PHENAZINES 83, 95
PHENOBARBITAL 186, 188
    nitration of 118
PHENOLPHTHALEIN 93, 213
    in chocolates 188
    in emulsions 187, 188
PHENOLS 112, 222
    coupling of 162
    in atmosphere 192
    in urine 192
    nitration of 116
    titration of 160, 162, 163
PHENOPLAST 216
PHENOSAFRANINE 95
PHENOTHIAZINES 96, 159
PHENYLACETYL CARBINOL 87
3(α-PHENYL-β-ACETYLETHYL)-4-
    HYDROXYCOUMARINE 141
PHENYLALANINE 192
    nitration of 117
p-PHENYLENEDIAMINES 83, 90
o-PHENYLENEDIAMINE, REACTION
    OF OXIDIZED ENEDIOLS WITH
    123
ψ-PHENYLESTER OF 2-BENZOYL-
    THIOBENZOIC ACID 93
PHENYL ETHYLAMINE 219
PHENYL ETHYL BARBITURIC ACID
    (see PHENOBARBITAL)
PHENYLGLYOXAL, ALKALINE DE-
    GRADATION OF 250
PHENYLGLYOXYLIC ACID 88
    imine of 90
    pH-dependence of waves of 16a
PHENYLHYDRAZINE 99
N-PHENYLHYDROXYLAMINE 83, 92
    nitrobenzene in presence of 46
3-PHENYL ISOINDOLINE 93
PHENYLISOTHIOCYANATE 92

PHENYLMERCURY 187
PHENYL PHENACYL SULPHIDE 92
threo-1-PHENYLPROPANE-1,2-DIOL
    144
PHENYLPROPIOLIC ACID 84
1-PHENYL PROPYL ALCOHOL 5
PHENYL RING 112
3-PHENYL SYDNONE 55, 56
PHENYL VINYL KETONE, REAC-
    TION OF AMINES WITH 236
PHOSPHATE 62
    besides mercaptans 152
    copper 139, 140, 183
    disodium 139
    trisodium 139
PHOSPHATE-BORATE BUFFER 213
PHOSPHATE BUFFER WITH AMMO-
    NIUM IONS 65
PHOSPHATE BUFFERS 14, 63, 109,
    134, 143, 159, 164, 176, 187,
    190, 199
PHOSPHOMOLYBDIC ACID, DEPRO-
    TEINATION WITH 173
PHOSPHORIC ACID 14, 133, 134
PHOTO-CATALYSIS 144
PHOTO-DECOMPOSITION OF NAPH-
    THOQUINONES 173
PHOTO-RECORDING POLAROGRAPHS
    41, 42, 43, 80, 81
PHOTOCHEMICAL REACTIONS 19
PHTHALADEHYDES 103
    reaction of amino acids with
    120f., 142
PHTHALAMIDES 94
PHTHALANHYDRIDE 94
PHTHALATE, POTASSIUM 212
PHTHALIC ACID 85, 234
    effect of 214
    in presence of naphthoquinone
    46
    isomers of 212
PHTHALIC ANHYDRIDE
    in alkyl resins 212
    maleic anhydride in 211, 212
    reaction with quinaldine 205
    saponification of 212

PHTHALIDES 93
PHTHALIMIDINE 93
PHTHALONIMIDE 97
PICRIC ACID 91
  as titrant 159
  production of 193
PILOT SUBSTANCE 76
PINACOLS,
  formation of 227
  stereoisomers of 228
PINENE HYDROPEROXIDE 93
PINENE NITROSOCHLORIDE 91
ω-PIPERIDINOACETOPHENONE
    METHOIODIDE 57, 58, 89,
    176
β-PIPERIDINOPROPIOPHENONE, IM-
    PURITIES IN 179
PIPERONAL REACTION OF PRIMARY
    AMINES WITH 124
$pK_a$-VALUES 232, 233
PLANTS,
  capsaicine in 163
  isolations from 230
PLASMA 144
PLASTICIZER 210
PLASTICS 209–216
  alkylphthalate esters in 212
  cells from 39
  salol in 213
PLATINUM CONTACTS 38
PLATINUM ELECTRODE,
  rotating 149, 153, 154, 156,
    157, 160, 161, 163
  stationary 208
POLAR EFFECTS 246
POLARIZATION, TRANSFER OF CON-
    CENTRATION 50, 52
POLAROGRAMS 42
  derivative 46
POLAROGRAPHIC BEHAVIOUR 107,
    108–110
POLAROGRAPHIC CURVES (see CUR-
    RENT-VOLTAGE CURVES)
POLAROGRAPHIC WAVES 5
  shape of 1

POLAROGRAPHICALLY ACTIVE SUB-
    STANCES 83–101
POLAROGRAPHS 32, 41–45, 150
  manual 41, 42, 43, 47
  pen-recording 41, 43, 81
  photo-recording 41, 42, 43, 80,
    81
  square-wave 78
POLAROGRAPHY,
  A.C. 44, 52
  constant current 44
  differential 47
  impulse 237
  multi-sweep 44
  oscillographic 44, 50, 54, 188
  partition 175
  single-sweep 44, 50, 54, 56
  square-wave 44
  Tast- 44
POLAROMETRIC TITRATIONS 43,
    102, 112, 142, 145–165, 177,
    206, 221, 222
  accuracy of 151
  equipment for 149, 150
  limitation of 151
  performance of 151
POLLEN ALLERGENS 192
POLYALCOHOLS, OXIDATION OF 133
POLYBUTYL METHACRYLATE 216
  monomer in 210
POLYCAPROLACTAM 216
POLYESTERS, MALEATE UNSATURA-
    TION IN 213, 214
POLYETHYLENE 216
POLYETHYLENE GLYCOL 202
POLYISOBUTYLENE 216
POLYMERS,
  analysis of 213–215
  as fillers 182
  disulphides in 156
  effect of 176
  identification of 214
  hydroquinone in 213
  pyrolysis of 214, 215, 216
  styrene in 143
  vinyl acetate in 143

POLYMETHACRYLATES,
  peroxides in 212
  pyruvate in 212
POLYMETHYLMETHACRYLATE 216
  benzoylperoxide in 212
POLYNITROBENZENES, ALKALINE
    CHANGES OF 113, 193
POLYOLS 195
  determination of 143
POLYPHENOLS BESIDES ADRENALINE
    135
POLYSTYRENE 216
  styrene in 211
POLYSULPHIDES, ORGANIC 206,
  207
POLYVINYL ALCOHOL 216
  carbonyl group in 214
  carboxy groups in 214
  1,2-glycol group in 214
POLYVINYLBUTYRAL 216
POLYVINYL CHLORIDE 216
POORLY BUFFERED SOLUTIONS (see
    UNBUFFERED MEDIA)
POPPY SEED, MORPHINE IN 118
POTASSIUM BROMATE 160, 163
POTASSIUM BROMIDE 160
POTASSIUM CHLORIDE 28, 32, 34,
    79, 127, 157, 182, 183, 192,
    200, 202, 206, 217, 219
POTASSIUM CHROMATE 102
POTASSIUM HYDROXIDE 117, 118,
    136, 137, 141, 191, 196, 212,
    215
POTASSIUM IODIDE 62, 134, 180,
    181, 182, 214
POTASSIUM IONS
  for potential measurements 80
  interference of 211
POTASSIUM METAL 102
POTASSIUM NITRATE 10, 103, 113,
    117, 137, 188, 218
POTASSIUM NITRITE 118, 119
POTASSIUM PERCHLORATE 193
POTASSIUM PERMANGANATE 118,
    134
POTASSIUM PHTHALATE 212

POTASSIUM SALTS 62
POTENTIAL,
  choice of 227
  liquid junction 79, 80
  oxidation-reduction 25
  standard 26
POTENTIAL RANGE, CHOICE OF 44,
    62, 241
POTENTIALS, HALF-WAVE 1, 6, 7,
    8, 10, 22, 24, 25, 26, 27, 34,
    38, 42, 46, 48, 57, 63, 64, 65,
    68, 72, 79–82, 104, 105, 107,
    108, 109, 110, 128, 135, 136,
    137, 138, 175, 183, 202, 207,
    215, 219, 227, 228, 232, 233,
    237, 238, 243, 245–248
POTENTIOMETER 2, 3, 150, 180
POTENTIOMETRIC TITRATIONS 57,
    162
POTENTIOMETRY 25
POTENTIOSTAT 53, 54, 55
POULTRY FEED, 2-METHYL-1,4-
    NAPHTHOQUINONE IN 173
PRECEDING REACTIONS 11, 15, 16,
    17
PRECIPITATES, DISSOLUTION OF
    135, 138–140, 149, 164, 165
PRECIPITATION, APPLICATIONS OF
    152–159, 172, 173
PRECISION (see ACCURACY)
PREPARATIONS,
  antibiotics in 198
  insecticides in 198
PREPARATIVE ELECTROLYSIS 227,
    228
PROCAINE PENICILLIN 186
  nitrosation of 120
PROCESS STREAMS 41
PRODUCTS,
  adsorption of 22
  electrolysis 48, 49, 50, 53–58
    identification of 177, 179
  reactive electrolysis 8
  reduction 78
  soluble 50
PROGESTERONE 65

PROLINE 221
in proteins 193, 194
PROPELLANTS,
centralite in 219
nitroglycerine in 215
pentaerithritol trinitrate in 217, 218
PROPIONALDEHYDE 127
besides acetaldehyde and butyraldehyde 175
PROPIOPHENONE 4, 5
PROPYLALCOHOL 203
PROPYLENE CHLOROHYDRINE 133
PROPYLENE DIAMINE, DETERMINATION OF 135
1,2-PROPYLENE GLYCOL, OXIDATION OF 132, 133, 145
PROSERINE 116
PROSTIGMINE 116
PROTEIN-BASED FIBRES 220–222
PROTEIN FRACTIONS, ANALYSIS OF 198
PROTEIN REACTION, FILTRATE 196, 197, 198
PROTEINS 20, 100
adsorption of 155
analysis of blood 179
aspartic acid in 131
catalytic wave of 192, 195, 196, 197, 198, 199, 220
cystine in 156
denaturation of 154, 155, 196
effect of 113, 154, 155, 164, 176, 193, 200
histidine in 164
hydroxyproline in 193
in wool 220
serine in 133
thiol groups in 155, 157
thyroxine in iodinated 192
PROTOANEMONIN 95
PROTON DONORS 16, 63
PROTON-TRANSFER 10, 11, 16, 27, 183, 232, 251
PROTONIZED KETOSTEROIDS 63
PROTONS, NUMBER OF 26

PROTOPINE, BICYCLIC FORM OF 250
PTERIDINES 96
substituent in 250
PTERINES 96, 249
PTEROYLGLUTAMIC ACID 96, 189, 190
PULSE POLAROGRAPHY 44
PURITY
of reagent grade chemicals 206
of technical products 203–206
PYRAZINIC ACID AMIDE 95
PYRAZOLANTHRONE 93
PYRAZOLONES 222
titration of 162
PYRIDAZINE-4-CARBOXYLIC ACID 95
PYRIDIL 88
PYRIDINE 100, 114, 115, 116, 218, 219
adsorption of 22
effect of 217
PYRIDINE-N-OXIDE 91
PYRIDINEALDEHYDES 88
PYRIDINALDOXIME 90
PYRIDINIUM ACETHYDRAZIDE 125
PYRIDINIUM CYCLOPENTADIENYLIDE 96
PYRIDINIUM IONS, N-ALKYL 96
PYRIDOIN 87
enediol form of 250
PYRIDOIN BIS-N-OXIDE 91
PYRIDOXAL 65, 66, 67, 68, 186
aldehydic form of 13
besides pyridoxal-5-phosphate 65, 125
hemiacetal form of 13, 66, 251
in pyridoxal-5-phosphate 206
kinetic wave of 238
pH-dependence of waves of 15
PYRIDOXAL-5-PHOSPHATE 65, 66, 67, 68
besides pyridoxal 65, 125
diffusion current of 238
hydrolysis of 238, 239
pH-dependence of wave of 15
purity of 206

PYRIDOXALDOXIME   65, 67
  formation of   125
PYRIDOXALDOXIME-5-PHOSPHATE
  65, 67
  formation of   215
PYRIDOXAMINE   89
PYRIDOXTHIOL   49
PYRIMIDINES   95, 100
PYRROLALDEHYDE   88
PYRROLSULPHONIC ACID   99
PYRUVATE
  in monomers   212
  in polymethacrylates   212
  sodium   234
PYRUVIC ACID   11, 47, 88
  ketimine of   89
  in biological material   126, 127
  in blood   178, 179
  in unbuffered media   11
  reaction of glycine with   234, 235
  reaction of histamine with   237
  reaction of histidine with   237


QUANTUM   CHEMICAL   METHODS
  246
QUATERNARY AMINES   62
QUERCETIN   186
QUERCITRIN, NITROSATION OF   120
QUINALDINE REMOVAL OF   205
QUINHYDRONE   10
  in unbuffered media   10
QUININE   97
  adsorption current of   22
QUINOID COMPOUNDS   83
QUINOID INTERMEDIATES   104, 252
QUINOLINE   100
  in coal-tar   205, 206
QUINOLINE CARBOXYLIC ACIDS   97
QUINONES   52, 233
  heterocyclic   233
  in coal extracts   209
  photochemical reaction of   19
QUINOPHTHALONE, FORMATION OF
  205
QUINOXALINE-N-OXIDES   91, 104

QUINOXALINES   95
QUOTIENT OF TWO WAVES   76


RADICALS,
  dimerization of   26
  formation of   8, 251
  free   101
  reactions of   8
RADIO   FREQUENCY   POLARIZATION
  44
RASPBERRIES   200
RATE CONSTANTS   247, 248
  computation of   243
  of electrode process   232
  of rapid reactions   17
REACTION   CONSTANT   $\rho$   105f.,
  207f., 247, 248
REACTION CURRENTS (see KINETIC
  CURRENTS)
REACTION KINETICS, APPLICATION
  OF POLAROGRAPHY IN   238–
  242
REACTION MIXTURE, COMPONENTS
  IN   242
REACTION RATES   232–243
  standard   234
REACTION SERIES   246
REACTIONS,
  antecedent   243
  consecutive   243
  fast   242
  half-time of   238, 239, 240
  heterogeneous   17, 18
  inactivation   26
  intermediates in chemical   250–
  251
  parallel   243
  photochemical   19
  preceding   17
  rate constants of rapid   17
REACTIVE FORMS   250–252
REACTIVITY,
  chemical   1
  electrochemical   1

REAGENT CHANGE OF WAVE-HEIGHT
    OF  141
REAGENT GRADE CHEMICALS, PUR-
    ITY OF  206
RECOMBINATION  11, 15, 16, 17
RECORDING
    of current-voltage curves 37,
        39, 41, 42, 43, 75, 80, 81, 102
    of time-changes of current 239,
        240
RECTANGULAR VOLTAGE, PERIODI-
    CALLY CHANGED  48, 52, 55,
    56
REDUCED FORM  48
    adsorption of  20
REDUCIBLE COMPOUNDS  83
REDUCTION,
    hindrance of  22
    of weak acids  11
REDUCTION MECHANISM  104
REDUCTION WAVE  12
REFERENCE ELECTRODES  2, 3, 32,
    33, 34, 35, 36, 38, 39, 40, 41,
    48, 50, 70, 79, 80, 81, 146,
    149, 150, 163, 180, 183
    for continuous analysers  41
    for nonaqueous solutions  79, 80
    non-polarizibility of  80
    polarization of  79
    position of  35
    potential of  80
    reproducibility of  80
    separated  2, 34, 35, 36, 38, 149
REGENERATION CURRENTS  18
REGENERATION PROCESSES  83
REGULATED DROP-TIME  51
REINECKE SALT AS TITRANT  159
REPRODUCIBILITY  33
RESERVOIR, MERCURY  2, 3, 7, 22,
    23, 25, 27, 28, 32, 70, 75,
    107, 109, 150, 197
RESIDUES, INSECTICIDES IN  198
RESINS, ALKYLPHTHALATE ESTERS
    IN  212
RESISTANCE,
    effect of  81, 82
RESISTANCE,
    in the circuit  2
    measurement of  81, 82
RESONANCE EFFECTS  246
RESORCINOL, NITROSATION OF  119
REVERSIBILITY,
    conditions for  48
    estimation of  48–50
    oscillographic  50
REVERSIBLE SYSTEMS  24, 26, 27,
    50, 83, 232, 233, 234, 237,
    238
RHODAMINE  96
RHODAN BENZENES  92
RHODANINE  99
RIBOFLAVIN  83, 96, 189, 190
RIBONUCLEIC ACID, HYDROLYSATE
    OF  194
RING-FORMATION, EFFECT OF  251
RING-OPENING REACTION  127
RODENTICIDES  141
    analysis of  198, 199, 202, 203
$p$-ROSANILINE, DIAZOTISED  159
ROUNDED MAXIMA  28
RUBBER, NATURAL  216
RUBBER FILLER  180, 181, 182,
    183
RUBIDIUM IONS FOR POTENTIAL
    MEASUREMENTS  80
RUTIN  186
    nitrosation of  120

SACCHARINE  94
    in food  199, 200
SALICYLALDOXIME  90, 158
SALICYLATES  168
    titration of  157
SALOL IN PLASTICS  213
SALT-BRIDGE  35
SANTONINE  168
    in Flores Cinae  174
SAUERKRAUT JUICE  47
SCHIFF'S BASE, FORMATION OF  237
SEDIMENTATION TEST  198
SEEDS, TERPENES IN  191

*Semen Cumini Cymini*, Cuminaldehyde in 176
Semicarbazide,
  reaction of aldehydes with 124
  reaction of ketones with 124
Semicarbazones 89
  comparison of aldimines and
    ketimines with 124
  formation of 120, 124, 125
Semimicro-Vessel 35, 36
Sensitivity 77–79
  change of 44
Separation Methods 107, 152,
  172–183
Serine,
  determination of 143
  in proteins 133
  oxidation of 133
Serum 196, 199
  dialysis of 176, 177
  thiols in 176, 177
Shape of Waves 1, 22, 24, 25, 42,
  78, 232
Sharp Maxima 28
Short Circuit System 150, 155,
  161, 163
Side-Chain, Reduction in 246
Silicotungstic Acid as Titrant
  158, 159
Silver Chloride Electrode 34,
  39, 40, 79, 81
Silver Compounds as Titrants
  152, 153, 155–156
Silver Nitrate 118, 207
  as titrant 152, 155, 156, 177
Silver Oxide 124, 194
Simultaneous Determinations
  110–111
Single Sweep Method 44, 50,
  54, 56, 215, 217, 218,
  237
Sintered Glass Membrane 35,
  39, 81
Skeleton, Type of 248
Skellysolve B, Extraction with
  203

Slope
  of irreversible waves 26
  of waves 24, 25, 26, 27, 107
Small Waves, Measurement of
  45, 46, 47, 48
Smoler Capillary 32, 33, 47
Sodium Acetate 75, 129, 134,
  163, 188, 207
Sodium Acetate Electrode 80
Sodium Amalgam 161
Sodium Bicarbonate 174
Sodium Bromide 129, 163
Sodium Carbonate 126, 133,
  174, 200
Sodium Chloride 14, 234
Sodium Hydroxide 14, 66, 68,
  109, 113, 114, 115, 119, 121,
  122, 124, 131, 140, 157, 174,
  189, 190, 193, 195, 206, 218,
  220
Sodium Metal 102
Sodium Nitrate 157
Sodium Nitrite 117, 118
Sodium Oxalate as Titrant 161
Sodium Pyruvate 234
Sodium Salts 62
Sodium Sulphate 34, 38, 126, 140
Sodium Sulphite 129, 202, 206
  reaction of
    cystine with 161
    ketones with 142
Sodium Tartrate 158
Solid Electrodes 34
Solubility Product, Effect of
  149
Soluble Product 50
Solution,
  motion of 20, 27
  volume of electrolysed 1
Solutions, Nonaqueous 61
Solvents 61
  effect of 110, 152
  nonaqueous 33, 107, 108
  organic 27, 61, 62, 70, 108, 109,
    142, 173, 182
  purification of 61

SORBITOL ESTERS 202
SPASMOLYTICS, TITRATION OF 159
SPECTROPHOTOMETRY 54
SPIRITS, ACETALDEHYDE IN 175, 199
SQUARE-WAVE POLAROGRAPHY 44, 78
STAINLESS STEEL CONTACT 37
STANDARD ADDITION METHOD 73–77
STANDARD POTENTIAL 26
STANDARD SUBSTANCE
  for determination of "m" 52, 53
  for potential measurement 80
STARCH, PROPERTIES OF 222
STARTING POTENTIAL 70
STEAM DISTILLATION 172, 176, 199, 219
STEARATE, CALCIUM 113
STEARIC ACID METHYLESTER 163
STEREOISOMERS, PREPARATION OF 228
STERIC EFFECTS 103, 246, 248
11-STEROID ALDEHYDES 104
STEROIDS 87
  acetaldehydogenic 195
  formaldehydogenic 195
STILBENE 84, 105
STOCK SOLUTIONS,
  preparation of 108
  stability of 108
STRAWBERRIES 200
STREAMING OF ELECTROLYTE 69
STREAMING MERCURY ELECTRODE 52
STREAMS, PROCESS 41
STREPTOMYCIN 186
  titration of 159
STRING-GALVANOMETER 50
STRUCTURAL ANALYSIS 248–250
STRUCTURE,
  determination of 248–250
  effect of 245–252
STRYCHINE
  in mixture with brucine 183
  nitration of 190, 191

STYRENE 84, 209, 213, 216
  effect of 214
  in benzene 203
  in copolymers 210
  in polymers 143
  in polystyrene 211
  reaction of mercuric acetate with 211
  titration of 163
SUBSTITUENT,
  effects of 81, 104, 245, 246
  identification of 248, 250
  position of 247
  type of 247
SUBSTITUENT CONSTANTS σ 247, 250
SUBSTITUTION 104
  application of 112, 132, 152, 163
  effect of 104
  reaction 152, 163
SUBTRACTIVE METHODS 45–48, 107, 111
SUCCUS LIQUIRITAE, GLYCYRRHIZIC ACID IN 191
SUGAR MIXTURES, ANALYSIS OF 127
SUGARS 62, 192, 200
  blood 144
  determination of 143
  enediol forms of 250
  reducing 145
  titration of 161
SULFANILIC ACID, DIAZOTISED 90
SULPHA-DRUGS 186
  titration of 162
SULPHAMIC ACID 219
SULPHATE 62
  ammonium 121, 182
  besides mercaptans 152
  copper 138
  ferrous 210
  lithium 14, 174, 191, 215
  manganous 133, 134
  mercurous 38
  sodium 34, 38, 126, 140

SULPHATE,
titration of 156, 158
zinc 134
SULPHIDE,
hydrogen 206, 207, 220
in keratin 221
SULPHIDE IONS, REMOVAL OF 207
SULPHIDES 206, 208
aromatic 208
formation of 220
SULPHIDIC SULPHUR 220
SULPHITE,
interference of 154
reaction of cystine with 221
removal of oxygen with 70
sodium 129, 202, 206
SULPHITE-BORATE BUFFER 218
SULPHONES 206, 208
formation of 208
SULPHONIUM SALTS 105
SULPHOSALICYLIC ACID, DENATURA-
WITH 173, 197
SULPHUR,
determination of 102
elemental 206, 207, 208, 220
in viscose rayon 220
sulphidic 220
thiocarbonate 220
total 220
xathogenate 220
SULPHUR DERIVATIVES 20, 21 100,
206, 207
SULPHUR DIOXIDE 221
S—S BONDS 93, 221
SULPHURIC ACID 9, 35, 38, 108,
113, 115, 117, 119, 126, 131,
134, 140, 141, 160, 165, 191,
205, 207, 212, 215, 219, 220,
221
polarography in 80
SULPHUROUS ACID, REACTION OF
KETONES WITH 142
SULPHYDRYL COMPOUNDS (see
THIOLS)
SULPHYDRYL GROUP (see THIOL
GROUP)

SUPPORTING ELECTROLYTE 4, 6,
12, 24, 27, 28, 34, 41, 46, 47,
52, 54, 57, 61–69, 71, 73, 75,
76, 77, 79, 81, 102, 107, 108,
109, 110, 121, 128, 129, 143,
151, 173, 177, 182, 185, 206,
208, 209, 213, 217, 218, 219,
227, 247
concentration of 61, 62
functions of 61
low concentration of 27
purification of 177
SURFACE, ELECTRODE 20, 27
SURFACE ACTIVE SUBSTANCES 28,
29, 34, 68, 69, 70, 83, 101,
110, 151, 154, 183, 197, 200
estimation of 29
SYDNONES 58, 94, 227
SYNCHRONIZED ELECTRODES 46
SYNTHESIS, APPLICATIONS IN 229–
230

TABLETS, ANALYSIS OF 185
TAFT EQUATION 105, 247, 250
TANNATE, LEAD 164
TANNIC ACID 141
separation from malic acid 178
TARTARIC ACID
as titrant 165
titration of 160, 161
TARTRATES 186
sodium 158
titration of 158
TAST-POLAROGRAPHY 44
TAUTOMERISM, KETO-ENOL 16
TECHNICAL PRODUCTS, PURITY OF
203–206
TEMPERATURE 70
control of 35, 40, 82
effect of 6, 7, 12, 22, 24, 25, 75,
76, 79, 109, 151, 183
influence on partition 182
TEMPERATURE COEFFICIENT 24, 25
TENSAMETRY 52
TEREPHTHALIC ACID 85, 212

TERPENE PEROXIDE 191
TERPENES 124, 249
  aldehydic 191
  ketonic 191
  unsaturated 186
  titration of 163
TESTOSTERONE 65
TETRA-ALKYLAMMONIUM SALTS 33, 62, 68
TETRA-ALKYLAMMONIUM HYDROXIDE 103
TETRABUTYLAMMONIUM CHLORIDE 211
TETRABUTYLAMMONIUM HYDROXIDE 62
TETRABUTYLAMMONIUM IODIDE 204, 208, 209, 210, 211
TETRACYANO ETHYLENE 85
TETRAETHYLAMMONIUM HYDROXIDE 62
  purification of 177
TETRAHYDROPHTHALIC ANHYDRIDE, FORMATION OF 143
TETRAMETHYLAMMONIUM BROMIDE 174, 210, 212
TETRAMETHYLAMMONIUM CHLORIDE 62, 215, 216, 217
TETRAMETHYLAMMONIUM IODIDE 208, 213, 214
TETRAPHENYLARSONIUM CHLORIDE 98
TETRAPHENYLCYCLOPENTADIENONE 87
TETRAPHENYLPHOSPHONIUM CHLORIDE 97
TETRAPHENYLSTIBONIUM CHLORIDE 98
TETRAZOLIUM SALTS 95
TEXTILE INDUSTRY 220–222
THALLOUS ION FOR POTENTIAL MEASUREMENTS 80
THALLOUS SULPHATE, REACTION OF CHLORIDES WITH 200
THERMOSTATING 75
8-THIABICYCLO-(1,2,3)-OCTANE-3-ONE METHOIODIDE 229

THIAMINE 99, 186, 189, 190
  oxidized form of 93
  thiol form of 250
  titration of 157, 159
THIAZINES 83
THIAZOLE-5-CARBOXAMIDE 94
THIENYLMETHYL KETONE 87
THIO-COMPOUNDS 100
THIOBARBITURATES 99, 101, 186, 189
THIOBENZAMIDE 92
THIOBENZOPHENONE 92
THIOCARBONATE SULPHUR 220
2-THIOCYANATOACETOPHENONE 92
THIOGENAL 189
THIOHYDANTOIN 100
THIOL GROUPS 103, 104, 152, 153, 155, 157
  in blood 196
  in proteins 155, 157
  in wool 221
THIOLS 152, 155, 159, 160, 206
  adsorption waves of 20
  besides ascorbic acid 122
  effect of 200
  identification of 249
  in biological material 154, 192
  in flour 156
  in fruit 200, 201
  in proteins 157
  in serum 176, 177
  in tomato 210
  in vegetables 200, 201
  reaction of
    heavy metals with 152
    Neohydrin with 221
  soluble 154
  titration of 177
THIOMERSALATE 187
THIONAPHTHENE-1-OXIDE 92
THIOPENTAL 156
THIOPHENE DERIVATIVES 206, 208
THIOPHENE DIOXIDES 208
THIOPYRIMIDINE 100
THIOSINAMINE, TITRATION OF 159, 160

THIOTHIOSULPHONATES 93
THIOUREA 99
  titration of 159, 160
THIOURONIUM SALTS, DEGRADA-
    TION OF 106
THIOXANTHONES 96
THREE ELECTRODE SYSTEM 40, 81
THYROXINE
  besides 3,5-diiodotyrosine 173,
    174
  in iodinated casein 173, 174
  in iodinated proteins 192
TIME, EFFECT OF 109
TIN,
  dichlorodiethyl 98
  triphenyl 98
TINCTURA IPECACUANHAE, CEP-
    HAELINE IN 120
TINCTURA OPII, MORPHINE IN
    158
TISSUES, ADENINE IN 194
TITANIUM TETRA CHLORIDE 209
TITRANTS 146, 147, 148, 149, 151,
    152, 154, 157, 159, 160, 161
  organic 159, 161
TITRATION CELL 149, 150, 161
TITRATION CURVES, TYPES OF 146,
    147, 148, 149, 151, 159, 162,
    164
TITRATIONS,
  amperometric 43, 102, 12,
    142, 145–165, 177, 206, 221,
    222
  iodimetric 242
  polarometric 43, 102, 112, 142,
    145–165, 177, 206, 221, 222
  potentiometric 57, 162
α-TOCOPHEROL 161, 186
TOLUENE,
  determination of 114
  in air 114, 192
  in blood 114, 192
  in breath 192
  in urine 114, 192
  nitration and oxidation of 116
  nitration product of 115

TOMATOES 200
  ascorbic acid in 201
  thiols in 201
TOXIC SUBSTANCES 193
TOXICOLOGY 188
  applications in 192
TRACES, DETERMINATION OF 45
TRACING OF CURVES (see RECORDING
    OF CURVES)
TRANSFER COEFFICIENT α 109, 243,
    245
TRANSFORMATION OF INACTIVE
    COMPOUNDS 112–141
TRAPANAL 189
TRICHLOROACETIC ACID 86
  deproteination with 194
1,1,2-TRICHLOROETHYLENE 129,
    130
TRIETHYLAMINE BUFFER 159
6-TRIFLUOROMETHYL-7-SULPHA-
    MYL-3,4-DIHYDRO-1,2,4-
    BENZOTHIADIAZINE 85
TRIMETHYAMINE BUFFERS 68
TRIMETHYLAMINOACROLEIN PER-
    CHLORATE 89
3-TRIMETHYL AMMONIUM PHENYL
    N,N-DIMETHYLCARBONATE
    116
TRIMETHYLGLYCYLHYDRAZIDE 125
TRINITROBROMOMETHANE 86
TRINITROTOLUENE 217, 218
TRIPHENYLSELENONIUM CHLORIDE
    98
TRIPHENYL SULPHONIUM CHLO-
    RIDE 92
TRIPHENYLTELLURONIUM CHLO-
    RIDE 98
TRIPHENYL TIN 98
TRIPPLE BONDS, CONJUGATED 246
TROPAEOLIN O 114
3-TROPINONE METHOIODIDE 229
TROPOLONE DERIVATIVES 230
TROPONE 87
TROPYL ALCOHOL 17
TROPYLIUM BROMIDE 51
TROPYLIUM ION 17, 26, 84

TRYPTOPHANE  192
  effect of  164
  nitration of  117
TUBERCULOSIS  199
TUMORS, SKIN  197
TYROSINE  192
  in peptides  118
  in serum albumin  118
  in wool  220, 222
  nitration of  117


UNBUFFERED MEDIA  69
  benzaldehyde in  10
  pyruvic acid in  11
  quinhydrone in  10
UNSATURATED BONDS, REACTION OF
    MALEIC ANHYDRIDE WITH
    129f., 142, 143
UNSATURATED COMPOUNDS  100
  addition of bromine to  129,
    142, 163
α,β-UNSATURATED KETONE  250
URACIL  22, 99
URAMIL-N,N-DIACETIC ACID  138
UREA, REACTION WITH NITROUS
    ACID  193, 194
URIC ACID  100
URINE,
  anti-tubercular drug in  193
  aromatics in  192
  benzene in  113, 114
  p-cresol in  116
  2,4-dinitrophenol  193
  21-hydroxy steroids in  195
  17-keto steroids in  194, 195
  mandelic acid in  134, 192
  nitrosamines in  193
  toluene in  114
U.V. LIGHT  19


VALERALDEHYDE  127
VANILLIN  87
VARIAMIN BLUE  90

VEGETABLES,
  ascorbic acid in  200
  thiols in  200, 201
VERONAL (see BARBITAL)
VERONAL BUFFERS  62, 63, 67, 79,
    109
VESSEL(S),
  electrolysis  2, 3, 32, 35–41, 43,
    44, 69, 70, 75, 78, 149, 150,
    176, 179, 180, 197, 214
  for continuous analysis  40
  from plastics  39
  of Nova'k  36, 37
  open  69
  semimicro  35, 36
  with a cellophane separated elec-
    trode  39, 40
  with temperature control  40
VICINAL HYDROXYLS, NUMBER OF
    144
VINYL ACETATE  209, 213
  besides acetaldehyde  211
  besides acetic acid  211
  besides croton aldehyde  211
  in polymers  143
  reaction of mercuric acetate with
    211
VINYL BUTYRATE, REACTION OF
    MERCURIC ACETATE WITH
    211
VINYLCHLORIDE  129, 130
VINYL ESTER OF ACETIC ACID
    132
VINYLIC MONOMERS, HYDROQUIN-
    ONE IN  213
VISCOSE RAYON, SULPHUR IN  220
VISCOSITY, EFFECT OF  76
VITAMIN A  189
VITAMIN B₁  189, 190
VITAMIN B₂  189, 190
VITAMIN B₁₂  78, 189
VITAMIN C  189, 190
VITAMIN D  189
VITAMIN K₃  173
VITAMINS  198
VITAMINS E  189

VITAMINS K  189, 190
VOLATILE COMPONENTS  70
VOLATILITY, APPLICATION OF  176
VOLTAGE,
  applied  50
  periodically changed rectangular
    48, 52, 55, 56
VOLTAGE SCANNING, RATE OF  44
VOLTAGE-SWEEP  50
VOLUME OF ELECTROLYSED SOLU-
    TION  33, 78

WALNUT,
  hydrojuglone in  230
  juglone in  230
WARFARIN  199
  determination of  141
WARING BLENDOR  199, 200
WASTES, CARBON DISULPHIDE IN
    129
WATER, INTERACTION WITH  27
WATER-BATH  40
WATER-JACKET  40
WATER SEAL  35, 39
WAVE-HEIGHT  5 (see also LIMITING
    CURRENTS)
  evaluation of  73–77
  measurement of  46
WAVES,
  anodic  4, 5, 10, 22, 26, 38, 55,
    56, 62, 71, 74, 83, 99, 102,
    103, 109, 122, 128, 129, 131,
    146, 148, 160, 164, 188, 189,
    190, 200, 201, 206, 207, 208,
    209, 213, 220, 221, 249
  cathodic  4, 5, 10, 34, 38, 45, 71,
    83, 109, 122, 146, 148, 190,
    221
  coincident  64
  course of  57
  distorted  28, 29
  false  28
  irreversible  26
  measurement of anodic  46

WAVES,
  measurement of small  45, 46,
    47, 48
  non-additivity of  8
  oxidation-reduction  190
  shape of  1, 22, 24, 25, 27, 42, 78
WEAK ACIDS,
  catalysis by  20
  reduction of  11
WEAK BASES, CATALYSIS BY  20
WINES, BENZALDEHYDE IN FRUIT
    199
WOOL,
  amino acids in  220
  cystine in  220, 221
  proteins of  220
  thiols in  221
  tyrosine in  220, 222

XANTHATES
  in fibres  220
  in flotation liquids  206
XANTHEN-9-CARBOXYLIC ACID
    159
XANTHOGENATE SULPHUR  220
XANTHONE  95
XYLENE  209
  nitration and oxidation of  116
  nitration product of  115
XYLENOL FRACTIONS, ANALYSIS OF
    163
XYLOSE  141

ZINC
  besides cysteine  153
  interference of  152
ZINC AMALGAM  69
  reduction with  156
  reference electrode  150
ZINC-EDTA  214
ZINC IONS, LIBERATION OF  214
ZINC MANGANITE  134
ZINC OXIDE  134
ZINC SULPHATE  134